THE STRUCTURE OF NEMATODES

THE STRUCTURE
OF NEMATODES

ALAN F. BIRD
Division of Horticultural Research
C.S.I.R.O.
Adelaide, Australia

 1971

ACADEMIC PRESS   New York and London

ACADEMIC PRESS, INC.
111 Fifth Avenue, New York, New York 10003

United Kingdom Edition published by
ACADEMIC PRESS, INC. (LONDON) LTD.
Berkeley Square House, London W1X 6BA

LIBRARY OF CONGRESS CATALOG CARD NUMBER: 79 - 163440

PRINTED IN THE UNITED STATES OF AMERICA

CONTENTS

9.   The Excretory System

10.   The Digestive System

11.   The Reproductive System

12.   The Egg

PREFACE

This book is an attempt to link recent research on the fine structure of nematodes, as seen with the aid of the electron microscope, with the mass of research that has been done on these animals with the aid of the light microscope. Knowledge and facilities for ultrastructural research on nematodes are, at the moment, restricted to comparatively few nematologists, but there is increasing interest in this field. I feel that there is a need for a book of this nature which will benefit those contemplating research along these lines as well as serving as a reference source for those interested in other aspects of nematology. In order to make the subject more interesting, I have endeavored, where possible, to equate function with the structures I describe.

This book is aimed at all workers interested in nematodes, irrespective of whether they do research on nematodes which are parasitic in animals or plants or are free-living in the soil, fresh water, or in the seas. It will thus, I hope, be of interest to zoologists, medical research workers, veterinarians, and to agricultural scientists. It is divided into twelve chapters including an introduction. A large chapter is devoted to modern techniques that have proved to be successful with nematodes. There are also chapters on the exoskeleton, molting, the hypodermis, musculature, the nervous system, the pseudocoelom, the excretory system, the digestive system, the reproductive system, and the egg.

Because this is essentially a descriptive book, there are many diagrams and photographs. Great care has been taken to include scales, where possible, so that an idea of the size of the structures being described can be obtained at a glance. As a further aid to the rapid understanding of the figures, their labels are fully written and are not just abbreviations whose meanings the reader has to glean from keys which are often placed on other pages.

This book draws attention to the many areas requiring further research, and it is hoped that it will stimulate such needed studies.

ALAN F. BIRD

ACKNOWLEDGMENTS

I am indebted to the following scientists for reviewing various chapters and offering helpful advice—Mr. M. R. Sauer and Dr. H. R. Wallace (C.S.I.R.O., Division of Horticultural Research), Dr. G. E. Rogers, Professor W. P. Rogers, and Dr. R. I. Sommerville (University of Adelaide), Dr. K. E. Dixon (Flinders University of South Australia), Professor J. F. A. Sprent (University of Queensland), and Dr. W. G. Inglis (South Australian Museum).

I am also most grateful to other colleagues in Australia as well as to those in the United States, England, and Canada who most generously supplied me with information and photographs which are acknowledged individually in the legends.

Academic Press, E. J. Brill, *Canadian Journal of Zoology, Experimental Cell Research, Journal of Cell Biology, Journal of Cell Science, Journal of Parasitology, Journal of Ultrastructural Research, Journal of Zoology* (*London*), *Parasitology, Proceedings of the Biological Society of Washington, Proceedings of the Helmintho-logical Society of Washington, Science,* and *Quarterly Review of Biology* all kindly permitted me to use material published in their journals.

I am grateful to the Chief of the Division of Horticultural Research C.S.I.R.O. (Dr. J. V. Possingham) for his support and for allowing me to use the facilities of the division.

Mrs. J. M. Smith (C.S.I.R.O.) prepared some of the photographic prints and many of the drawings, and Mr. D. Eddy (C.S.I.R.O.) translated all the German and some of the French articles. I am most grateful for their help.

Finally, I am deeply indebted to my wife Jean, who did all of the typing, translated most of the French articles, and whose knowledge of both biology and grammar resulted in the elimination of many of the rough spots.

THE   STRUCTURE   OF   NEMATODES

1
GENERAL INTRODUCTION

An interesting account of the history of nematology from the records of Egyptian physicians in 1550 B.C. until the early part of this century is given by Chitwood and Chitwood (1950) in their classic work on nematode anatomy "An Introduction to Nematology." A more recent and equally interesting account of this subject, as seen through the eyes of a zoologist interested in the functional aspects of nematology, is given by Crofton (1966) in the introduction to his book "Nematodes."

The first detailed papers on the structure of nematodes were published at the end of the nineteenth century following the development of suitable microtomes and microscopes. Most of this work was done between 1880 and 1910 on the large nematodes parasitic in animals. This 30-year period of discovery was followed by 30 years during which relatively little research was done on the anatomy and morphology of nematodes. During this period, which includes the two great world wars and the years between them, a great deal of work was done on the taxonomy and physiology of nematodes, particularly in the later part of the period. The reason for this pattern of research is, I think, partly due to the fact that the microscopes available to the worker in the second period were not much better than those available to the worker in the first. Also, the trend toward physiological research in the early twentieth century was accelerated by the supply of instruments which made the technological aspects of this research much easier. The taxonomists were able to continue their work without, usually, requiring resolution greater than that provided by the light microscope. At this time there was an increasing demand for workers trained in this branch of nematology, to identify the increasing numbers of small parasitic forms that were becoming more important in the applied sciences of medicine and agriculture.

As I see it, at the moment we are in the midst of a second period of anatomical discovery which started with the development of the electron microscope on a commercial scale in the 1950's and which is, at present, gathering impetus as more electron microscopes become available to nematologists throughout the world.

Typical nematodes are spindle-shaped, unsegmented, and bilaterally symmetrical pseudocoelomates with four main longitudinal hypodermal cords, a triradiate pharynx, a circumenteric nerve ring, and no circulatory or respiratory organs. They have one or two tubular gonads which open separately in the female and into the rectum in the male which also has copulatory spicules. There are, of course, exceptions to this general definition of a nematode but they are rare. Until as recently as 1965, it was thought that nematodes did not have any cilia but the electron microscope studies of Roggen *et al.* (1966) on *Xiphinema index*, Yuen (1967) on *Ditylenchus dipsaci*, and Ross (1967) on larval stages of *Haemonchus contortus* have clearly demonstrated that cilia do occur in nematode sensory organs.

The need for an instrument, such as the electron microscope, to assist the microanatomist in his studies was apparent for many years. It was reflected in the numerous published drawings of small nematodes which incorporated dotted lines to define structures. Research in experimental pathology has shown that nematodes can act as virus vectors for diseases in both animals and plants (Shope, 1941; Hewitt *et al.*, 1958). However, viruses have not yet been detected in nematode organs, although they have been shown, by means of the electron microscope, to be present in the lumen of the buccal capsule of *Longidorus elongatus* (Taylor and Robertson, 1969) and Weischer (1968) has reported that they can survive in an infective state, in association with nematodes, for several months at least. This raises the whole question of the relationship between microorganisms and nematodes, as yet little explored, and leads to the need of the study of nematode pathology. Little is known about the internal parasites of nematodes although a number of microorganisms come into this category. Protozoans (Williams, 1960, 1967) have been reported as causing disease in both free-living and plant parasitic nematodes. A virus (Loewenberg *et al.*, 1959) has been reported as damaging a plant parasitic nematode. The fungus *Catenaria* (Birchfield, 1960) can exist as a parasite within the tissues of various nematodes and yeastlike microorganisms and rod-shaped bacteria have been observed and photographed under the electron microscope in the intestine of *Aspiculuris tetraptera* (Lee and Anya, 1968) where their presence in large numbers at the cell surface greatly reduces the number of microvilli that are present. Another aspect of nematode pathology which is beginning to receive attention is the study of experimentally induced tumors; Kämpfe (1967) has obtained these tumors in free-living nematodes in response to various carcinogenic substances.

Despite these pioneer works it is clear that much more information on the fine structure of normal tissues is necessary before any changes associated with diseased tissues can be understood and this is particularly true of virus–nematode interrelationships. If one may be permitted to speculate on the future, nematode pathology must surely develop one day into an active branch of science just as its insect equivalent has. As a subject it has considerable potential as the basis for a much more sophisticated approach toward controlling nematodes that are economically undesirable.

It is not difficult to predict that within the next decade or two a great deal more information will become available on the fine structure of nematodes and doubtless some of the ideas that are currently held about their structure will be shown to be wrong.

Despite the fact that they are so numerous and are such a versatile group and have filled so many ecological niches, both as free-living animals and parasites, nematodes show surprising conformity of structure and only comparatively few depart from their remarkably constant cylindrical shape and characteristic arrangement of their internal organs. It remains to be seen if this pattern is reflected in their ultrastructure; the work done so far indicates that this is so.

REFERENCES

Birchfield, W. (1960). *Mycopathol. Mycol. Appl.* **13**, 331.
Chitwood, B. G., and Chitwood, M. B., eds. (1950). "An Introduction to Nematology," 213 pp. Monumental Printing Co., Baltimore, Maryland.
Crofton, H. D. (1966). "Nematodes," 160 pp. Hutchinson, London.
Hewitt, W. B., Raski, D. J., and Goheen, A. C. (1958). *Phytopathology* **48**, 586.
Kämpfe, L. (1967). *Biol. Rundsch.* **5**, 177.
Lee, D. L., and Anya, A. O. (1968). *J. Zool.* **156**, 9.
Loewenberg, J. R., Sullivan, T., and Schuster, M. L. (1959). *Nature (London)* **184**, 1896.
Roggen, D. R., Raski, D. J., and Jones, N. O. (1966). *Science* **152**, 515.
Ross, M. M. R. (1967). *Science* **156**, 1494.
Shope, R. E. (1941). *J. Exp. Med.* **74**, 49.
Taylor, C. E., and Robertson, W. M. (1969). *Ann. Appl. Biol.* **64**, 233.

Weischer, B. (1968). *Mitt. Biol. Bundesanst. Land- Forstwirt Berlin-Dahlem* **128**, 24.
Williams, J. R. (1960). *Nematologica* **5**, 37.
Williams, J. R. (1967). *Nematologica* **13**, 336.
Yuen, P. H. (1967). *Can. J. Zool.* **45**, 1019.

2
TECHNIQUES

Many of the advances that have been made in experimental science are due to the development or use of special techniques and this is particularly true in biology when small organisms are being studied.

The techniques described in this chapter are limited to those that are connected in some way with resolving the various structures of nematodes together with their particular functions. These are techniques that are applied to whole organisms and not to cell cultures, homogenates, or hydrolyzates.

Cairns (1960) has written a comprehensive general review of methods used in the study of nematodes and this is recommended for background reading.

The nematologist's most important tool of trade is, of course, the microscope, but a wide variety of techniques have been developed which supplement and extend the use of this instrument. I propose to deal with these various methods in chronological sequence starting with various techniques used to collect the nematode from its environment and maintain it in a physiological state.

I. Collection and Maintenance

It is essential that all specimens be obtained alive and examined, photographed, and drawn in normal physiological state so that any distortion brought about by subsequent treatment may be noted. The systematics and taxonomy of nematodes are largely based on the measurement of structures such as cuticular appendages and buccal structures, e.g., teeth and stylets, the position of various orifices and copulatory spicules, etc., which do not become distorted during chemical treatment. Methods of fixation will be considered later in this chapter but it is worth noting here that fixation by chemicals and killing by gentle heating using standard procedures (Goodey, 1963) may be responsible for artifacts which make the resolution of some internal structures under the light microscope much more difficult than when the nematode is alive (Bird, 1967).

Marine and freshwater nematodes are generally easier to collect and maintain than parasitic ones. The marine nematode *Deontostoma californicum*, for instance, has been collected from seaweed at low tide and stored at 5°C in aerated seawater which was replenished at weekly intervals (Croll and Maggenti, 1968).

The soil-inhabiting nematodes, i.e., those that remain in the soil throughout their whole life cycle or the free-living stages of various parasitic forms, may be stored for several weeks in shallow, well-aerated distilled water or shaken in distilled water in Warburg flasks at various temperatures. Under these conditions the nematode is, of course, deprived of food and its food reserves in the intestine become depleted, thus making other internal systems easier to see. Goodey (1959) has made use of this in a technique that he describes for demonstrating the excretory system of *Paraphelenchus myceliophthorus*. Various techniques have been devised for separating nematodes from plants and soil and these have been described in detail by Goodey (1963). Many of these methods are capable of providing a quantitative estimate of numbers of nematodes in the soil and so are particularly useful for ecological studies on the variations of field populations, etc. Fortunately, the morphologist does not normally need to know the exact numbers that he collects so that simple qualitative methods are adequate.

Forms parasitic in animals may be dissected from their hosts and stored for several hours in Ringer's solutions maintained at the body temperature of the host. Thus, nematodes parasitic in mammals may often be collected from slaughterhouses and maintained at 38°C in 0.9% sodium chloride solution in a vacuum flask during transport back to the laboratory where they should either be examined immediately or fixed (Hobson, 1948).

A number of different species of nematodes can be readily and conveniently maintained in axenic cultures, notably various rhabditids (Dougherty *et al.*, 1959; Nicholas *et al.*, 1959).

The classic example of axenic cultivation of nematodes is that of the oxyurid *Neoaplectana glaseri* which, in 1958, had been grown by Stoll (1959) for 14 years continuously on kidney tissue in dextrose–agar slants with no noticable diminution in growth capacity over the 219 generations recorded during this period of time. However, no obligate parasitic nematode of mammals has been cultivated axenically through successive generations and, in fact, it is easier to cultivate the hosts of many parasitic nematodes, whether they be plants or animals, and to grow the parasites in these than to maintain sterile cultures.

II. Anesthetics

A solution consisting of 2 drops of dichloroethyl ether in 50 ml of water will anesthetize and immobilize nematodes mounted in it (Goodey, 1963); recovery takes place when they are transferred into freshwater. No information on the lengths of time of exposure to this anesthetic required before immobility is achieved in different genera or the length of time that they can be exposed to the anesthetic before they succumb is available.

Another anesthetic which has been used successfully with some free-living and plant parasitic nematodes is 3-phenoxypropanol (propylene phenoxetol) (Ellenby and Smith, 1964). A 0.5% solution of this chemical has been found to be particularly useful for examining the morphology of the larvae of *Meloidogyne javanica* (Bird, 1967) as these nematodes can tolerate exposure to this solution for 2 hr, during which time they may be examined and photographed at high magnification on ringed slides. After this treatment they recover in water and are physiologically perfectly normal. This anesthetic is clearly a very useful one for work with certain free-living and plant parasitic nematodes although the times of exposure vary among different genera. It apparently has no anesthetic effect at these concentrations on strongyle larvae such as *Haemonchus contortus* and *Nippostrongylus muris*.

The immobilization of nematodes by treatment with various gases has been studied in some detail by Maggenti and Viglierchio (1965), who found that while inert gases such as nitrogen and helium were unsatisfactory, gases such as Freon-12 and Freon-22 immobilized the nematodes within 4 hr and carbon dioxide at pH 4.5 produced this effect within 2 hr. Carbon dioxide and Freon-22 improved the clarity of the nematodes, which suggests that physiological changes might have taken place within them, although these were apparently reversible.

Thus, for accurate morphological examination of nematodes, particularly for internal structures of microscopic specimens whose recovery may be required for physiological purposes, either dichloroethyl ether, 3-phenoxypropanol, or carbon dioxide should prove to be suitable anesthetics for a wide range of nematodes. Information on the mode of action of these or other potential anesthetics for nematodes is lacking.

III. Measurement

While the largest nematodes can readily be measured with the naked eye or under dissecting microscopes, the vast majority of adult forms and all eggs and larvae are best measured at the limit of resolution of the light microscope and in most cases their cell components can only be measured satisfactorily under the electron microscope. Measurement under the light microscope can be done with either an ocular micrometer, an ocular screw micrometer, or by means of an image-splitting eyepiece. All of these devices are first of all calibrated by means of a stage micrometer. This consists of a scale, usually 2 mm in length and divided into minor divisions which are 10 μ apart and major divisions which are 100 μ apart. This scale is enclosed between a microscope slide and a coverglass and the ocular micrometer is focused upon it so that the spacings or rulings in the ocular micrometer can be calibrated. This calibration depends, of course, on the magnification of the objectives and oculars used.

The stage micrometer may be used for calibrating photographs by photographing and printing it at the same magnification as the photographs.

Both the ocular screw micrometer and the image-splitting eyepiece use a micrometer screw which consists of a drum on which is engraved a scale. It is this scale that is calibrated at different magnifications by means of the stage micrometer. The screw micrometer consists of a scale beneath which intersecting cross-graticule lines and a pair of double lines are moved by turning the drum. The double lines are set on the scale and the edge of the specimen to be measured is brought to the intersecting lines by means of the microscope stage. The drum is then turned until the intersecting lines reach the other limit of measurement and the readings on the scale are added and comparison is made to a calibration chart.

The image-splitting eyepiece is more useful for measuring irregular or moving objects. It makes use of a principle that has been used by astronomers for centuries to determine variations of the angular diameter of the sun. The method consists of splitting the image into two identical images which can be placed edge-to-edge and then superimposed by means of a screw micrometer which is calibrated for different magnifications. This system has been developed (Dyson, 1960) as an accessory which can be fitted directly into the eyepiece tube of a conventional microscope. The reading on the screw micrometer scale is noted and the screw is turned until the images are superimposed when the reading on the scale is again noted. The width or length of the image can be calculated by reference to a calibration chart.

Measurements under the electron microscope are made by photographing the object at required magnifications obtained by altering the currents in the intermediate and projector lenses. Electron microscopes may be calibrated by photographing structures such as polystyrene spheres of known diameter at set magnifications and comparing these with those expected theoretically. Alternatively, in some instruments, the intermediate screen is engraved with two circles so that when the intermediate lens is excited to a set value and a 70 μ aperture is focused on to this screen, its image will lie between the diameters of the inner and outer circles if the machine is correctly calibrated.

While it is relatively simple to weigh large nematodes, it is difficult to obtain rapid accurate weighings, even by Cartesian diver methods, for those that are about 0.5 mm long and about 20 μ wide. The weight of several thousand freeze-dried specimens of these dimensions can be measured rapidly on a Cahn electrobalance (Van Gundy et al., 1967) but the total procedure is time-consuming and relies on accurate counting. Provided that the width and length of the nematode can be measured and the specific gravity is known the weight may be calculated (Overgaard Nielsen, 1949; Andrássy, 1956). Andrássy (1956) rapidly calculates the weights of various small nematodes by means of a formula

$$G = (a^2 \times b)/(16 \times 100,000)\,\mu g$$

where a is the greatest body width, b is the body length, and 16 is an empirical value calculated mathematically by Andrássy.

This formula does not appear to hold exactly for large worms such as *Ascaris* which can be weighed directly and which are found to have greater values than those calculated from Andrássy's equation. This may be due to a variation in the empirical value when dealing with large nematodes or, more probably, to the fact that the specific gravity varies with the size and physiological state of the nematode.

IV. Fixatives

Prior to fixation, nematodes may be killed by gentle heating in a cavity slide until heat rigor occurs, when they straighten out (Goodey, 1963), or by pouring a hot (almost 100° C) solution of 0.5% acetic acid over the nematodes in a small drop of water (Seinhorst, 1962). Killing and fixation may be combined by using a hot solution of 40% formaldehyde:acetic acid:water (10:1:89) commonly known as FA 4:1 (Seinhorst, 1966).

An alternative method of killing and storing nematodes prior to fixation is to quick-freeze them (Hoff and Mai, 1964). This is done by rapidly placing a nematode suspension into approximately four times its volume of liquid nitrogen and then maintaining the temperature at $-35°$C.

Vapor-phase perfusion as a method of killing nematodes prior to fixation has been studied in detail by Maggenti and Viglierchio (1965), who have also made a comprehensive study of fixation and the processing of nematodes into glycerine. They are aware that "there is no technique for preserving all tissues in a whole mount eternally and in a lifelike condition" and that the different properties of the tissues in whole mounts preclude any one procedure from preserving each tissue at optimum quality.

Cytologists would, perhaps, feel a little uneasy about some of the methods that have been described above but it should be remembered that nematodes are surrounded by a barrier, the cuticle, which impedes the entry of chemicals, so that the methods that are suitable for tissues that are cut from whole organisms are often quite unsuitable for small nematodes.

Fixatives may be divided into two groups, according to their effects on proteins (Baker, 1958). Substances such as methanol, ethanol, and acetone act as coagulants while substances such as formaldehyde, osmium tetroxide, and acetic acid are noncoagulants. Fixatives are often mixtures of a number of chemicals which act better in this fashion than when used on their own. Baker's (1958) book is recommended for a more comprehensive and detailed account of fixatives.

In recent years, with the advent of the electron microscope, particular care has been given to the use of buffered isotonic fixatives of the noncoagulant type such as osmium tetroxide and aldehydes such as formaldehyde and gluteraldehyde. The methods of preparation and use of these fixatives are described in detail by Pease (1964) in his excellent book on histological techniques for electron microscopy.

Various fixatives have been used on nematodes for ultrastructural studies. In addition to those listed above, potassium permanganate and acrolein have been used with success on both marine and soil-inhabiting nematodes (Wright and Jones, 1965).

I have found (Bird and Saurer, 1967) that the following technique gives very satisfactory fixation of a number of plant parasitic nematodes for studies under both the UV microspectrograph and the electron microscope.

1. The nematodes are cooled in a small volume of distilled water in a covered dish for 30 min at 5°C. Time and temperature will probably vary for different nematodes. The temperature should be low enough to straighten the nematode and yet maintain it in a physiological state so that it recovers if brought back to room temperature. If the nematode is fixed in a bent shape high-resolution photomicrography or sectioning for electron microscopy is difficult.

2. The nematodes are fixed by pouring cold (5°C) 4% buffered formal-

dehyde (pH 7.3) over them and leaving them at this temperature for 30 min.

3. After this they are concentrated by centrifugation, placed in a drop of fixative on a clean slide, and cut by chopping with a sharp scalpel. This procedure removes the cuticle barrier and permits better subsequent fixation of internal structures which have already been fixed enough to prevent the extrusion of the body contents which takes place when living nematodes are cut open.

4. After cutting, the pieces of nematodes are replaced in fresh fixative at 5°C for periods of from 30 min to 2 hr, after which they are washed in distilled water and are then ready for treatment with enzymes, substrates, or stains.

The cuticle acts as a barrier to many of these substances and uncut nematodes often remain unstained and give evidence of poorer fixation under the electron microscope.

The buffer that I have found most satisfactory for use with fixatives for preserving the fine structure of nematodes is Millonig's phosphate buffer (Millonig, 1961, 1962) without 0.5% glucose. This buffer is made by adding a solution of sodium hydroxide to one of monosodium phosphate. The pH is adjusted between 5.4 and 8.0 by varying the amount of alkali. A pH of 7.3 is obtained by adding 17 ml of 2.52% sodium hydroxide to 83 ml of 2.26% monosodium phosphate. Instead of using formalin, which may contain traces of methanol, paraformaldehyde powder is used. Four grams is dissolved in the buffer by warming it up to 60°C and adjusting the pH to 7.3 by adding drops of sodium hydroxide solution. The solution eventually becomes clear and the pH of the fixative is checked on a meter. Further information on this method of preparation of a formaldehyde fixative and of various other well-tried fixatives including Zetterqvist's osmium tetroxide fixative, which is also useful for nematodes, is available in detail (Pease, 1964).

V. Dehydration and Embedding

Whole small nematodes or parts of large nematodes are often examined as permanent mounts in substances such as glycerine, lactophenol, balsam, or various neutral mounting media. While nematodes treated in this manner can never give as true a picture as living anesthetized specimens do, nevertheless, certain taxonomical characters are often shown more clearly by these methods and the specimens can be stored for long periods of time with no apparent changes in their morphology. In fact, the mounting of small nematodes in glycerine is a standard procedure which is described in detail in various texts (Goodey, 1963; Thorne, 1961). There are two methods, one taking several weeks and the other about an hour.

The former consists of placing the fixed nematodes in a 1.5% solution of glycerine (containing a trace of thymol or copper sulfate to prevent mold growth) in a desiccator for 4 to 6 weeks, during which time the water evaporates slowly leaving the nematodes in pure glycerine. The short method (Baker, 1953) takes about 1 hr. It consists of gently heating the nematodes in lactophenol to 65°C and then transferring them through a graded series of reagents consisting of mixtures of formalin, phenol, lactic acid, water, and glycerine. With each step the concentration of glycerine is increased and eventually the specimens are mounted in anhydrous glycerine. The cover slips of glycerine-mounted material are always ringed with a hard setting mountant which prevents subsequent water uptake by the glycerine and movement of the coverglass when immersion oil is being removed.

Glycerine is unusual in that it acts both as a dehydrant and a mounting medium. In most cases the mounting medium is selected because it has a refractive index close to that of glass. A substance such as balsam, for instance, is insoluble in dehydrants such as various alcohols and after dehydration the specimen must be passed through an intermediate chemical, such as benzene or xylene, which is soluble in alcohols and balsam.

Methods of dehydration and embedding are described in detail in various modern textbooks. For background reading, the chapter on microtomy in Baker's book on cytological technique (Baker, 1950) is recommended. This deals with frozen sections, paraffin embedding, and celloidin embedding; Pearse (1968) gives a comprehensive account of cryostat methods in his most recent text on histochemistry.

I find redistilled ethanol to be as good a dehydrant as any and routinely use the following procedure for embedding prior to microtomy, both for the light and electron microscopes.

A. Washing

The material is washed three times in distilled water (10 min each time) to remove as much of the unbound fixatives, such as osmium tetroxide, as possible.

B. Dehydration

Dehydrate in a graded series of ethanol for 30 min each as follows: 30, 50, 70 (the material may be left overnight at this stage), 80, 90%, and finally two changes of 30 min each in absolute ethanol.

C. Embedding

1. *Light Microscopy*

Place in the following mixtures for 30 min each at room temperature: (1:1) ethanol:xylene, pure xylene. The material is then placed in a small vacuum desiccator in an oven at 60°C for 30 min in (1:1) xylene:Paraplast *in vacuo*. (Paraplast is a compound of paraffin and plastic polymers produced by Arthur H. Thomas company, Philadelphia, Pa. It has a melting point of 56°– 57°C. Various other paraffin waxes with different melting points may be used.) Finally, the material is transferred to pure Paraplast *in vacuo* at 60°C, two changes are made within 30 min, and the tissue is finally embedded using two solid brass L pieces which, when slid against each other, give various-sized molds for the blocks. These are placed in a shallow flat glass dish whose surface and that of the L pieces are smeared with a (9:1) solution of 60% ethanol:glycerine and these are placed in a deep freeze to cool. When the brass pieces are at the temperature of the deep freeze, the Paraplast is poured into the mold and the tissue is then orientated in the block with the aid of a hot needle or spatula. The dish is then returned to the deep freeze. The cold blocks are easily removed when required. I find this method better than the conventional ones in which paper, metal, or plastic boats with iced water are used.

2. *Electron Microscopy*

The details of embedding materials for use in electron microscopy have been comprehensively described in recent texts and reviews (Pease, 1964; Wischnitzer, 1967). Of the four principal embedding media—methacrylate, epoxy resins, polyester resins, and a group of water-soluble embedding media such as glycol methacrylate, aquon, and durcupan—the epoxy resins have been found to be the most consistently useful for many organisms, including the nematodes. These epoxy resins are Araldite, Epon, and Maraglas. The low-viscosity epoxy resin described by Spurr (1969) may also prove to be useful.

Epon is an aliphatic resin and its monomer is more fluid than that of the aromatic Araldite and thus it is handled more easily. I find the following two formulas for Epon and Maraglas to be both convenient and satisfactory for the embedding of small nematodes and better than the durcupan–Epon method previously described (Bird, 1964b) although dehydration with fat solvents must lead to some artifacts. However, thorough embedding and the production of a hard block are more important.

Epon	ml
Epon 812	47.0
DDSA (dodecenyl succinic anhydride)	20.0
MNA (methyl nadic anhydride)	33.0
BDMA (benzyldimethyl amine)	1.6

Maraglas	
Maraglas 665	68.0
Cardolite NC 513	20.0
DBP (dibutyl phthalate)	10.0
BNMA (benzyldimethyl amine)	2.0

These reagents are measured out, mixed carefully, and stored in the deep freeze until used in plastic specimen tubes.

The nematodes are placed in a (1:1) ethanol:Epon mixture (overnight in capped vials or specimen tubes). They are then placed in fresh Epon *in vacuo* at room temperature for 2 hr and are then polymerized in plastic or gelatin capsules for 48 hr at 60°C.

Specimens are treated in a similar fashion if Maraglas is used except that propylene oxide is used as an intermediary between ethanol and the Maraglas mixture. Thus the nematodes go through a (1:1) ethanol:propylene oxide mixture and then into two changes of pure propylene oxide over 30 min and can then be left overnight in a (1:1) propylene oxide:Maraglas mixture. They are then placed in fresh Maraglas *in vacuo* for 2 hr and polymerized in plastic molds for 48 hr at 60°C.

The orientation of small nematodes in the embedding medium is very important. A number of methods have been used with satisfactory results for a variety of genera. Nematodes may be orientated in slits in 1–3% agar blocks (Wright and Jones, 1965). They are sealed into this position by means of a molten (45°C) drop of agar. The agar block is trimmed to orientate the nematodes and fit snugly into a gelatin capsule. The material is dehydrated by normal procedures and the agar is infiltrated with either Epon or Maraglas. An alternative, and perhaps even better method is to orientate the nematodes in slits of polymerized blocks or sheets of Epon or Maraglas and to seal them in with a drop of the epoxy resin which is then polymerized in the normal way. After this the nematode can be fitted snugly into a capsule and polymerized in the normal way (Ross, 1967).

Another way of orientating small nematodes that I find useful is to use a cut-down Beem capsule. The sloping part of the capsule is held in a hole in a wooden block and the nematode is placed into position with fine needles under a dissecting microscope. For transverse section, for which a vertical specimen is required, repeated attention during the early stages of polymerization is required. The shaped block is removed after 18 hr at 60°C and placed in a whole Beem capsule into which it fits snugly, epoxy resin is added to the top of the capsule—any trapped air is removed by down-ward pressure with a needle—and the whole block is polymerized.

VI. Microtomy

Because of the difference in technique, microtomy is perhaps best con-sidered under the two headings microtome and ultramicrotome.

A. THE MICROTOME

A great deal of information has been obtained about the internal struc-tures of the larger nematodes by examination of stained sections of paraffin-embedded material. The basic methods, and microtomes capable of cutting 5–10 μ-thick serial sections, have been available since the end of the nine-teenth century and are largely responsible for the advances in knowledge of nematode anatomy made with such genera as *Ancylostoma* (Looss, 1905) and *Ascaris* (Goldschmidt, 1908, 1909, 1910).

Since this time there have been improvements in embedding media and design of microtomes but the basic technique remains the same. Because of the susceptibility of nematodes to distortion during sectioning of paraffin-embedded material, collodion has been used in conjunction with paraffin for many years. It has been used to cover the sections before cutting them (Looss, 1905) or the nematodes may be double embedded (Wright, 1966). Both ester wax (Kan and Davey, 1968) and Paraplast appear to be better embedding media for nematodes than pure paraffin wax.

Excellent and comprehensive descriptions of the techniques of wax sectioning are given in the textbooks of Baker (1950) and Jensen (1962).

The development of cold microtomes or cryostats is much more recent but although commercial models have been available over the last twenty years, they have not been used much by nematologists. These instruments have many advantages over the old type of carbon dioxide-cooled freezing microtome which, nevertheless, can be utilized to great advantage with large nematodes using phase contrast microscopy (Bird, 1958). By means of the cryostat, it is now possible to cut thin serial sections with ease. An up-to-date description of the theory and techniques associated with these instruments is given by Pearse (1968).

B. THE ULTRAMICROTOME

The majority of nematodes are too small to be sectioned satisfactorily using conventional wax embedding or frozen methods. The development of ultramicrotomes using low-power binocular microscopes to observe sections of material embedded in epoxy resins being cut with glass or diamond knives onto a fluid surface has revolutionized the study of fine structures in nematodes. For the first time, the detailed anatomy of small nematodes and various larval stages can be examined and the relationships of nematodes with various microorganisms established.

The different makes of ultramicrotomes and their methods of operation have been adequately described in the literature (Pease, 1964) and need not be repeated here beyond pointing out a few of the essential requirements of a good ultramicrotome. It should be equipped with a low-power binocular dissecting microscope with good illumination, a range of magnifications, and easy adjustment, so that both observation of the sectioning process and trimming of the specimen block can be done with a minimum of disruption. There should be a wide range of cutting speeds and easy adjustment of the correct knife height and angle. Cutting speeds as low as 0.5 mm/sec are necessary for some nematodes. The range of distances that the block is advanced at each stroke should be sufficient to allow one to cut the required thickness of section and this, of course, varies with the hardness of the material and embedding medium being used. The lighting used should permit rapid assessment of section thicknesses by their interference colors. The distance that the specimen is advanced at each stroke may be either mechanically or thermally controlled or both may be used, in which case the former is used for thicker sections. It is an advantage to have an ultramicrotome that can also cut sections of known thickness for use with the light microscope. In thermal advance instruments a cooling fan is useful. Perhaps the three greatest worries for the ultramicrotomist are drafts, dust, and vibration and if satisfactory results are ever to be obtained, these factors must be considered in positioning ultramicroromes in laboratories.

Details of glass knife preparation and sources of diamond knives are given by Pease (1964). Glass knives are preferable to diamond knives because the latter are fragile and can easily be damaged by the inexperienced worker. Also, it is apparently difficult to standardize their manufacture, as their quality varies. Glass knives, on the other hand, are readily replaced if damaged, can be made rapidly and effectively using a machine designed for this purpose and are just as effective, if not better, for cutting nematode material.

Ultrathin sections are cut on to a fluid surface which may be either distilled water or something like 10% acetone which wets glass better. I find that distilled water, which has been passed through a bacterial filter to remove dust and debris, works well. The various methods for making troughs for glass knives are described in detail in various texts and in the microtome manufacturers' manuals. I find adhesive tape of a little under 1 cm in width suitable; the heel of the trough can be neatly sealed with nail varnish rather than with hot wax or rubber cement.

Methods of cutting sections and correcting faults tend to be specific for different ultramicrotomes and are best described and illustrated in the manufacturers' manuals. It takes more experience and technical ability to operate an ultramicrotome than an ordinary microtome. When the knife is cutting well and factors such as knife height and angle and level of fluid in the trough are correct, it is advisable to continue to use the knife for as long as possible before changing it. It often helps to spread sections by holding a small strip of filter paper soaked in trichlorethylene over them using a fine clamp mounted on a holder. The section should be watched carefully during this maneuver to ensure that the expansion is gentle. Sections are easily picked up on coated grids by placing the grids, held by forceps, on top of them, lifting them out, and tilting them on to filter paper to remove excess fluid. Care should be taken to ensure that the sections lie across the middle of the grid so that their localization when viewed under the electron microscope is easier.

The various methods of coating grids are described in detail in Chapter 6 of Pease's book (Pease, 1964). The grids which I find most convenient for work with small nematodes are those of 150 mesh. They are coated with a 0.5% solution of Parlodion (trade name of a nitrocellulose plastic; Mallinckrodt Chemical Works, St Louis, Missouri), in amyl acetate as follows: An ordinary 1 × 3 in microscope slide is dipped in this solution and dried in an oven at 60°C. With the tip of a scalpel blade the film is cut on all four sides about 0.25 in from the edge of the slide which is then slid gently at an angle under the surface of some distilled water so that the rectangular sheet of Parlodion floats off as a raft. The container for the distilled water is built so that it can be drained from the bottom and it also contains a 1 × 3 in strip of brass gauze which sits on a three-sided metal form that raises the gauze strip about an inch from the bottom of the container. Now the Parlodion raft is guided over the gauze strip on which are placed a number of grids. The tap at the bottom of the container is gently opened so that, as the water level falls, the Parlodion settles on the gauze and the grids. All the water is now drained from the container and the strip of gauze is removed, drained on filter paper, and dried in a partly covered dish in an oven at 60°C. When dry, the gauze strip and grids are stored in a covered dish until required. The grids are then lifted off and the coated surface of the grid touched against a clean slide to remove any loose strips of film before being placed over the sections.

Great care must be taken at all times in the preparation of materials for electron microscopy to keep the working area clean and dust-free. It is well worthwhile to examine coated grids under the phase contrast microscope before they are used to collect sections and this procedure itself may be wasted if any dust has settled on the fluid in the trough or if stains used in postsectional staining are not filtered or even if, during loading into the specimen holder of the electron microscope, the grid happens to fall onto a dusty surface.

VII. Observation

Generally speaking, observations on the structure of living nematodes have paralleled the development of techniques which are a compromise between keeping the nematodes alive and healthy and permitting maximum resolution. Hanging drop slides have been used to study the larvae of nematodes parasitic in animals (Lapage, 1935) and various observation chambers have been used to demonstrate feeding in plant parasitic nematodes (Linford, 1937, 1942). Linford obtained particularly good photographs using a ×40 water-immersion objective and cooled incident light. His work has only been bettered in more recent times by Doncaster (1962, 1966) using high- and medium-power apochromatic objectives and a metallurgical objective as a condenser. He (Doncaster, 1964) has described in detail four different types of observation chamber that he has used to study the behavior and morphology of plant parasitic and soil-inhabiting nematodes under the ordinary light microscope at high magnification. These are (1) an observation dish for agar cultures, (2) a variable depth sealed observation chamber, (3) a perfusion chamber, and (4) a moisture-controlled observation chamber.

The moisture-controlled observation chamber is intended for observations on nematodes penetrating or within an entire seedling while the perfusion chamber is intended for observations of nematodes on their own or in portions of host tissue. The perfusion chamber described by Doncaster (1962) is a modification of one described by Paul (1957) that I have found particularly useful for studies with nematodes (Bird, 1959, 1968b). This consists of a plastic center section carrying two reservoirs which are connected to the culture chamber by two channels that run underneath it (Fig. 1A). When the chamber is assembled and screwed together so that the rubber gaskets seal and make it watertight, these channels act as ducts. The medium is added to one reservoir and removed from the other. With a little experience, air bubbles are easily removed and the specimen located in the center of the coverslip area. If specimens move due to the flow of the

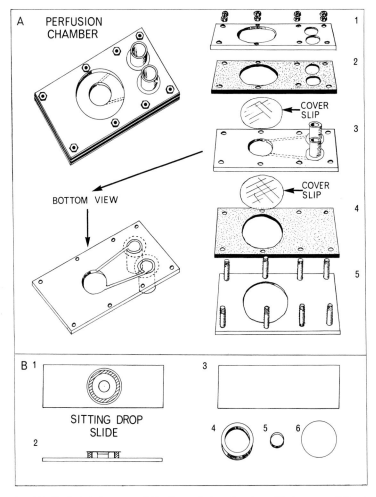

FIG. 1. (A) Exploded diagram of Paul's perfusion chamber; (B) diagram of Gautheret's sitting drop slide.

perfusing fluid, they can be "anchored" in the center by adhesion to a small drop of agar jelly or placed within a ring of soft wax painted thinly on the center of the lower coverslip (Doncaster, 1964). A great advantage of Paul's perfusion slide is that it enables either media or stains to be rapidly and easily replaced so that it is readily used for certain types of histochemical studies (Bird, 1968b).

A simpler and more convenient type of observation chamber for nematodes is the sitting drop slide (Fig. 1B). This was designed by Gautheret and is described in White's book (White, 1954). It consists of an ordinary glass slide, a brass ring about 20 mm in diameter and about 4 mm high, an optically ground glass disc 7 mm in diameter and 3 mm high, and a 22-mm round coverglass. The ring is attached to the slide with petroleum jelly or an adhesive which gives greater rigidity if so required. The disc is placed in the middle of the cavity on a small drop of water large enough to attach it by capillarity without air bubbles, but small enough to prevent it from slipping sideways. The top of the brass ring is painted with molten petroleum jelly and the nematodes in their medium are placed on top of the disc, experience determining the correct size of the drop of fluid used, and the coverslip is then placed on top of the ring so that an optically continuous system is established between the top of the coverglass and the bottom of the slide. In this respect it is much superior to the hanging drop slide. I find this system to be ideally suited for examining nematodes and their eggs for periods of up to a week or more (Bird, 1959, 1968a).

Another simple type of observation chamber which has yielded good results with high power observations on the feeding of a plant parasitic nematode and which could presumably be used with a wide range of nematodes has been described by McElroy and Van Gundy (1968). It consists of two concentric rings in which the smaller fits tightly inside the larger. The material to be examined, which has been growing in agar, is cut out and sandwiched between two pieces of polyethylene stretched tight by the rings.

VIII. Staining

The use of different staining techniques has contributed significantly to increase our knowledge of nematode morphology, even though these techniques are invariably nonspecific.

Early staining methods were used to increase the contrast of sections of nematodes viewed under the microscope using normal transmitted light without having to close the iris diaphragm of the condenser and so decrease resolution. With the advent of modern optical techniques, such as phase or interference contrast microscopy, in which contrast is enhanced without loss of resolution, stains were used more to define the chemical composition of the cells and tissues under examination. Histochemistry is becoming more and more important in correlating structure and function in all nematodes. There are numerous excellent textbooks on histochemistry. Of these, at least two (Jensen, 1962; Pearse, 1968) are particularly useful in that they provide concise accounts of a wide variety of methods.

The use of dyes as an aid to the study of nematode structure and function may, perhaps, be considered under the following headings.

A. General Staining

Dyes may be divided into three major groups (Baker, 1958), namely, the quinonoid dyes, the azo dyes, and the nitro dyes. The quinonoid dyes include dyes such as hematoxylin, carmine, and the fuchsins that have been used extensively by various early workers studying nematode structure under the microscope.

Details of the origin and isolation of the active components of these and many other dyes are given by Baker (1958), together with an account of the chemistry of mordanting in microtechnique. Mordants, of course, are substances which alter the behavior of particular dyes so that when the tissue–mordant–dye complex has been formed, it becomes insoluble in various neutral fluids and dehydrating agents; consequently, further washing, staining with other dyes, and dehydration in alcohols need not be hurried.

A good general stain for nematodes of all types is Heidenhain's hematoxylin (Baker, 1958) with a 2.5% solution of ferric alum as the mordant (Maggenti, 1961) and 0.5% fast green as a counterstain (Elsea, 1951).

Another good general stain for nematodes is Mallory's triple stain. This gives better differentiation of the layers of the cuticle than other stains that I know of (Bird and Deutsch, 1957).

The staining procedure is as follows (after Pantin, 1946):

1. Bring slides to water
2. Mordant in saturated $HgCl_2$ in 5% acetic acid (10 min)
3. Rinse in distilled water
4. 0.1% acid fuchsin (5 sec)
5. Differentiate in distilled water (10 sec)
6. Mordant in 1% phosphomolybdic acid (20 sec)
7. Wash in distilled water (10 sec)
8. Stain in Mallory's stain (0.5 gm aniline blue WS:2.0 gm orange G:2.0 gm oxalic acid/100 ml water) (25 sec)
9. Drain and wipe back of slide
10. 90% ethanol (10 sec)
11. Absolute ethanol I (10 sec)
12. Absolute ethanol II (10 sec)
13. Rinse in xylene
14. Mount in balsam

B. Chromosome Staining

The chromosome stains are histochemical stains for nucleic acids. They are associated with special techniques of fixation, mordanting, chemical and physical treatment which result in the chromosomes being displayed in a prominent manner. These techniques are described in detail by Darlington and la Cour (1960). The classic and comprehensive work of van Beneden (1883) with *Ascaris megalocephala* (*Parascaris equorum*), which took full advantage of the small number of chromosomes involved, clearly showed for the first time that the chromosomes of the offspring were derived equally from the nuclei of the egg and the sperm, thus establishing one of the fundamentals of genetics. Van Beneden used a variety of techniques involving borax carmine or picrocarmine as stains and glacial acetic, nitric, or osmic acids as fixatives.

As a result of modern techniques, the chromosomes of the smaller free-living and plant parasitic nematodes have been studied by various workers and some excellent photographs have been obtained of their often minute and numerous chromosomes.

Three of the most useful techniques used on these nematodes are Feulgen (Nigon and Brun, 1955; Triantaphyllou, 1963) and the propionic–orcein (Mulvey, 1955; Triantaphyllou, 1963) or acetic-orcein methods (Triantaphyllou and Hirschmann, 1966). The former is usually used on sections and the latter two on smears. The smear or squash technique is both rapid and efficient. The method used by Triantaphyllou and Hirschmann (1966) is as follows:

1. Smear the material, either egg-laying females or young males, onto a clean slide and submerge in 1 N hydrochloric acid for 3 min
2. Place in ethanol:acetic acid (3:1) for 15 min
3. Stain in 2% acetic orcein (2% orcein in 45% acetic acid) for 15 min
4. Wash away excess stain in 45% acetic acid for a few seconds
5. Make slides permanent by quick freezing (Conger and Fairchild, 1953) as follows:

(a) Remove the slide from the 45% acetic acid and place on top of a flat block of Dry Ice and press on this until frozen (approx. 30 sec)

(b) Place the frozen slide immediately into 95% ethanol (5 min)

(c) Transfer it to absolute ethanol (5 min)

(d) Remove from absolute ethanol and mount in Euporal *without* draining away the alcohol, as the excess of alcohol over the cells at the time the mounting medium is applied prevents the collapse of the cells at this step

C. Histochemical Staining

The range of techniques available to the investigator is large and increasing all the time. However, very few are quantitative for a particular chemical. Perhaps the best known and most widely used quantitative histochemical staining technique is the Feulgen method for deoxyribonucleic acid in which the color produced is proportional to the amount of DNA present. Nevertheless, there are a number of histochemical techniques that are both reliable and specific for a number of chemical compounds. These compounds include enzymes whose substrates have been synthesized and are available. With the aid of various controls, inhibitors, and these substrates, the presence of enzymes can be detected in various different types of nematodes.

A number of these techniques, which I have found to be most useful when working with cut whole mounts of small nematodes, are described below. Most of them have been used on wax sections of larger nematodes.

Both of these methods involve cutting the cuticle and exposing the internal structures to the stains. The method using cut whole mounts is to be preferred to wax sections because it does not involve the eluting processes of various dehydrating agents nor the inactivating effect of heating associated with wax embedding. There are some chemicals which make the cuticle more permeable to stains, particularly when heated, but again these procedures accelerate inactivation of substances such as enzymes.

The nematodes are cooled, fixed, and cut as described above for the electron microscope. After an hour in the buffered formaldehyde, the nematodes do not extrude their body contents when cut and are then ready for treatment with histochemical stains after being washed several times in buffer or distilled water. Washing of these cut nematodes is all done by centrifugation.

1. Carbohydrates

The periodic acid–Schiff technique (PAS) is a most reliable method. The periodic acid oxidizes the 1:2 glycol groups of the carbohydrate to dialdehydes, which combine with Schiff's reagent to give a substituted dye that is red in color. The procedure is as follows (after McManus, 1948).

1. Oxidize in 0.5% periodic acid (5 min)
2. Wash in distilled water
3. Place in Schiff's reagent (prepared by bubbling sulfur dioxide into a 1% solution of basic fuchsin in distilled water) (15 min)
4. Three changes in sulfurous acid (2 min each) prepared by bubbling sulfur dioxide into distilled water
5. Wash several times in water
6. Mount in distilled water and photograph or dehydrate, clear in xylene, and mount in a neutral mounting medium for permanent slides

Controls are treated with salivary amylase for 3 hr at 37°C and the reaction is prevented by acetylation.

2. *Lipids*

A good general stain is Sudan black B (after McManus, 1946) used as follows:
1. Take up to 70% ethanol
2. Stain in saturated Sudan black B in 70% ethanol (30 min)
3. Wash in 70% ethanol to remove excess dye
4. Wash in water
5. Mount in water and photograph or mount in glycerine jelly

For controls use various lipid solvents.

3. *Nucleic Acids*

A particularly useful stain is gallocyanin–chromalum (after Einarson, 1951). The method is as follows.
1. Wash in water
2. Stain for 48 hr in gallocyanin–chromalum (prepared by dissolving 5 gm of chromalum in 100 ml of distilled water, adding 0.15 gm gallocyanin, bringing to boil and refluxing for 5 min; filter when cool and make up to 100 ml with distilled water
3. Wash briefly in water
4. Dehydrate in ethanol series
5. Clear in xylene and mount in neutral mounting medium

For controls use deoxyribonuclease, ribonuclease, and various nucleic acid solvents.

There is a stoichiometric relationship between this dye and the nucleic acids (Sandritter *et al.*, 1963; Kiefer *et al.*, 1967).

4. *Histones (after Alfert and Geschwind, 1953)*

1. Wash in water
2. Extract nucleic acids by placing in 15% trichloroacetic acid at 90°–100°C for 15 min or in 15% trichloroacetic acid at 60°C for 1 hr
3. Wash 3 times in 70% ethanol
4. Stain 30 min in 0.1% fast green F.C.F. at pH 8.0 (adjusted with 0.1 N NaOH)
5. Wash in distilled water (5 min)
6. Place in 95% ethanol
7. Dehydrate, clear in xylene, and mount in a neutral mounting medium

5. *Proteins*

The mercuric–bromophenol blue method (after Bonhag, 1955).

1. Wash in water

2. Stain for 2 hr at room temperature in a solution consisting of 0.05% bromophenol blue in 2% acetic acid and containing 1% mercuric chloride

3. Wash in 0.5% acetic acid for 20 min

4. Place directly into tertiary butanol (3 changes over 3 hr)

5. Clear in xylene and mount in neutral mounting medium

6. *Neurosecretions*

Reports on neurosecretory cells are becoming more common, particularly in large nematodes such as *Ascaris* (Davey, 1964) which are the easiest to section and stain. The aldehyde–fuchsin method used (Cameron and Steele, 1959) is as follows:

1. Wash in water

2. Oxidize in a solution consisting of 0.3% potassium permanganate in 0.2% sulfuric acid (1 min)

3. Wash in sulfurous acid solution (see Section VIII, C, 1, step 4) to remove stain (a few seconds)

4. Wash in distilled water

5. Take to 70% ethanol through 30% ethanol (5 min)

6. Stain in an aldehyde–fuchsin solution (10 min). This solution consists of 0.5% aldehyde–fuchsin in 70% ethanol. The aldehyde–fuchsin is made as follows: 1 gm of basic fuchsin is added to 200 ml of boiling water, boiled for 1 min, cooled, and filtered; 2 ml of concentrated hydrochloric acid and 2 ml of paraldehyde are added to the filtrate. This is left in a stoppered bottle at room temperature and tested each day by removing a drop and placing it on filter paper. When the solution has lost its red color (3–4 days) it is filtered and the filtrate is discarded. The precipitate is dried on filter paper at 60°C and the crystals, which should weigh a little less than 2 gm, are stored in a sealed container

7. Rinse in 95% ethanol

8. Wash in 95% ethanol (5 min)

9. Bring to water through 70% and 30% ethanol and photograph or

10. Wash twice in absolute ethanol after step (8)

11. Clear in xylene and mount in a neutral mounting medium

A positive result for this test should be followed by a search for neurosecretory granules using the electron microscope.

7. *Enzymes*

The number of histochemical tests for enzymes increase as more enzymes are discovered and more of their substrates are synthesized. The syntheses of various dyes and substrates are described, together with various methods of enzyme histochemistry, by Burstone (1962).

The techniques described below are chosen for their reliability and simplicity, involving the minimum number of changes through various solutions, an important consideration when dealing with small organisms, and because they have all been used on nematodes that are parasitic in either animals or plants.

a. Esterase. Of several methods used on nematodes, Holt's (1958) indigogenic method was found to be the most satisfactory. The procedure (Bird, 1966) is as follows:

1. Wash in water
2. Incubate for 1 hr at 30°C in fresh stain–substrate solution made up as follows: 2 ml of 0.1 M tris buffer (pH 8.5); 1 ml of (1:1) potassium ferricyanide: potassium ferrocyanide, both 5×10^{-2} M; 0.1 ml of 1 M calcium chloride; 5 ml of 2 M sodium chloride; 0.1 ml of absolute ethanol containing 1.5 mg of 5-bromo-4-chloroindoxyl acetate; 1.8 ml of distilled water
3. Mount in water under a coverslip sealed with dental wax or petroleum jelly and photograph. Controls consist of either heating the nematodes for 10 min in distilled water in a boiling water bath before incubation in the substrate, or using specific inhibitors such as eserine, or omitting the substrate.

b. Catechol Oxidase (Smyth, 1954). If this enzyme is present in the tissues it will react with catechol, its substrate, to produce *o*-quinone which in turn will combine with adjacent protein molecules and "tan" them a brown color. The method is as follows:

1. Wash in water (30 min)
2. Place in 0.1% freshly prepared catechol at 40°C (90 min)
3. Wash in water (15 min)
4. Either mount in water under a sealed coverslip and photograph or dehydrate in ethanol, clear in xylene, and mount permanently in a neutral mounting medium.

Controls consist of either excluding the substrate or inhibiting the reaction with 0.001 M sodium diethyl dithiocarbamate.

c. Acid Phosphatase. The use of naphthol AS phosphates as substrates for acid phosphatase was first reported by Burstone (1958). A method that has been used successfully with small nematodes (Van Gundy *et al.*, 1967) is as follows:

1. Wash in water
2. Incubate in the following solution at 35°C (1 hr): 0.5 ml of

dimethyl formamide containing 5 mg of naphthol AS-BI phosphate; 50 ml of 0.1 M acetate buffer (pH 5.2); 10 mg fast red violet LB

3. Mount in distilled water under a sealed coverslip and photograph

Controls consist of either heating the nematodes (as for Section VIII, C, 7, *a*), leaving out the substrate or inhibiting the reaction with 0.001 M sodium fluoride.

d. Leucine Aminopeptidase. Recent investigations have shown that this enzyme can be detected in various nematodes by histochemical techniques, both in the hypodermis (Roggen *et al.*, 1967) and excretory glands (Davey and Kan, 1967). The method used by these workers is as follows (after Nachlas *et al.*, 1957):

1. Wash in water

2. Incubate at 37°C for 1 hr in a substrate solution made up as follows: 1 ml of 1-leucyl-β-naphthylamide (8 mg/ml); 10 ml of 0.1 M acetate buffer (pH 6.5); 8 ml of 0.85% sodium chloride; 1 ml 2 × 10^{-2} M potassium cyanide; 10 mg fast blue B salt

3. Wash in saline (2 min)

4. Place in 0.1 M cupric sulfate (2 min)

5. Wash in saline

6. Mount in distilled water under a sealed coverslip and photograph

or

7. Dehydrate in ethanol series, clear in xylene, and mount in a neutral mounting medium

D. VITAL STAINING

Most manufacturers of dyes list a variety of so-called vital stains which can be used to stain living organisms without damaging them and thus can be used to increase their contrast. A number of these compounds have been used on nematodes. Methylene blue is, perhaps, one of the best known. It can be used to stain internal structures, such as parts of the nervous system in some of the large ascarids. The nematodes obtained fresh from their hosts can be maintained alive for some days in 0.9% saline at 38°C. Methylene blue (10 mg/100 ml) is added to the saline and after 18 hr the nematodes are removed, frozen, and cut in a cryostat. The stained areas are readily observed in transverse sections. This dye, neutral red, and Janus green B have been used as vital stains on ascarids (Mueller, 1929) and methylene blue, neutral red, and indigo carmine have been used in this manner on rhabditids (Chitwood, 1930).

Methyl red and neutral red (Doncaster and Clark, 1964) have been used as pH indicator dyes in the intestinal walls of free-living soil nematodes and the redox indicator 1-naphthol-2-sodium sulfonate indophenol is taken up by *Panagrellus redivivus* and stains its excretory system (Smith, 1965). Chrysoidin (Doliwa, 1956), New Blue R (Shepherd, 1962) and eosine-Y are useful stains for differentiating between living and dead nematodes (Moriarty, 1964; Chaudhuri *et al.*, 1966). These three stains are not, perhaps, vital stains in the commonly accepted sense because, in the case of New Blue R and eosine-Y, for instance, only dead nematodes stain. However, staining occurs in both living and dead nematodes in chrysoidin.

Useful vital stains for basic protein are 0.1% fast green FCF at pH 8.0 and aqueous 0.1% bromophenol blue. They are particularly useful for staining the buccal exudations of a plant parasitic nematode (Bird, 1968b). Furthermore, they may be washed away with successive washes in distilled water so that several staining techniques may be used on the one structure while the nematode remains alive. Since for most dyes the cuticle acts as a barrier, the dye has either to be ingested or act directly on exudations from the nematode.

The uptake of acid vital stains, such as thymol blue, bromophenol blue, bromocresol green, methyl red, bromothymol blue, and phenol red, by the animal parasitic nematode *Graphidium strigosum* after its host had been injected with the stain has been studied by Enigk (1938). Using this technique in addition to incubating nematodes in dye solutions and injecting the dyes directly into the body cavity of the worm, Behrenz (1956) has used a wide range of vital and fluorescing dyes on many different genera of nematodes parasitic in animals. These dyes included trypan blue, toluidine blue, neutral red, and Sudan III and the following fluorescing dyes—fluorescein, phloxine, eosine, erythrosine, acridine orange, auramine, berberine sulfate, and coriphosphine. A dye is said to be fluorescent if, upon absorbing light of one wavelength, it emits light of another wavelength within 10^{-7} sec. The emitting light is always of longer wavelength than the exciting light. Some fluorescent stains fade much more rapidly than others upon exposure to the exciting light and this should be taken into account even for qualitative studies.

When 3rd- and 4th-stage larvae of *Haemonchus contortus* are incubated *in vitro* in diluted normal serum conjugated to lissamine rhodamine B (Sommerville, 1966) and then examined under a fluorescence microscope, the fluorochrome can be detected in the lumen of the alimentary tracts of the 4th-stage larvae but not in those of the 3rd stage. Thus, under these conditions, the 4th-stage larvae appear to be able to ingest the medium whereas the 3rd stage are unable to do so.

Details of the equipment required to obtain fluorescence are given later in this chapter.

E. Serological Techniques

By means of serological techniques it is possible to demonstrate the presence of substances exuding from orifices, such as the excretory pore, that would normally be invisible. This particular serological technique is known as the fluorescent antibody technique. The methods involved have been described in detail (Cherry et al., 1960; Pearse, 1968). Essentially, they take advantage of the fact that mammals respond to foreign substances (antigens), which are usually proteins but may be polysaccharides or complexes of lipid, carbohydrate, and protein, by producing antibodies, located in the globulin fraction of their serum, which react with the antigens to give precipitates. A fluorescent dye is coupled to a specific antibody and when this reacts with its antigen the dye is incorporated in the resulting precipitate and is readily located under the fluorescence microscope. This precipitate was first observed in nematodes in antiserum by Sarles (1938) and has since been verified by numerous workers in animal and plant parasitic nematodes, where it has been used as an aid to taxonomy. That the precipitates result from true antibody–antigen reactions has been shown by using fluorescein-tagged antibody in *Ascaris suum* (Taffs and Voller, 1962), *Trichinella spiralis* (Jackson, 1959), *Nippostrongylus muris* (Jackson, 1960), and *Meloidogyne javanica* (Bird, 1964a). These techniques give some indication of the nature of substances exuded from nematodes. The resolution of the method can be increased and brought to the electron microscope level by conjugating ferritin to the antibody. The use of ferritin-labeled globulins to identify specific antigens in nematodes appears to be a technique with some potential.

For background reading on the nature of immunity in general I refer the reader to Burnet (1962) and in its relationship to nematodes in particular to Sprent (1963).

F. Staining for Electron Microscopy

This subject is dealt with comprehensively by Pease (1964). All the electron microscope stains are electron dense and serve to scatter the electrons and so enhance contrast. They include salts of lead, uranium, vanadium, chromium, and permanganate, as well as osmium tetroxide and phosphotungstic acid. It is particularly important that identical stains and fixatives be used when comparing similar structures in nematodes. An example of induced differences in similar structures brought about by the use of different stains and fixatives is seen in sections of the dorsal esophageal gland of a plant parasitic nematode (Bird, 1969). For instance, material fixed in osmium and stained in a 1:1 solution of 1% potassium per-

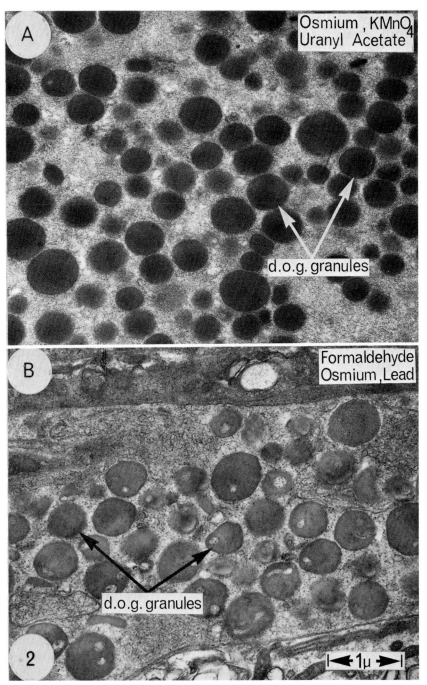

Fig. 2. Morphological differences induced by different methods of fixation and staining in the dorsal esophageal gland (d.o.g.) region of adult female *Meloidogyne javanica*. Both A and B at similar magnification (×20,000). (Bird, 1969.)

30

manganate: saturated uranyl acetate (Fig. 2A) looks quite unlike similar material treated with formaldehyde, osmium, and lead (Fig. 2B).

I find that a most reliable and useful stain for nematodes, following the fixation procedures outlined earlier in this chapter, is lead citrate (Reynolds, 1963). The method used is similar to that described by Pease (1964). The solution, which has a pH of about 12, is prepared by mixing 1.33 gm of lead nitrate and 1.76 gm of sodium citrate in 30 ml of distilled water. This is shaken for 30 min and then 8 ml of 1 N sodium hydroxide is added and the final solution is made up to 50 ml with distilled water. The final solution is clear. However, it should be filtered and stored in the refrigerator in a clean glass screw-capped bottle with a piece of fine plastic sheeting between the cap and the bottle. The staining process takes place at room temperature, the grids being placed face downward on drops of the stain on a ring of dental wax sitting on filter paper soaked with 0.02 N sodium hydroxide in a petri dish. After staining, the grids are removed and held by forceps while being rapidly washed in a jet of 0.02 N sodium hydroxide from a plastic wash bottle, followed by several similar washes in distilled water. After this they are dried by tilting the grid against filter paper and are then stored on filter paper in a clean petri dish. The most important criterion is that this staining is done in a clean and dust-free environment. An alternative and simpler method (Normann, 1964) is to place the grid between two sheets of Whatman No. 1 filter paper held together by paper clips. This material is then immersed in the lead solution and stained for 15–30 min (epoxy sections). It is then removed and blotted dry with filter paper, the grid is taken from between the filter paper sheets and is ready for examination under the electron microscope. Provided that the blotting is done immediately after staining and the grid is not removed from between the filter papers until it is dry there is no contamination by precipitated lead carbonate.

A number of methods have been described for staining 1-μ thick epoxy sections for use with the light microscope. One of the best of these for nematode tissues is that of Richardson *et al.* (1960). The method is as follows:

1. Pick up sections and place on a small drop of distilled water on a slide
2. Leave slide in an oven at 60°C until completely dry
3. Add a drop of 1% periodic acid and leave for 5 min at room temperature
4. Wash with distilled water and dry
5. Add a drop of 1% aqueous Azure II:1% methylene blue in 1% borax solution (1:1), fresh and filtered, and place in an oven at 60°C for 5 min
6. Wash in distilled water

7. Dry in an oven at 60°C, clear in xylene, and mount in a neutral mounting medium

IX. Radioautography

The techniques of radioautography (Rogers, 1967) have scarcely been used to relate form and function in nematodes and, even then, only at the level of the light microscope (Dissanaike et al., 1957) at very low magnification. The potential of these techniques in studies on the host–parasite relationships of some nematodes has been discussed (Dropkin, 1960). The use of electron microscope radioautography offers enormous scope in studies on all types of nematodes, despite the fact that the resolving power of this technique is about 700 Å compared with about 10 Å for the electron microscope and it is unlikely that future improvements in technique will bring the resolution below 100 Å.

The reader is referred to Rogers (1967) for a comprehensive and detailed account of known techniques for both light and electron microscopes up to this date.

X. The Light Microscope

As I have said earlier, the microscope is the nematologist's most important tool of trade. However, one commonly finds instruments which cannot give the maximum resolution for the particular lens system being used because they are not properly set up for Kohler illumination or because they have become slightly contaminated with substances such as dust. The adjustments for obtaining maximum resolution for all lens systems used in modern microscopes are simple. If an instrument is to be used for critical research work it should be kept in a special microscope cupboard which can be made vibration- and draft-free. It enables the operator to work with less eye strain, even in a brightly lit room, and assists in keeping the equipment clean and dust-free.

Microscopy was put on a firm scientific basis toward the end of the nineteenth century, due principally to the brilliant physicist Ernst Abbe, who expressed the fraction of a wavefront admitted by a lens as the numerical aperture (N.A.) and showed that it is related to the refractive index of the medium between the object being observed and the lens and the diameter and focal length of the lens. This number is marked on the objectives of all modern microscopes, together with their magnification, mechanical tube lengths (in most this is 160 mm), and their serial numbers and maker's name.

It has been shown by mathematicians that the limit of resolution (r) of a microscope is given by the formula

$$r = 0.61 \; \lambda/\text{N.A.}$$

where λ is the wavelength of light used. Thus, greater resolutions are obtained with higher numerical apertures and shorter wavelengths.

Some idea of the resolution of a good microscope is given by the following example (Barer, 1953). Assuming a numerical aperture of 1.4 (oil-immersion objective) and taking λ as the wavelength of green light (0.55×10^{-4} cm), as achromatic objectives are designed to give their best performance with green light, then by the formula given above

$$r = (0.61 \times 0.55 \times 10^{-4} \text{ cm})/1.40$$

Thus, $r = 0.24 \times 10^{-4}$ cm or $0.24 \; \mu$, so that under normal conditions, the limit of resolution of the light microscope is about $0.25 \; \mu$. These conditions can only be achieved by using an oil-immersion objective.

Pioneer work on homogenous immersion objectives by Abbe (1879) showed that an increase in resolution was obtained if immersion fluids with refractive indices similar to glass were used. Abbe's partnership with Zeiss resulted in the commercial production, for the first time, of apochromatic objectives corrected for spherical and chromatic aberration at three different wavelengths. These objectives were used at the turn of the century by a number of workers studying the structure of nematodes, notably Looss (1905). Modern biologists, who are sometimes surprised at the details observed by earlier workers, perhaps forget that these workers were equipped with microscopes that could resolve suitably stained material as well as the modern microscope. However, various methods have been evolved which make the modern microscope a much more versatile instrument. Some of the types of microscopes available and the methods by which they can be used for observations on nematodes are described below.

A. NORMAL TRANSMITTED-LIGHT MICROSCOPY

All makers of modern microscopes sell these instruments with a wide range of components which can be attached to the basic instrument, thus enabling it to be used for different purposes. All modern instruments are binoculars, which are much more comfortable for observation than monoculars, although a monocular tube is necessary for photographic work. Better still is a trinocular, which permits observations to be made in comfort while a camera is attached and ready for photography if required. A prism may be substituted for the camera for projection and drawing. A rotating mechanical stage is essential, as it not only permits orientation of small nematodes for photography or drawing but is also necessary for the interference and polarizing microscopes.

The revolving nosepiece in most modern microscopes holds five objectives; I have found the following five objectives particularly useful for work with nematodes under normal bright field or phase contrast: (1) either $\times 6.3$ or $\times 10$ phase achromat; (2) either $\times 16$ or $\times 20$ phase achromat; (3) $\times 40$ phase fluorite; (4) $\times 40$ water-immersion phase achromat; (5) $\times 100$ phase fluorite or apochromat.

Usually the differences between fluorites and apochromats are so slight that the latter do not warrant the extra expense involved. However, for critical work at the limit of resolution, an oil immersion apochromat may be desirable. Certainly one of the most useful objectives is the $\times 40$ phase-contrast, water-immersion achromat which has both a higher numerical aperture and a much greater minimum working distance than the dry $\times 40$ objectives. The normal range of magnification of eyepieces lies between $\times 5$ and $\times 20$. The normal eyepiece for low power achromats is the Huyghens eyepiece but special compensating eyepieces are used with apochromats and high-power achromats. Generally speaking, the maximum magnification should not exceed $\times 1000$ N.A. of the objective and should not be less than $\times 250$ N.A. of the objective in order to take full advantage of its resolving power.

Most makers provide a range of condensers, including revolving ones, for both phase and bright-field work. Condensers with N.A.'s of up to 1.4 are available and needed for the most critical work, although a second condenser with a long focal length is particularly useful for work with nematodes, especially for the examination of living material under the water-immersion objective. Oil-immersion objectives have been used as condensers for high-resolution work with small nematodes (Thorne, 1961; Doncaster, 1966) using normal bright-field illumination.

All modern microscopes have a built-in light source and Kohler illumination is readily obtained by focusing the diaphragm of the light source onto the object by means of the condenser, thus achieving a uniformly illuminated field of view.

B. Dark-Field Microscopy

The normal condenser is replaced by a special dark-field condenser which is designed so that no direct light reaches the objective. The specimen under observation receives oblique light that would not normally pass into the objective. This light is diffracted by the specimen and some of it passes into the objective; consequently the specimen appears light against a dark background. The method has not been used much with nematodes, although it is potentially a most useful technique for many microorganisms, particularly if used in conjunction with fluorescence microscopy. The only extra equipment needed is the condenser and a funnel stop for the oil-immersion objective. This consists of a small funnel-shaped piece of metal which fits behind the back lens of the objective and reduces the N.A. below 1.0. Alternatively, some oil-immersion objectives incorporate an iris diaphragm and this merely needs to be closed slightly.

C. FLUORESCENCE MICROSCOPY

For a comprehensive review of the principles, techniques, and history of fluorescence microscopy, the papers of Ellinger (1940) and Young (1961) are recommended for further reading.

The components for this technique consist of normal achromatic objectives, a dark-field condenser, a high-pressure mercury light source (HBO 200), and two filters, one in front of the lamp to cut out visible light rays and the other in front of the eyepiece to cut out any blue rays.

It is not necessary to buy expensive quartz components for fluorescence microscopy. The normal glass optics do not show enough autofluorescence or absorb enough ultraviolet light to interfere with routine fluorescence microscopy using dark-field illumination. In fact, good results with nematodes can be obtained with standard optical components and illumination (Matthaei, 1950; Hicks and Matthaei, 1955) using filters consisting of an 8 oz clear glass plane-walled medicine bottle with an inside clearance of 2.5 cm containing a solution consisting of 8.33 gm of $CuSO_4 \cdot 5H_2O$:100 ml concentrated aqueous ammonia (specific gravity 0.88): 160 ml water. This is placed in front of the light source and it removes light of wavelength greater than 500 mμ. Blue light is removed at the eyepieces by using either Kodak G15 or Ilford 110 gelatin filters, a small disc being placed over the field lens inside the eyepiece. For high-resolution work, however, a combination of high-intensity illumination, dark-field condenser, and an objective such as a × 50 water immersion with an N.A. of 1 is desirable.

D. POLARIZED LIGHT

The polarizing microscope is an extremely sensitive instrument. Under ideal conditions a retardation of 0.1 Å can be detected on objects 0.2 μ

wide but the limit with a typical biological object is probably about 0.5 Å.

In its simplest form it consists of an ordinary microscope with a rotating stage and two polarizers which are either Nicol prisms or more commonly, sheets of Polaroid. One of these is mounted below the condenser and is called the polarizer and the other is located in the body of the microscope between the objective and the eyepiece and is called the analyzer. When the polarizer and the analyzer are rotated so that their planes of vibration are at right angles to each other they are said to be crossed. Thus, no light is transmitted and the field of view is dark. Under these conditions a viewed object may appear dark like the rest of the field. Such a substance is isotropic, that is, it is the same in all directions. Isotropic substances include liquids at rest and unstrained amorphous solids. Objects which exhibit light when viewed under crossed polarizers are anisotropic or birefringent. Birefringence may be *intrinsic* or *crystalline*, in which case it is due to the arrangement of atoms and molecules in a regular structure or it may be *form* birefringence which is due to the orientation of micelles in a surrounding medium of different refractive index. Form birefringence can be distinguished from intrinsic birefringence in an object by immersing the object in liquids of different refractive index. As the refractive index increases, the birefringence decreases and then rises. If the birefringence reduces to zero, it is completely due to form birefringence but, if at the minimum, some birefringence remains it is intrinsic in nature. Birefringence is measured by means of compensators introduced into the microscope below the analyzer. For quantitative work special strain-free optics are used. So far, polarized light microscopy has only been used qualitatively on nematodes but it has proved to be a most effective means of studying structures such as the cuticle in the larger parasitic nematodes (Czermak, 1852; Fauré-Fremiet and Garrault, 1944; Bird and Deutsch, 1957) and the intestinal cells of smaller free-living nematodes (Cobb, 1914).

E. PHASE-CONTRAST MICROSCOPY

This relatively simple and particularly useful method of increasing the contrast of unstained objects without decreasing the N.A. and resolution of the microscope was discovered by Zernike while working on diffraction gratings about 1930 and he has described the manner in which this came about (Zernike, 1955). The phase-contrast microscope (Zernike, 1942a,b), which makes differences in refractive index appear as differences in light intensity, consists of rings of clear glass in opaque glass discs in the condenser which are of such a size that each forms an image in the back focal plane of the particular objective being used. The back focal plane of the objective contains a disc of glass with a circular trough etched into it. Light passing through this trough has a phase difference of a quarter of a wavelength from that passing through the rest of the disc.

These two rings are superimposed by means of screws on the condenser. During this operation, the back focal plane of the objective is viewed by means of a phase telescope which is inserted in place of the eyepiece. When this has been done and the specimen is properly illuminated, it acts as a diffraction grating. The undiffracted light passes through the phase ring in the objective and is reduced in intensity and given a $1/4 \lambda$ shift from the diffracted light. The image formed results from the interference of the diffracted and undiffracted light.

Phase contrast may be positive in which the phase is advanced and the object appears darker than the background, or it may be negative in which the phase is retarded and the object appears brighter than the background.

The phase-contrast microscope can be set up rapidly and simply. It has proved to be extremely useful in examining unstained frozen sections of large nematodes (Bird and Deutsch, 1957) and small, living, anesthetized nematodes (Bird, 1967). The method is characterized by the presence of background halos caused by the imperfect separation of direct and diffracted light, as some of the diffracted light passes through the phase ring together with the direct light. This in no way detracts from the resolution of the method, which has enormous potential in studying the structure of nematodes.

F. THE INTERFERENCE MICROSCOPE

This instrument enables quantitative measurements to be made on objects so that their thickness, mass, and refractive index can be determined. Qualitatively, it results in images without the characteristic halos of phase contrast but with interference colors which can be used to emphasize certain structures. However, the adjustments and alignments of interference microscopes are more complicated than those of phase-contrast microscopes.

At the moment, phase-contrast microscopy, because of its simplicity and ease of adjustment and because it is less sensitive to variations in the slide and coverslip, is undoubtedly the instrument of choice for routine morphological work. However, interference microscopes are only just starting to be used and obviously have a great deal of potential in both physiological and morphological research with nematodes.

Various different types of interference microscopes are now available and information on their optical systems and methods of use is adequately provided in the various manufacturers' manuals.

Qualitatively, different types of interference microscopes have been used to study changes in the morphology of the larvae of plant parasitic nematodes (Van Gundy et al., 1967; Bird, 1968a) and quantitative measurements have been made on the water content of a free-living nematode (Ellenby, 1968a) and the larvae of nematodes parasitic in either plants or animals (Ellenby, 1968b,c).

G. PHOTOMICROGRAPHY

This subject has been extensively reviewed in a number of books, notably by Shillaber (1944) and Allen (1958). The use of electronic flash in photomicrographic work with nematodes is described by Doncaster (1956). Electronic flash equipment is made by a number of well-known firms for their microscopes. This equipment is easy to operate and is particularly useful for taking photographs of living nematodes as eggs, larvae, or adults (Bird, 1967, 1968a).

If electronic flash equipment is not available, good photographs of living nematodes under anesthesia may be taken using fast, high-contrast films such as Ilford HP 4. All films used must, of course, be calibrated for particular light settings and exposures and once this has been done the exposure meters provided by the various microscope manufacturers are particularly useful in saving both time and film.

H. MICROSPECTROPHOTOMETERS

These are expensive instruments as they incorporate quartz optics, for observations in ultraviolet light, and various devices for obtaining quantitative results. They are particularly useful for obtaining chemical measurements at high resolution in different structures in small nematodes (Bird and Saurer, 1967; Bird, 1968b).

Measurements with these machines are made by using either photoelectric or photographic methods. The former have the advantage of showing the light absorption directly and are thus much more rapid than the photographic method which involves scanning the photographic plate with a microdensitometer. An advantage of the photographic method is that it is more sensitive toward the short wave side of ultraviolet because it uses a hydrogen lamp which, though insufficient for photoelectric measurements, is ideal for photographic absorption measurements. The hydrogen beam, however, causes gross damage to living nematodes within a few seconds and thus it must be used on fixed material. The following method has been found most suitable for the preparation of small nematodes prior to their examination with the UV microspectrograph:

1. Cool and fix the nematodes in 4% buffered formaldehyde (pH 7.3) at 5°C for 30 min

2. Cut the nematodes and leave for another 30 min in the fixative

3. Wash and mount in distilled water using a quartz slide and coverslip sealed with wax

The use of these instruments with nematodes has been rather limited to date. However, they have considerable potential in helping to integrate form and function in these organisms.

The microspectrograph that we have used for measurements on small nematodes is a combination of a reflecting microscope and a spectrograph. Details of its construction and manipulation are given by Ruch (1960).

XI. The Electron Microscope

The great advantage of the electron microscope is, of course, its increase in resolving power; its great disadvantage is that material must be examined in a dehydrated or nonliving state. The increase in resolution is attained by using electrons which have a much shorter wavelength than light and the dry condition of the specimen is essential because the presence of air or moisture in the column of the electron microscope would lead to diffraction of the electron beam and interfere with focusing.

Wherever possible, an attempt should be made to compare measurements of living material photographed at high magnification using the light microscope with electron micrographs to determine the extent of shrinkage, if any, of the fixed and embedded material. The degree of fixation artifact is (usually) apparent in high resolution electron micrographs. With modern techniques of fixation, staining, and embedding, an improvement in quality of electron micrographs of sections of nematodes depicted in various journals is quite noticeable.

The electron microscope is undoubtedly going to play a major role in future studies of nematode fine structure. Most modern instruments are capable of resolving to at least 5–10 Å although exceptionally thin and well-stained sections of biological material are needed to take advantage of this resolution.

All the manufacturers provide comprehensive manuals on the maintenance and use of their instruments; although the nematologist cannot be expected to undertake even routine maintenance of the instrument, it is an advantage to know how, for instance, to change a filament or clean apertures, as this makes the operator aware of the care that must be taken in keeping the machine clean. It is necessary to know how to use the instrument and how to take photographs with it and how to reload the camera, etc., as this enables the nematologist to focus and photograph structures rapidly before they have time to become contaminated, in the electron beam as can happen while he attempts to explain to an operator exactly what he wants photographed.

Some of the commoner problems associated with the observation and photography of objects in the electron microscope are dealt with by Pease (1964).

A relatively new type of instrument, the stereoscan electron microscope (Oatley *et al.*, 1965), is used to obtain pictures with great depth of focus on the outer surface of specimens. It has been used to examine the cuticles of various nematodes (Green, 1967) and the buccal stylet of a larval plant parasitic nematode (Ellenby and Wilson, 1969). Despite its poor resolving power compared with the conventional electron microscope, it may prove to be particularly useful in studies on the nematode exoskeleton. A number of methods used in the preparation of small nematodes for examination by the stereoscan electron microscope are described by Green (1967).

Another method which has, as far as I know, not yet been used on nematodes, but which has considerable potential as a means of determining ultrastructure of microorganisms, is the freeze-etching technique. This method, discovered by Steere (1957) and developed into a practical technique by Moor *et al.* (1961), consists of using a freezing ultramicrotome to cut the specimen down to the particular area being examined. A thin layer of ice is then removed from the cut surface by sublimation in high vacuum. This etched surface is shadowed with a heavy metal and the thin film obtained is strengthened by carbon evaporation. This replica, which is a true image of the etched cut surface, is detached from the specimen and placed on a coated specimen grid for examination under the electron microscope.

XII. X-Ray Diffraction

This technique permits a three-dimensional study to be made of the molecular structure of the specimen. A narrow incident X-ray beam is used which sets the electrons within the specimen oscillating so that they act as subsidiary sources of X-rays. These interact with each other and form a pattern on a photographic plate around a dark spot caused by the undeflected X-rays.

In low-resolution studies, such as have been done on some large nematodes (Fauré-Fremiet and Garrault, 1944; Picken *et al.*, 1947), only the main regions of high electron density are defined, although at the limit of resolution of the method, individual atoms of lower atomic number can be located.

High-resolution work involves analyses of various X-ray diffraction patterns taken at different angles and the incorporation of atoms of relatively high atomic weight to act as markers. The methods are complicated and, at the moment, are more of academic than practical interest as techniques to be used for defining the fine structure of nematodes, partly because of the difficulty in obtaining structures from small nematodes that are not contaminated with material from adjacent structures.

REFERENCES

Abbe, E. (1879). *J. Roy. Microsc. Soc.* **2**, 812.
Alfert, M., and Geschwind, I. I. (1953). *Proc. Nat. Acad. Sci. USA* **39**, 991.
Allen, R. M. (1958). "Photomicrography," 441 pp. Van Nostrand, New York.
Andrássy, I. (1956). *Acta Zool. (Budapest)* **2**, 1.
Baker, A. D. (1953). *Can. Entomol.* **85**, 77.
Baker, J. R. (1950). "Cytological Technique," 211 pp. Methuen, London.
Baker, J. R. (1958). "Principles of Biological Microtechnique," 357 pp. Wiley, New York.
Barer, R. (1953). "Lecture Notes on the Use of the Microscope," 76 pp. Blackwell, Oxford.
Behrenz, K. W. (1956). *Z. Wiss. Zool., Abs. A* **159**, 129.
Bird, A. F. (1958). *Parasitology* **48**, 32.
Bird, A. F. (1959). *Nematologica* **4**, 31.
Bird, A. F. (1964a). *Exp. Parasitol.* **15**, 350.
Bird, A. F. (1964b). *Nature (London)* **203**, 1300.
Bird, A. F. (1966). *Nematologica* **12**, 359.
Bird, A. F. (1967). *J. Parasitol.* **53**, 768.
Bird, A. F. (1968a). *J. Parasitol.* **54**, 475.
Bird, A. F. (1968b). *J. Parasitol.* **54**, 879.
Bird, A. F. (1969). *J. Parasitol.* **55**, 337.
Bird, A. F., and Deutsch, K. (1957). *Parasitology* **47**, 319.
Bird, A. F., and Saurer, W. (1967). *J. Parasitol.* **53**, 1262.
Bonhag, P. F. (1955). *J. Morphol.* **96**, 381.
Burnet, F. M. (1962). "The Integrity of the Body," 189 pp. Harvard Univ. Press, Cambridge, Massachusetts.
Burstone, M. S. (1958). *J. Nat. Cancer Inst.* **21**, 523.
Burstone, M. S. (1962). "Enzyme Histochemistry and its Application in the Study of Neoplasms," 621 pp. Academic Press, New York.
Cairns, E. J. (1960). *In* "Nematology" (J. N. Sasser and W. R. Jenkins, eds.), pp. 33–84. Univ. of North Carolina Press, Chapel Hill, North Carolina.
Cameron, M. L., and Steele, J. E. (1959). *Stain Technol.* **34**, 265.
Chaudhuri, N., Dick, R. I., Engelbrecht, R. S., and Austin, J. H. (1966). *Nematologica* **12**, 337.

Cherry, W. B., Goldman, M., and Carski, T. R. (1960). Fluorescent Antibody Techniques in the Diagnosis of Communicable Disease, *U.S. Pub. Health Serv. Publ.* **729**, 73 pp.

Chitwood, B. G. (1930). *J. Morphol. Physiol.* **49**, 251.

Cobb, N. A. (1914). *J. Parasitol.* **1**, 40.

Conger, A. D., and Fairchild, L. M. (1953). *Stain Technol.* **28**, 281.

Croll, N. A., and Maggenti, A. R. (1968). *Proc. Helminthol. Soc. Wash.* **35**, 108.

Czermak, J. (1852). *Sitzungsber. Kaiserl. Akad. Wiss. Wien, Math.-Naturwiss. Kl.* **9**, 755.

Darlington, C. D., and la Cour, L. F. (1960). "The Handling of Chromosomes," 248 pp. Allen & Unwin London.

Davey, K. G. (1964). *Can. J. Zool.* **42**, 731.

Davey, K. G., and Kan, S. P. (1967). *Nature (London)* **214**, 737.

Dissanaike, A. S., Dissanaike, G. A., Niles, W. J., and Surendranathan, R. (1957). *Exp. Parasitol.* **6**, 261.

Doliwa, U. (1956). *Wiss. Z. Univ. Rostock, Math.-Naturwiss. Reihe* **5**, 133.

Doncaster, C. C. (1956). *Nematologica* **1**, 51.

Doncaster, C. C. (1962). *Nematologica* **8**, 313.

Doncaster, C. C. (1964). *Nematologica* **10**, 306.

Doncaster C. C. (1966). *Nematologica* **12**, 417.

Doncaster, C. C., and Clark, S. A. (1964). *Nematologica* **10**, 136.

Dougherty, E. C., Hansen, E. L., Nicholas, W. L., Mollett, J. A., and Yarwood, E. A. (1959). *Ann. NY. Acad. Sci.* **77**, 176.

Dropkin, V. H. (1960). *In* "Nematology" (J. N. Sasser and W. R. Jenkins, eds.), pp. 103–108. Univ. of North Carolina Press, Chapel Hill, North Carolina.

Dyson, J. (1960). *J. Opt. Soc. Amer.* **50**, 754.

Einarson, L. (1951). *Acta Pathol. Microbiol. Scand.* **28**, 82.

Ellenby, C. (1968a). *Experientia* **24**, 84.

Ellenby, C. (1968b). *Proc. Roy. Soc., Ser. B* **169**, 203.

Ellenby, C. (1968c). *J. Exp. Biol.* **49**, 469.

Ellenby, C., and Smith, L. (1964). *Nematologica* **10**, 342.

Ellenby, C., and Wilson, E. M. (1969). *Nematologica* **15**, 290.

Ellinger, P. (1940). *Biol. Rev. Cambridge Phil. Soc.* **15**, 323.

Elsea, J. R. (1951). *Proc. Helminthol. Soc. Wash.* **18**, 53.

Enigk, K. (1938). *Z. Parasitenk.* **10**, 386.

Fauré-Fremiet, E., and Garrault, H. (1944). *Bull. Biol. Fr. Belg.* **78**, 206.

Goldschmidt, R. (1908). *Z. Wiss. Zool.* **90**, 73.

Goldschmidt, R. (1909). *Z. Wiss. Zool.* **92**, 306.

Goldschmidt, R. (1910). *Festschr. Hertwigs* **2**, 253–354.

Goodey, J. B. (1959). *Nematologica* **4**, 157.

Goodey, J. B. (1963). *Min. Agr., Fish Food, Tech. Bull.* **2**, 72 pp. H. M. Stationery Office, London.

Green, C. D. (1967). *Nematologica* **13**, 279.

Hicks, J. D., and Matthaei, E. (1955). *J. Pathol. Bacteriol.* **70**, 1.

Hobson, A. D. (1948). *Parasitology* **38**, 183.

Hoff, J. K., and Mai, W. F. (1964). *Phytopathology* **54**, 869.

Holt, S. J. (1958). *Gen. Cytochem. Methods* **1**, 375.

Jackson, G. J. (1959). *J. Infec. Dis.* **105**, 97.

Jackson, G. J. (1960). *J. Infec. Dis.* **106**, 20.

Jensen, W. A. (1962). "Botanical Histochemistry," 408 pp. Freeman, San Francisco, California.

Kan, S. P., and Davey, K. G. (1968). *Can. J. Zool.* **46**, 723.

Kiefer, G., Kiefer, R., and Sandritter, W. (1967). *Exp. Cell Res.* **45**, 247.

Lapage, G. (1935). *J. Helminthol.* **13**, 115.

Linford, M. B. (1937). *Phytopathology* **27**, 824.

Linford, M. B. (1942). *Phytopathology* **32**, 580.

Looss, A. (1905). *Rec. Egypt. Govt. Sch. Med.* **3**, 1.

McElroy, F. D., and Van Gundy, S. D. (1968). *Phytopathology* **58**, 1558.

McManus, J. F. A. (1946). *J. Pathol. Bacteriol.* **58**, 93.

McManus, J. F. A. (1948). *Stain Technol.* **23**, 99.

Maggenti, A. R. (1961). *Proc. Helminthol. Soc. Wash.* **28**, 118.

Maggenti, A. R., and Viglierchio, D. R. (1965). *Hilgardia* **36**, 435.

Matthaei, E. (1950). *J. Gen. Microbiol.* **4**, 393.

Millonig, G. (1961). *J. Appl. Phys.* **32**, 1637.

Millonig, G. (1962). *Electron Microsc., Proc. 5th Int. Congr., Philadelphia* **2**, 8.

Moor, H., Mühlethaler, K., Waldner, H., and Frey-Wyssling, A. (1961). *J. Biophys. Biochem. Cytol.* **10**, 1.

Moriarty, F. (1964). *Nematologica* **10**, 644.

Mueller, J. F. (1929). *Z. Zellforsch. Mikrosk. Anat.* **8**, 361.

Mulvey, R. H. (1955). *Can. J. Zool.* **33**, 295.

Nachlas, M. M., Crawford, D. T., and Seligman, A. M. (1957). *J. Histochem. Cytochem.* **5**, 264.

Nicholas, W. L., Dougherty, E. C., and Hansen, E. L. (1959). *Ann. NY. Acad. Sci.* **77**, 218.

Nigon, V., and Brun, J. (1955). *Chromosoma* **7**, 129.

Normann, T. C. (1964). *Stain Technol.* **39**, 50.

Oatley, S. W., Nixon, W. C., and Pease, R. F. W. (1965). *Advan. Electron. Electron Phys.* **21**, 181.

Overgaard Nielsen, C. (1949). *Natura Jutl.* **2**, 1.

Pantin, C. F. A. (1946). "Notes on Microscopical Technique for Zoologists" 73 pp. Cambridge Univ. Press, London and New York.

Paul, J. (1957). *Quart. J. Microsc. Sci.* **98**, 279.

Pearse, A. G. E. (1968). "Histochemistry Theoretical and Applied," Vol. 1, 3rd Ed., 759 pp. Churchill, London.

Pease, D. C. (1964). "Histological Techniques for Electron Microscopy," 381 pp. Academic Press, New York.

Picken, L. E. A., Pryor, M. G. M., and Swann, M. M. (1947). *Nature (London)* **159**, 434.

Reynolds, E. S. (1963). *J. Cell Biol.* **17**, 208.

Richardson, K. C., Jarett, L., and Finke, E. H. (1960). *Stain Technol.* **35**, 313.

Rogers, A. W. (1967). "Techniques of Autoradiography," 335 pp. Elsevier, Amsterdam.

Roggen, D. R., Raski, D. J., and Jones, N. O. (1967). *Nematologica* **13**, 1.

Ross, M. M. R. (1967). *Science* **156**, 1494.

Ruch, F. (1960). *Z. Wiss. Zool., Abt. A* **64**, 453.

Sandritter, W., Kiefer, G., and Rick, W. (1963). *Histochemie* **3**, 315.

Sarles, M. P. (1938). *J. Infec. Dis.* **62**, 337.

Seinhorst, J. W. (1962). *Nematologica* **8**, 29.

Seinhorst, J. W. (1966). *Nematologica* **12**, 178.

Shepherd, A. M. (1962). *Nematologica* **8**, 201.

Shillaber, C. P. (1944). "Photomicrography in Theory and Practice," 773 pp. Wiley, New York.

Smith, L. (1965). *Comp. Biochem. Physiol.* **15**, 89.

Smyth, J. D. (1954). *Quart. J. Microsc. Sci.* **95**, 139.

Sommerville, R. I. (1966). *Exp. Parasitol.* **52**, 127.

Sprent, J. F. A. (1963). "Parasitism," 145 pp. Univ. of Queensland Press, St. Lucia, Australia.

Spurr, A. R. (1969). *J. Ultrastruct. Res.* **26**, 31.

Steere, R. L. (1957). *J. Biophys. Biochem. Cytol.* **3**, 45.

Stoll, N. R. (1959). *Ann. N. Y. Acad. Sci.* **77**, 126.

Taffs, L. F., and Voller, A. (1962). *J. Helminthol.* **36**, 339.

Thorne, G. (1961). "Principles of Nematology," 553 pp. McGraw-Hill, New York.

Triantaphyllou, A. C. (1963). *J. Morphol.* **113**, 489.

Triantaphyllou, A. C., and Hirschmann, H. (1966). *Nematologica* **12**, 437.

van Beneden, E. (1883). *Arch. Biol. (Paris)* **4**, 265.

Van Gundy, S. D., Bird, A. F., and Wallace, H. R. (1967). *Phytopathology* **57**, 559.

White, P. R. (1954). "The Cultivation of Animal and Plant Cells," 239 pp. Ronald Press, New York.

Wischnitzer, S. (1967). *Int. Rev. Cytol.* **22**, 1.

Wright, K. A. (1966). *Can. J. Zool.* **44**, 329.

Wright, K. A., and Jones, N. O. (1965). *Nematologica* **11**, 125.

Young, M. R. (1961). *Quart. J. Microsc. Sci.* **102**, 419.

Zernike, F. (1942a). *Physica (Utrecht)* **9**, 686.

Zernike, F. (1942b). *Physica (Utrecht)* **9**, 974.

Zernike, F. (1955). *Science* **121**, 345.

3

THE EXOSKELETON

I. Introduction

The exoskeleton of nematodes may be defined as the outer covering or cuticle together with its invaginations and outgrowths. Structures such as mouth parts and copulatory spicules, although part of the exoskeleton, will not be considered in this chapter but will be dealt with in the appropriate chapters on the digestive and reproductive systems.

The cuticle is a multilayered structure which functions both as a barrier to undesirable elements in the environment and as a flexible skeleton (Harris and Crofton, 1957; Wisse and Daems, 1968). It invaginates at the mouth, rectum, cloaca, vagina, and excretory pore. It invaginates also at the anterior end in association with a pair of lateral sensory organs, the amphids, and at the posterior end, in some nematodes, in association with a pair of sensory organs, the phasmids. These sensory organs and other sensory appendages of the cuticle and sensory structures such as papillae and setae will be described in the chapter on the nervous system.

II. External Structures

The markings on the surface of the cuticle are varied and complex and

45

have been used extensively by taxonomists to assist in the identification of various species. Work on these various external cuticular structures has been comprehensively reviewed (Chitwood and Chitwood, 1950; de Coninck, 1965). These authors have done considerable work on the external cephalic structures of nematodes.

It is generally agreed that the cephalic structures arose from a primitive hexaradiate or six-lipped form. The six lips may have become fused or otherwise modified. The head region and its sensory structures will be considered in the chapter on the nervous system.

A. Punctations

Punctations, when viewed under the light microscope, commonly appear as minute, round areas which are often arranged in a pattern. They are particularly common in the Rhabditidae, Diplogasteridae, Chromadoridae, and Cyatholaimidae (Chitwood and Chitwood, 1950) and are considered by Inglis (1964) to be the openings of punctation canals, or their derivatives, viewed end on. However, Wright and Hope (1968) in recent electron microscope studies of *Acanthonchus duplicatus*, a member of the Cyatholaimidae, use the great increase in resolution of this instrument to show that these rodlike structures are not always hollow. They consider that the punctations act as structures for strengthening the cuticle rather than as pore canals through which cuticular proteins may be transported. In addition to punctations, members of the family Cyatholaimidae have characteristic circular structures running in longitudinal rows along the lateral, dorsal and ventral

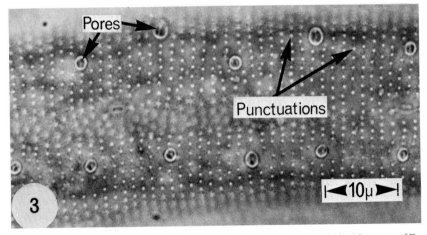

Fig. 3.   Surface view of the cuticle of *Acanthonchus duplicatus* (× 2,000). (Courtesy of Dr. K. A. Wright; Wright and Hope, 1968.)

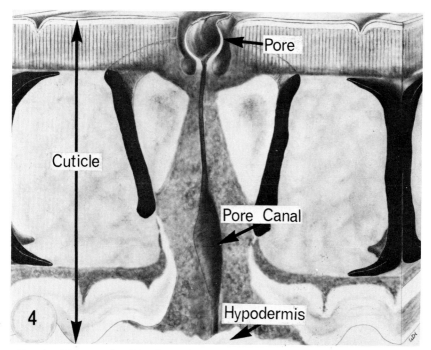

FIG. 4. Diagram of cuticle of *Acanthonchus duplicatus*. (Courtesy of Dr. K. A. Wright; Wright and Hope, 1968.)

surfaces of the body (Fig. 3). These structures have been viewed under the light microscope by Inglis (1963), who thought that they resembled campaniform receptors of insects. However, the electron microscope studies of Wright and Hope (1968) (Fig. 4) show that they are pores which connect the surface of the cuticle with a cell in the hypodermis by means of a continuous channel which penetrates the cuticle. The function of these cells is not known although they resemble hypodermal glands.

B. TRANSVERSE MARKINGS

These take the form of transverse striations or annulations and are found in most, if not all, nematodes giving them a segmented appearance. These annulations are very pronounced in some families of marine nematodes, such as the Epsilonematidae, Draconematidae, and Desmoscolecidae, many families of the large nematodes parasitic in animals, such as the Ascaridae, Strongylidae, Spiruridae, and Oxyuridae, and many families of the smaller plant parasitic nematodes, such as the Tylenchidae, Heteroderidae, and particularly the Criconematidae where the annulations are so pronounced that they become outgrowths and are known as scales.

Electron microscope examination of members of the Dorylaimidae (Wright, 1965; Roggen et al., 1967; López-Abella et al., 1967; Raski et al., 1969) show that they do have a cuticle with transverse annulations, although these are not shown in the literature in various drawings done with the aid of the light microscope. It may be that transverse annulations are present in varying degrees in all nematodes and are associated with their characteristic dorsoventral undulatory movement. Their presence may be necessary to allow dorsoventral flexures (Wisse and Daems, 1968).

The width of the annuli varies in different nematodes. It lies between 1 and 2 μ for the larval stages of many species parasitic in either animals or plants (Table I). This distance is much the same for the adults of many plant parasitic or free-living nematodes but is usually much greater in the adults of forms parasitic in animals. The distances between the annulations vary in the same nematode and are usually less in the anterior region and greater in the posterior region. In nematodes which are either molting or carrying the cast cuticle as a sheath, the internal cuticle usually has striations which are closer together than the outermost cuticle.

C. LONGITUDINAL MARKINGS

These usually take the form of longitudinal ridges or of alae.

1. *Ridges*

These are raised areas which run the length of the body and occur on the submedian as well as the lateral surface. They are pronounced in trichostrongyloids and are depicted very clearly by Lee (1965b) in a stereogram of a portion of the middle region of an adult *Nippostrongylus brasiliensis* which has fourteen longitudinal ridges extending from its cephalic area to its posterior end. The arrangement of ridges is used by taxonomists as an aid to species identification as, for example, in the identification of heligmosomids parasitic in rodents (Durette-Desset, 1966).

2. *Alae*

These are thickenings or projections of the cuticle which occur in the lateral or sublateral region. They are divided as follows:

a. *Caudal Alae.* These are found in the posterior region and are restricted to males as copulatory bursae. They will be considered in greater detail in the chapter on reproduction.

TABLE I

DISTANCES BETWEEN TRAVERSE STRIATIONS IN DIFFERENT NEMATODES

Nematode	Measurement (μ)	Reference
Larval stages		
Necator americanus	1.5	Inatomi *et al.* (1963)
Ancylostoma duodenale	1.3	Inatomi *et al.* (1963)
Ancylostoma caninum	1.1	Inatomi *et al.* (1963)
Trichostrongylus orientalis	1.2	Inatomi *et al.* (1963)
Strongyloides stercoralis	0.9	Inatomi *et al.* (1963)
Strongyloides fülleborni	0.9	Inatomi *et al.* (1963)
Strongyloides ratti	1.1	Inatomi *et al.* (1963)
Nippostrongylus brasiliensis	1.3	Inatomi *et al.* (1963)
Nippostrongylus brasiliensis	1.5	Lee (1966a)
Nippostrongylus brasiliensis	1.8	Jamuar (1966)
Meloidogyne javanica	0.9	Bird (1968)
Meloidogyne hapla	0.4	Ibrahim and Hollis (1967)
Heterodera schachtii	1.4–1.7	Gunther and Kämpfe (1966)
Heterodera rostochiensis	1.6	Wisse and Daems (1968)
Haemonchus contortus	0.9	Rogers (1968)
Adults of free-living, plant, and invertebrate parasitic nematodes		
Rhabditis pellio	1.0–1.5	Beams and Sekhon (1967)
Xiphinema index	0.9	Wright (1965)
Xiphinema index	1.5	Roggen *et al.* (1967)
Tylenchorhynchus martini	1.0–1.5	Ibrahim (1967)
Euchromadora vulgaris	2.0	Watson (1965a)
Acanthonchus duplicatus	1.6–3.8	Wright and Hope (1968)
Meloidogyne javanica	1.6–2.0	Bird and Rogers (1965)
Trichodorus	3.0	Raski *et al.* (1969)
Adults of nematodes parasitic in vertebrates		
Ascaris lumbricoides	10	Bird and Bird (1969)
Parascaris equorum	9–10	Hinz (1963)
Enterobius vermicularis	7	Tsubota (1966)
Trichuris myocastoris	5	Wright (1968)
Aspiculuris tetraptera	2–3	Anya (1966a)
Oxyuris equi	25	Bird (1958a)
Strongylus equinus	4	Bird, (1958a)

b. Cervical Alae. These are confined to the anterior part of the body in certain families of nematodes parasitic in animals, namely, Strongylidae, Ascaridae, and Spiruridae. They are formed from the cortical and median layers of the cuticle.

c. Longitudinal Alae. These delimit the lateral fields and are known as lateral alae. Transverse sections of their fine structure have been examined with the aid of the electron microscope and it has been shown (Inatomi *et al.*, 1963; Eckert and Schwarz, 1965; Wu, 1967; Van Gundy *et al.*, 1967), for many different species of nematodes, that their form varies considerably in different species and is characteristic for a particular species. Not only does the shape of the lateral alae vary but they are traversed by striations or furrows varying in number from one to twelve. Functionally, they probably assist locomotion and may permit slight changes in the width of the animals.

III. Internal Structures

A. THICKNESS OF CUTICLE

Recent reviewers of the structure of the nematode cuticle (Inglis, 1964; Lee, 1966b; Bird and Bird, 1969) are in agreement that, although in some forms there is considerable variation in thickness and complexity, there is, in almost all forms, a basic pattern.

Examination of electron micrographs in which the ratio of thickness of cuticle to diameter of nematode can be measured reveals (Table II) that the average ratio is about 1:34. Extremes of this include the large ascarids (1:100) which are atypical, although the ratio for their larvae is normal (1:30) and the adult Strongylina, e.g., *Ancylostoma* (1:10) which are characterized by having a very thick cuticle. Also, this ratio appears to be different in the head region where the cuticle appears to retain much of its thickness, although the diameter decreases due to a decrease in diameter of the whole nematode as it tapers toward the anterior end. For example, the head region of male *Meloidogyne javanica* is 1:15 and that of adult *Xiphinema americanum* is 1:12. In the middle of the nematode the ratio would be closer to the average of 1:34. However, in some thick-cuticled nematodes, such as *Trichodorus*, a 1:13 ratio exists even in the middle of the nematode.

B. LAYERS OF THE CUTICLE

Perhaps the greatest problem which confronts the readers of papers on cuticle structure is the diversity in nomenclature of the different layers. Inglis (1964), Lee (1966b), and Johnson *et al.* (1970) agree that it is basically a three-layered structure and consists of an outer layer (cortical), a middle layer (matrix), and an inner layer (basal).

It is clear (Bird and Bird, 1969) that the nematode cuticle nearly always consists of at least two major layers, the cortical and the basal layers. An

TABLE II
RATIO OF THICKNESS OF CUTICLE TO DIAMETER OF NEMATODE

Species	Type (Male, female, or larva)	Ratio (Cuticle: Diameter of Nematode	Reference
Heterodera rostochiensis	Infective larva	1:27	Wisse and Daems (1968)
Meloidogyne javanica	Infective larva	1:30	Van Gundy et al. (1967); Bird (1968)
Trichinella spiralis	Larva	1:25	Beckett and Boothroyd (1961)
Tylenchulus semipenetrans	Infective larva	1:40	Van Gundy et al. (1967)
Ditylenchus dipsaci	Adults and larvae	1:28	Yuen (1967, 1968a)
Panagrellus silusiae	—	1:50	Yuen (1968b)
Acanthonchus duplicatus	—	1:38	Wright and Hope (1968)
Xiphinema americanum	Adult (head)	1:12	López-Abella et al. (1967)
Trichodorus sp.	Adult	1:13	Bird (unpublished)
Neoaplectana carpocapsae	Normal 3rd stage larva	1:45	Poinar and Leutenegger (1968)
Neoaplectana carpocapsae	Infective 3rd-stage larva	1:30	Poinar and Leutenegger (1968)
Ascaris lumbricoides	3rd-stage larva	1:30	Thust (1967)
Ascaris lumbricoides	Adults (male and female)	1:100	Light microscope measurement: Bird (unpublished)
Meloidogyne javanica	Male (head)	1:15	Bird (unpublished)
Ancylostoma duodenale	Males and females	1:10	Looss (1905)
Ancylostoma duodenale	Larva	1:50	Inatomi et al. (1963)
Ancylostoma caninum	Larva	1:50	Inatomi et al. (1963)
Strongyloides stercoralis	Larva	1:24	Inatomi et al. (1963)
Nippostrongylus brasiliensis	Larva	1:40	Inatomi et al. (1963)
Trichostrongylus orientalis	Larva	1.30	Inatomi et al. (1963)
Necator americanus	Larva	1.30	Inatomi et al. (1963)

exception to this general rule is found in the insect parasitic nematode
Bradynema sp. Here the normal cuticular structure has been replaced by
microvilli (Riding, 1970). In some nematodes there are only two layers as
in the adult females of the family Heteroderidae (Wieser, 1953; Ferris and
Siegel, 1957; Bird and Rogers, 1965; Kämpfe, 1966) and the cuticle of the
mature larva of *Trichinella spiralis* (Beckett and Boothroyd, 1961). All these
nematodes are parasitic and have an initial rapid period of growth of about
3 weeks duration in their hosts. In the Heteroderidae this takes place in the
roots of plants and in *Trichinella spiralis* in the muscles of animals. It seems

probable that this two-layered structure may be a consequence of the rapid period of growth once the animal is within its host and in an environment where movement is not required. This may give rise to a modification of the basic three-layered structure which is found in preparasitic larvae and males of the Heteroderidae and in the adults of the Trichuridae (Sheffield, 1963; Wright, 1968). In the Heteroderidae, preparasitic infective larvae have a basic cuticular structure which resembles that of a similar stage in many other species of nematodes (Fig. 9) (Bird, 1968; Wisse and Daems, 1968). In the case of *Meloidogyne javanica*, this basic three-layered structure changes, within a week of entry into the host, into the typical two-layered structure of the parasitic larva and sedentary adult female (Fig. 5). This early change, which is associated with a marked decrease in the ability of the larva to move through sand (Bird, 1967) due to muscular atrophy, is clearly an adaptation to the parasitic mode of life of this nematode. It seems reasonable to suggest that a similar process takes place in *Trichinella spiralis* for similar reasons, and that both are modifications of the basic three-layered pattern and are induced by a parasitic environment characterized by the absence of need for active undulatory movement and by sudden rapid growth.

It has been suggested by Thust (1966), with regard to the basic three-layered structure of nematode cuticles, that the term "median layer" be used instead of "homogeneous" or "matrix layer." Because it is clear that in many cases this layer is not homogeneous and because matrix is defined in the biological sense as "the substance situated between animal or vegetable cells" I feel that Thust's definition is the more correct and should be used. However, I refer to what Thust (1967) calls, in the larva of *Ascaris*, the "median layer" as the "basal layer" so that the basal layer of the larva corresponds with the basal layer of the adult (Fig. 6).

As stated earlier, the diversity in nomenclature of the various layers of the nematode cuticle has resulted in some confusion. I have attempted to overcome this by presenting cuticles as scale histograms in which the various layers are depicted. The larval stages of parasitic forms are usually similar in thickness and structure (Fig. 6A). For instance, the larval stages of *Ascaris lumbricoides* (0.3 μ), *Meloidogyne javanica* (0.5 μ), and *Nippostrongylus brasiliensis* (0.4 μ) are all very similar whereas the adult stages of these nematodes are completely different (Fig. 6B). Here *Ascaris lumbricoides* is depicted as being nearly 50 μ thick, although it varies from 30 μ to 80 μ (Watson, 1965b). *Meloidogyne javanica* is 6 μ thick and *Nippostrongylus brasiliensis* 10 μ thick. Other examples of the general constancy of thickness of the cuticles of infective larvae are shown in Table III. The average thickness of the cuticles of the fourteen different species of larvae comes to about 0.4 μ and it seems reasonable to assume that this is a typical thickness for all types of infective larvae. A similar state of uniformity of cuticle thickness

TABLE III

CUTICLE THICKNESS IN VARIOUS NEMATODES

Species	Thickness (μ)	Reference
Parasitic adults		
Strongylus equinus	50	Bird (1958a)
Oxyuris equi	15	Bird (1958a)
Trichuris myocastoris	9	Wright (1968)
Enterobius vermicularis	4	Tsubota (1966)
Aspiculuris tetraptera	5	Anya (1966a)
Xiphinema index	4	Roggen et al. (1967)
Xiphinema americanum	3	López-Abella et al. (1967)
Heterodera rostochiensis	7	Ferris and Siegal (1957)
Trichodorus allius	3	Raski et al. (1969)
Trichodorus sp.	4	Bird (unpublished)
Free-living adults		
Rhabditis pellio	2.25	Beams and Sekhon (1967)
Euchromadora vulgaris	2.1	Watson (1965a)
Acanthonchus duplicatus	2.1	Wright and Hope (1968)
Infective Larvae		
Filipjevimermis leipsandra	0.5	Poinar et al. (1968)
Heterodera rostochiensis	0.65	Wisse and Daems (1968)
Neoaplectana carpocapsae	0.4	Poinar and Leutenegger (1968)
Cooperia punctata	0.35	Eckert and Schwarz (1965)
Trichostrongylus colubriformis	0.44	Eckert and Schwarz (1965)
Haemonchus contortus	0.26	Eckert and Schwarz (1965)
Bunostomum trigonocephalum	0.30	Eckert and Schwarz (1965)
Necator americanus	0.35	Inatomi et al. (1963)
Ancylostoma duodenale	0.29	Inatomi et al. (1963)
Ancylostoma caninum	0.38	Inatomi et al. (1963)
Trichostrongylus orientalis	0.30	Inatomi et al. (1963)
Strongyloides stercoralis	0.25	Inatomi et al. (1963)
Strongyloides fülleborni	0.39	Inatomi et al. (1963)
Strongyloides ratti	0.24	Inatomi et al. (1963)

in thickness from 3 μ for *Xiphinema americanum* to 50 μ for *Strongylus equinus*. This variability in thickness is probably largely due to the variability in size of the parasitic adult forms.

It is generally agreed that the nematode cuticle is a three-layered structure in its most basic form and consists of cortical, median, and basal layers. I propose to consider these three layers as they occur in the three major ecological groups of nematodes, namely, those parasitic in animals or plants, their infective larvae, and the free-living nematodes.

1. Cortical Layer

In the larger nematodes the cortical layer is often divided into an external cortical layer and an internal cortical layer. The surface of the external cortical layer is exposed to the nematode's environment. It has been shown that, in the large ascarids, this layer is a very thin osmiophilic layer which is less than 100 mμ thick in *Ascaris lumbricoides* (Bird and Deutsch, 1957; Watson, 1965b) and is about 45 mμ thick in *Parascaris equorum* (Hinz, 1963). As a result of work on drug penetration into *Ascaris lumbricoides* Trim (1949) suggested that a thin lipid layer was present on the surface of the cuticle. This lipid layer is so thin that it cannot be detected by staining frozen sections of *Ascaris lumbricoides* with histochemical reagents (Bird, 1957). However, its presence has been detected by removing it by dipping ligatured ascarids into a lipid solvent, concentrating the solvent, and applying it as a spot to filter paper where it can be stained with fat stains (Bird, 1957). It has been suggested that this layer may, in fact, be a triple-layered membrane common to all nematodes (Lee, 1965b; Roggen *et al.*, 1967). It has so far been detected in many of the nematodes examined under the electron microscope and its apparent absence in others may be due to overstaining so that all three layers appear equally electron-dense. An example of this can be seen in the high-resolution pictures of the cuticles of larvae of *Meloidogyne javanica* (Fig. 5A, B, and C) in which the heavily stained outermost layer, which is about 35 mμ thick, corresponds to a less densely stained three-layered structure of similar dimensions in similar material belonging to another section (Fig. 7A).

Measurements of this layer in the highest resolution electronmicrographs of nematode cuticle that are available, indicate that it varies from 25 to 40 mμ in thickness. It can be subdivided into an outer membrane which is about 7 mμ thick and may correspond with a plasma membrane as it is a triple-layered membrane itself (Fig. 7A), a middle, relatively nonosmiophilic layer of about 10 to 20 mμ in thickness and an inner osmiophilic layer which varies from about 10 to 20 mμ in larval and free-living forms. This three-layered structure should not be called a triple-layered membrane as this term leads to confusion with the classical triple-layered "unit membrane" of cells (Robertson, 1959) which corresponds only with the outermost 7-mμ layer of the three-layered structure on the surface of nematode cuticles. The whole structure can be called the external cortical time of their formation they were actually a part of living cells" receives some support from electron microscope studies although the structure of the cuticle bears no relationship to a living cell and chemical studies (see below) indicate that the cuticle is a living structure and may, in many cases, be secreted from the hypodermis (Bird and Rogers, 1965). Bonner and his coworkers (Bonner *et al.*, 1970) conclude that, in *Nematospiroides dubius*, the cuticle is formed by both secretion and hypodermal differentiation.

There is considerable variation in the structure of the cortical layer. As mentioned above, it exists in all forms as an external cortical layer which varies from a basic three-layered structure to a much modified and thickened structure which appears granular or filamentous, at high resolution, in parasitic forms. In the majority of nematodes the cortical layer may be divided into two layers, the external cortical layer and the internal cortical layer (Figs. 6–8).

The external cortical layer has a complex chemical composition in the large parasitic nematodes; because of their size, they are the only nematodes in which the chemistry of the individual layers has been examined. It has been considered to be a keratin because of its sulfur content (Flury, 1912; Chitwood, 1936), the presence of disulfide and sulfhydryl groups (Carbonell and Apitz, 1961; Anya, 1966a), and the similarity of its histidine:lysine:arginine ratio to that obtained for keratins (Savel, 1955). However, this layer gives a collagen-type X-ray diffraction pattern (Fauré-Fremiet and Garrault, 1944) although its resistance to collagenase activity (Dawson, 1960) and failure to detect hydroxyproline in hydrolyzates of it suggest that it is not a typical vertebrate collagen (Savel, 1955; Bird, 1957). However, it does not act like a typical vertebrate keratin either as it is not completely dissolved by 0.5% thioglycollate (Bird, 1957, 1958b; Anya, 1966a) and is soluble in hot dilute alkali (Fairbairn, 1957). Furthermore, there is so much variation in the histidine:lysine:arginine ratios of keratins that this ratio has ceased to be of much significance in determining different types of protein (Crewther *et al.*, 1965). Sulfhydryl groups and sulfur-containing amino acids are found in other layers of the cuticle as well as the external cortical layer but disulfide groups appear to be peculiar to this layer and may be partly responsible for its resistant properties. Quinone tanning, which would also make this a more resistant layer, has been shown to occur in this layer in various species of nematodes together with catechol oxidase and polyphenols (Brown, 1950; Bird, 1957, 1958b; Monné, 1960; Ellenby, 1946, 1963). Quinone tanning does not appear to occur in some nematodes (Lee, 1965b; Anya, 1966a). The classic example of quinone tanning in the nematode cuticle is that of the female of *Heterodera rostochiensis* (Ellenby, 1946). This is a rather specialized case as the

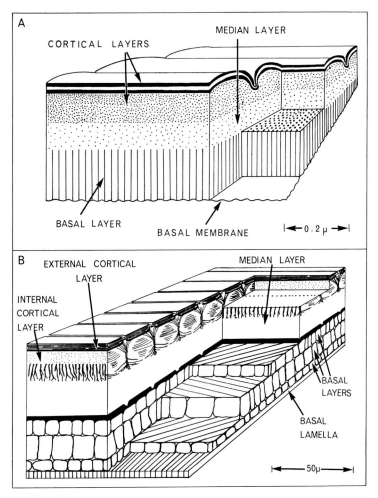

FIG. 8.   Diagrams of nematode cuticle layers. (A) Typical infective larva; (B) adult *Ascaris lumbricoides.*

cuticle of this nematode becomes a cyst wall on the death of the female and acts as a protective cover over the eggs. It is thought to aid in slowing down the rate of desiccation of the eggs under dry conditions (Ellenby, 1968a). Ellenby and Smith (1967) have examined the activity of the catechol oxidases responsible for tanning the cyst walls of a number of species of *Heterodera* and have observed that this enzyme in *H. rostochiensis* is more active at low temperatures than the enzymes of either *H. schachtii* or *H. avenae.* They think that this may be because *H.*

rostochiensis originates from a colder climate than the other two, namely, the high Andes of South America.

The internal cortical layer varies considerably in thickness in different nematodes. In preparasitic larval forms it may be only about 0.15–0.25 μ thick, whereas in the larger ascarids it is about 10 μ thick (Fig. 8B). It has a fibrous structure. In the large ascarids the fibers are 75–100 mμ in diameter (Watson, 1965b). There is no clear line of demarcation separating the internal cortical layer and the median (homogeneous or matrix) layer.

In many of the large nematodes parasitic in animals, the internal cortical layer is traversed by structures which lie under the transverse grooves. These structures have been referred to by various authors as "circular lamellae," "*Saftbahnen*," "fibers," "strands of condensed material," "pore canals," "thick fibrous masses," and "reflections of the plasticity of the matrix layer" (van Bömmel, 1895; Toldt, 1899; Goldschmidt, 1904; Chitwood and Chitwood, 1950; Bird, 1958a; Bogiavlenskii, 1958; Hinz, 1963; Inglis, 1964; Watson, 1965b).

These various statements are not as contradictory as they might seem at first sight. They all imply function as skeletal supports or channels through which materials may move more rapidly to the surface of the cuticle. It seems possible that they may function in both these respects and that morphologically different but functionally similar structures may occur throughout the Nematoda.

Studies on cuticle growth of *Ascaris lumbricoides* (Watson, 1965b) suggest that these structures could function as transporting canals as, in young forms, they extend into the basal (fiber) layers. An increase in thickness of the cuticle of this nematode is proportional to growth from 2 cm to over 30 cm in length and, in particular, a marked increase in thickness of the median (matrix or homogeneous) layer takes place. Indeed, a greatly thickened median layer seems to be a characteristic of the cuticles of the large nematodes parasitic in animals. The cuticles of these nematodes reflect adaptations to their parasitic environment and cannot be regarded as typical for the Nematoda.

The cortical layer of the cuticle in adult female *Mermis nigrescens* is penetrated by canals which extend from the tranverse grooves of the cuticle to the layer beneath the cortex (Lee, 1970).

Inglis (1964) suggests that all modifications of the nematode cuticle are based on a system of punctation canals which evolved "as a method of allowing the cuticle to grow by the incorporation of additional materials from processes of the hypodermis" (epidermis or subcuticle).

The internal cortical layer varies from 0.3 to 0.5 μ in thickness in free-living nematodes such as *Acanthonchus duplicatus, Euchromadora vulgaris,* and *Rhabditis pellio* (Wright and Hope, 1968; Watson, 1965a; Beams and

Sekhon, 1967). In the cuticles of larvae of parasitic nematodes it is about 0.15 to 0.25 μ thick in forms such as *Nippostrongylus brasiliensis, Meloidogyne javanica,* and *Heterodera rostochiensis* (Lee, 1966a; Bird, 1968; Wisse and Daems, 1968). A layer of similar dimensions and morphological appearance in the cuticles of various infective strongyle larvae (Eckert and Schwarz, 1965) has been named the homogeneous (median) layer. I feel that this is a misnomer and that these forms, like the adults of *Meloidogyne javanica* and the mature larva of *Trichinella spiralis* mentioned above, do not have a median layer. They are peculiarly modified for their potentially parasitic mode of life in having the partly shed cuticle of the 2nd-stage larva enveloping the infective larva as a protective sheath. It has been shown (Ellenby, 1968b) that this structure helps prevent desiccation of the larva. Thus the two-layered structure (cortical and basal) of the cuticle of these 3rd-stage infective larvae is a modification of the basic three-layered structure brought about by adaptation to this particular preparasitic stage of their life cycle.

Ribonucleic acid, ATPase, and acid phosphatase have been detected in the internal cortical layers of *Aspiculuris tetraptera, Syphacia obvelata,* and *Ascaris lumbricoides,* and ascorbic acid has been detected in this layer in *Aspiculuris* and *Ascaris* (Anya, 1966a). Furthermore, Anya (1966b) suggests that the cuticle itself is capable of synthesizing some of its own protein. However, in the larval and adult cuticles of *Phocanema decipiens* tests for nucleic acids and esterases were negative (Kan and Davey, 1968) although tests for ATPase, acid phosphatase, and ascorbic acid were not carried out.

2. *Median Layer*

As mentioned above, the synonyms for this layer are matrix and homogeneous. In the large ascarids the median layer is homogeneous and devoid of structure as evidenced by studies with phase-contrast, polarizing, and electron microscopes (Bird and Deutsch, 1957; Watson, 1965b). In many other nematodes, however, the median layer is far from homogeneous. In the adults of *Nippostrongylus brasiliensis* it is a fluid-filled region containing struts or skeletal rods and is traversed by fibrils which are apparently composed of collagen as they exhibit the characteristic periodic cross-banding of this protein visible when viewed under the electron microscope (Lee, 1965b; Jamuar, 1966). These are the first morphological demonstrations of collagen in the nematode cuticle. The struts in the hemaglobin containing fluid-filled median layer are suspended by these collagen fibrils and they also connect the cortex to the basal (fiber) layer.

The median layer of preparasitic larvae belonging to the family *Heter-*

oderidae (Bird, 1968; Wisse and Daems, 1968) is largely electron transparent and contains globular electron-dense bodies. This layer is particularly clear in the larva of *Heterodera rostochiensis* and is thought to be filled with fluid. It is traversed by thin columns of material which connect the cortical layer to the basal layer. The median layer is fluid in a number of different species of nematodes.

In many of the free-living nematodes this layer is traversed by dense rods or interlocking units which are called punctation canals and blocks by Inglis (1964, 1969). In forms such as *Euchromadora vulgaris* there is great structural variation in different parts of the cuticle. Electron micrographs of the cuticle of this nematode (Watson, 1965a) show that the median layer consists of a series of overlapping plates whose internal structure appears homogeneous. They are traversed by canals which connect the hypodermis (epidermis) with the outer portions of the cuticle. Inglis (1969) points out that these observations are mostly confined to the dorsal or ventral regions of nonpunctate cuticle, whereas the lateral region is much thicker and is marked by "punctations which correspond to the layers of rods sandwiched between the two other layers like teeth of a comb." Each annulus in this nematode is not a simple ring as in many forms but laterally it is narrow and thick with punctation processes and ventrally and dorsally it is a thin, wide, wedge-shaped sector. Clearly, further research is required on the complex cuticles of these marine forms. In the marine form *Acanthonchus duplicatus* (Wright and Hope, 1968) the median layer of the cuticle appears as an elctron-translucent zone which is traversed by electron-dense material; the arrangement of this material as rings and rods (Fig. 4) produces the light microscope image of pores and punctations mentioned earlier in this chapter. These structures resemble the "pore canals" of *Ascaris* in that radial processes branch out from each end of these rods (Fig. 8B).

In *Rhabditis pellio* the median layer is more electron dense than the internal cortical and basal (fiber) layers on each side of it (Beams and Sekhon, 1967). It is uniformly granular and is not traversed by struts or other skeletal elements. In the oxyurid *Aspiculuris tetraptera* the median (matrix) layer is also more electron dense than the layers on each side of it. In this case, the fibrils are arranged into a series of wavelike structures. These fibrils are similar to those in the internal cortical layer and, as in the ascarids, there is no clear line of demarcation between the two layers.

As mentioned above, it is in the median layer of ascarids that the greatest growth in the cuticle occurs during increases in size of the adult nematodes. This may also be true of other nematodes but no other measurements of this nature have yet been made. This layer can increase from 8 to 35 μ in thickness during growth of adult *Ascaris lumbricoides* (Watson, 1965b). Average thicknesses of the median layer range from 0.1 μ for the larvae of *Meloidogyne* and

Heterodera to 0.5 μ for *Rhabditis*. This layer is 5–10 μ in large parasitic forms such as *Strongylus*, *Phocanema* and *Oxyuris* and averages about 20 μ in *Ascaris* and *Parascaris*.

The median layer undergoes marked increases in width in *Hemicycliophora arenaria* (Johnson *et al.*, 1970) as it grows through the larval stages to become an adult nematode. The median (matrix) layer of this nematode is about 0.2 μ in width in the 2nd-stage larva and about 0.7 μ in width in the adult female.

Generally speaking, the median layer shows considerable structural variability in different nematodes. Chemically, it consists of proteins which resemble collagen which has been demonstrated both morphologically and chemically in different nematodes. A nonspecific esterase, acid mucopolysaccharide, and some lipid have also been detected in this layer. It does not appear to be as metabolically active as the cortical layers, however, and, so far, no other enzymes or free or bound polyphenols have been detected in it (Bird, 1957; Dawson, 1960; Monné, 1960; Novelli, 1961; Lee, 1961, 1962, 1965a; Anya, 1966a).

3. *Basal Layer*

In the free-living and marine nematodes, such as *Rhabditis pellio, Euchromadora vulgaris,* and *Acathonchus duplicatus* that have been examined under the electron microscope, this layer varies from about 0.2 to 0.5 μ in depth. It is made up of fibers or filaments which may be transversely orientated but which do not form the layered trellis of crossed fibers characteristic of some of the larger nematodes parasitic in animals (Watson, 1965a; Beams and Sekhon, 1967; Wright and Hope, 1968).

Studies with the electron microscope have revealed that the basal layer of preparasitic larvae is remarkably similar in different nematodes irrespective of whether the final host is an animal or a plant (Figs. 5, 8A, and 9). It consists of regularly arranged vertical rods or striations. These structures were first reported by Peebles (1957) in the cuticle of adult *Rhabditis strongyloides* and subsequently shown by Inatomi and his co-workers (1963) in the cuticles of infective larvae of *Necator americanus, Ancylostoma duodenale, Ancylostoma caninum, Trichostrongylus orientalis, Nippostrongylus brasiliensis, Strongyloides ratti, Strongyloides stercoralis,* and *Strongyloides fülleborni*. They have also been observed by Watson (1962) in *Turbatrix aceti*; by Eckert and Schwarz (1965) in the infective larvae of *Haemonchus contortus, Trichostrongylus colubriformis, Cooperia punctata, Bunostomum trigonocephalum, Strongyloides ransomi,* and *Strongyloides papilosus*; by Lee (1966a) and Jamuar (1966) in *Nippostrongylus brasiliensis*; by Yuen (1967, 1968a, b) in *Ditylenchus dipsaci* and *Panagrellus silusiae*; by Ibrahim and Hollis (1967) in the larva of *Meloidogyne hapla*; by Bird (1968) in the larva of *Meloidogyne*

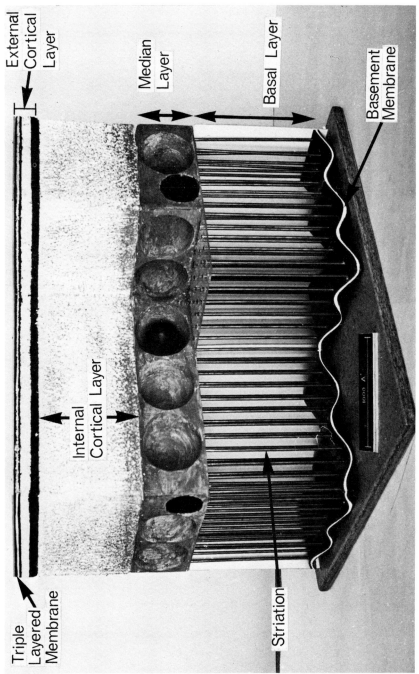

External Cortical Layer

Median Layer

Basal Layer

Basement Membrane

Internal Cortical Layer

Triple Layered Membrane

Striation

FIG. 9.   Model of the cuticle of a typical infective larva.

javanica; by Wisse and Daems (1968) in the larva of *Heterodera rostochiensis*; and by Johnson *et al.* (1970) in *Hemicycliophora arenaria*, *Aphelenchus avenae*, *Hirschmanniella gracilis*, and *Hirschmanniella belli*. I have observed them also in *Tylenchulus semipenetrans*.

These structures have been variously referred to as "subcortical parallel columellae," "the striped layer," "regularly arranged rods or canals," "regularly spaced striations," "regularly arranged crystalloid structures," and "a palisadelike array." They have been included in all of the three principle layers, but when their position in the cuticle is examined comparatively in various different nematodes, I think that it becomes clear that they are part of the basal layer. Some idea of the three-dimensional appearance of this striped layer was first provided by Eckert and Schwarz (1965) and Jamuar (1966), who cut saggital sections through the cuticle and showed that it consists of a lattice work made up of parallel rows of the rodlike structures crossing each other at right angles. Furthermore, Jamuar (1966) measured these periodicities and found that the lateral periodicity shown in transverse sections was greater (27 mμ) than the anterior–posterior periodicity shown in longitudinal section (18 mμ). In the larva of *Heterodera rostochiensis* (Wisse and Daems, 1968) these periodicities are 24 mμ and 18 mμ, respectively. The mean periodicity is thus about 20 mμ and an identical measurement to this has been found in *Meloidogyne javanica* larvae (Bird, 1968). These periodicities appear to vary slightly in different species and these differences are probably due more to differences in methods of fixation, embedding, and calibration of the electron photomicrographs than to actual differences between species, as different values have been obtained by different workers for the same species of nematode.

Wisse and Daems (1968) have used the goniometer stage of the Philips EM 300 electron microscope to tilt transverse sections through an angle of 12° and thus demonstrate support for the assumption that the sharp striation is caused by the projection of several rods to a single image and this can also be demonstrated by manipulating a three-dimensional model (Fig. 9). If sections of about 600 Å thickness are examined under the electron microscope, they will contain several parallel lines of stripes, striations, or columns. While the periodicity of approximately 20 mμ between the stripes appears to remain fairly constant, the depth of this type of basal layer varies in different species and in different stages of the same species. For instance, it is about 125 mμ thick in *Meloidogyne javanica* larvae, but is 250 mμ thick in *Heterodera rostochiensis* larvae and 500 mμ thick in the adult male of *M. javanica*.

So far, all the nematodes in which the basal layer has this striped or striated structure are forms which are exposed to environments that can fluctuate. Lee's suggestion (1966a) that its regular spacings exist because it is composed of a protein with very close linkages between the molecules, resulting in a resistant layer that would protect the nematode from a fluctuating environment, seems a reasonable one. This seems most likely in forms such as *Meloidogyne javanica* (Fig. 5) in which the preparasitic larva and the male, which can be exposed to a fluctuating environment, have it, whereas the parasitic larva and the female, which lie within the plant, do not.

The uniformity of this type of cuticle (Fig. 8A) is so great among such widely divergent species that it is tempting to regard it as the basic cuticular type from which the more elaborate ones have evolved.

As mentioned above, the basal layer of some free-living and marine forms consists of a layer of fibers or filaments which varies in thickness from 200 to 500 mμ. The adults of many parasitic nematodes, however, have a thick basal layer which is often made up of layers of fibers which cross each other to form a lattice. In these forms, this layer ranges in thickness from about 2 μ in the plant parasitic nematode *Xiphinema index* (Roggen *et al.*, 1967) to 25 μ in *Strongylus equinus* and the large ascarids (Bird, 1957, 1958a; Hinz, 1963; Watson, 1965b). These crossing fiber layers were first observed in the large ascarids over a hundred years ago (von Siebold, 1845; Czermak, 1852). Their presence can be readily demonstrated under the light microscope (Figs. 8B and 10). It has been shown that this trellislike arrangement permits a 10–15% elongation (Fauré-Fremiet and Garrault, 1944; Harris and Crofton, 1957). Each fiber layer consists of parallel strands which run in spirals at about 75° to the longitudinal axis of the worm. The middle of the three layers in *Ascaris* crosses the other two at an angle of 135° to form a mobile lattice which Harris and Crofton (1957) consider provides for an anisometric expansion and contraction under the action of the longitudinal muscles, (Fig. 11).

Under the electron microscope it can be shown that these layers are made up of irregularly shaped fibers which consist of bundles of tightly packed fibrils, each less than 10 mμ in diameter (Watson, 1965b). These fibrils do not show the banding visible in vertebrate collagen fibrils and in the median layer of adult *Nippostrongylus brasiliensis* described above under the electron microscope, but X-ray diffraction studies (Fauré-Fremiet and Garrault, 1944; Picken *et al.*, 1947) and various chemical tests (Chitwood, 1936; Bird, 1957; Dawson, 1960) indicate its close affinities with the collagens.

The basal layer and the hypodermis are separated by a highly convoluted triple-layered plasma-membrane or basement membrane (Figs. 5, 8, and 9). The occurrence of this membrane is so universal over such a wide range of nematodes that reports of its absence may, perhaps, be due to differences in fixing and staining techniques. The interesting observation of Hinz (1963) that this membrane is part of the hypodermal endoplasmic reticulum in *Parascaris equorum*, because of the implications that it suggests concerning

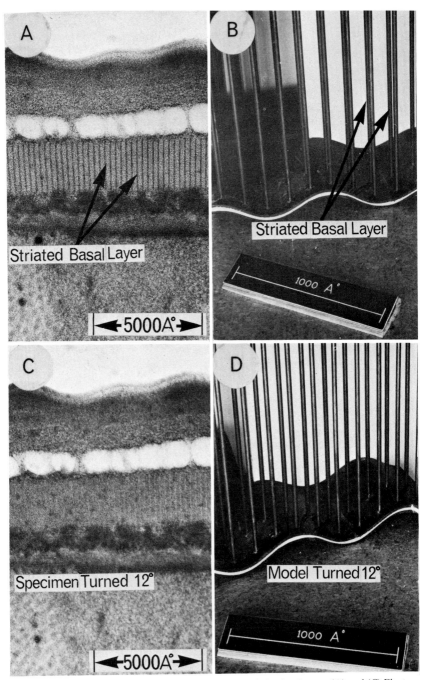

FIG. 10. Structure of striated basal layer of typical infective larvae. (A) and (C) Electron micrographs of transverse sections showing the effect of tilting the specimen 12° within the electron microscope. (×61,000). (Courtesy of Dr. E. Wisse; (Wisse and Daems, 1968.) (B) and (D) Similar effect caused by turning model of cutcle through 12°. (Approx. ×450,000).

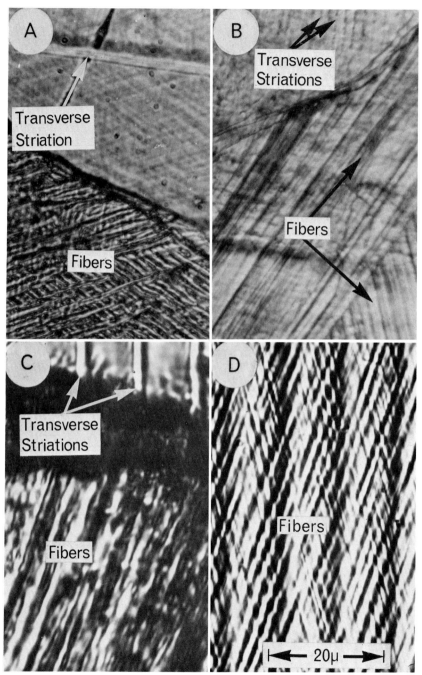

FIG. 11. Surface views of several nematode cuticles showing various layers exposed by a stripping technique. (A) *Oxyuris equi*; (B) *Strongylus equinus*; (C) and (D) *Ascaris lumbricoides*. (× 1600).

matters such as protein synthesis in the cuticle and the position of the limiting membrane of the hypodermis, requires further testing at the limit of
resolution of the electron microscope during various stages of cuticle growth
and development. Observations of *Meloidogyne javanica* under these conditions, however, (Bird and Rogers, 1965; Bird, 1968) indicate that these
membranes resemble plasma membranes and not the double membranes
of the endoplasmic reticulum which occur in other parts of this nematode
(Bird, 1968).

C. CHEMICAL COMPOSITION OF THE CUTICLE

Our knowledge of the chemical composition of the nematode cuticle is
based largely on experiments with the larger ascarids. The reason for this is,
of course, that the majority of nematodes are far too small for microdis-
section of cuticles free of adhering noncuticular material. This makes
chemical analysis impossible and, as the cuticles in many larval forms are
not thick enough to be resolved clearly with the light microscope, even
histochemical staining techniques are not feasible. The exceptions to this
have been the outermost cuticle or sheath of 3rd-stage infective larvae of
various strongyles (Bird and Rogers, 1956) and the 4th-stage larval cuticle
of *Nippostrongylus muris* (Simmonds, 1958). These structures are less than
0.5 μ thick in most strongyle larvae (Inatomi *et al.*, 1963; Eckert and
Schwarz, 1965).

The methods used to obtain these delicate structures take advantage of
two facts. First, the larvae can be induced to shed their cuticles either by
treatment with dilute hypochlorite solutions in the case of 3rd-stage larvae
or in salt solutions in the case of the 4th-stage larvae. Second, they can be
separated from the living larvae by differential centrifugation as the relative
density of the sheaths is greater than that of the larvae. By means of these
techniques, pure samples of isolated larval cuticles are obtained for chemical
analysis.

As a result of the investigations of numerous workers, mostly on the
cuticles of the larger ascarids, but also of some smaller forms including the
larvae mentioned above, it has been established that the chemical composition of the nematode cuticle, apart from water, consists predominantly of
protein with traces of lipid and carbohydrate. It is flexible and, as has been
mentioned, is capable of some distension. The amino acid composition of
this protein in *Ascaris lumbricoides* has been estimated quantitatively by two
groups of workers. First by Rees and Baston (Bird, 1957) and later by Watson
and Silvester (1959). The results obtained from these separate analyses are
very similar (Table IV). With the exception of valine, there was close agree-

ment in the quantities of amino acids present. Hydroxyproline, whose presence was not tested for by the column technique by the first group of workers, was nevertheless located by paper chromatographic methods using specific reagents (Bird, 1957). This amino acid has been shown to be present in all whole cuticles which have been chemically analyzed. However, it does not appear to be present in the external cortical layer, the most stable and resistant layer of the cuticle, which is characterized by the presence of sulfur-containing groups and quinone tanning in many nematodes in addition to the thin superficial lipid layer mentioned above. Although the external cortical layer has some of the characteristics of a keratin, it differs in having an X-ray diffraction pattern which resembles collagen and in its solubility in hot dilute alkali and insolubility in 0.5% thioglycolate. The

TABLE IV

Amino Acid Composition of *Ascaris lumbricoides* Cuticle Given as Grams of Amino Acid Nitrogen[a]

Amino acid	After Bird (1957)	After Watson and Silvester (1959)
Alanine	5.6	6.0
Amide N	—	3.39
Ammonia	4.3	—
Arginine	11.2	12.5
Aspartic acid	5.2	5.4
Glutamic acid	5.9	6.0
Glycine	18.1	20.4
Histidine	1.94	2.09
Hydroxylysine	—	0.0
Hydroxyproline	—	1.58
Isoleucine	1.44	1.25
Leucine	1.94	1.55
Lysine	7.7	6.2
Methionine	1.00	0.77
Phenylalanine	0.88	0.67
Proline	22.1	22.7
Serine	1.78	1.82
Threonine	1.44	1.47
Tyrosine	0.50	0.24
Valine	4.25	1.29
Unknown	1.51	—
Total	96.8	95.3
Method of hydrolysis	80% formic acid–11.7 N HCl (1:1)	6 N HCl at 110° for 24 hr
Method of analysis	Stein and Moore (1950)	Moore and Stein (1951)

[a]Values per 100 gm of total nitrogen.

other layers of the cuticle resemble collagens in their X-ray diffraction patterns, amino acid composition, hydrothermal properties, and response to collagenase. Here again, however, their chemical composition and fine structure differ in some respects from those of typical vertebrate collagens. Nematode cuticles are perhaps best described (Bird and Bird, 1969) as being made up of secreted collagens unique to and characteristic of the Nematoda, which are made more resistant and stable at the surface of the cuticle by the presence of disulfide groups and quinone bonds.

The presence of enzymes, ribonucleic acid, ascorbic acid, and hemaglobin in some cuticles, together with their observed growth after molting, supports the hypothesis that the cuticle is an active living structure and not just an inert covering.

IV. Function

The cuticle acts as a barrier between the nematode and harmful elements in its environment. The fact that nematodes are found in almost every ecological niche bears testimony to the amazing survival value of animals which have the cuticle as a flexible exoskeleton. I shall now consider its principal functions.

A. PERMEABILITY

The cuticle is permeable to water, certain ions, and nonelectrolytes including some organic nematocides. Nematodes exhibit a selectivity toward the molecules that enter them. This is characteristic of the living nematode and is lost when the nematode dies. This dynamic equilibrium between the nematode and its aqueous environment varies, depending on the nature of the environment in which the nematode normally lives. The cuticles of marine nematodes, for instance, are usually more permeable to chemicals than those of soil-inhabiting forms.

Work on permeability of the nematode cuticle has been comprehensively reviewed and discussed in a number of books (Rogers, 1962; Lee, 1965a; Von Brand, 1966). Recently, however, a number of papers have appeared on this topic dealing with nematodes inhabiting widely divergent environments.

The permeability of the cuticles of a number of plant parasitic and soil-inhabiting nematodes to various radiolabeled chemicals has been examined by Marks et al. (1968). These workers measured the specific rates of entrance and exit of these chemicals from living and dead *Aphelenchus avenae* and also carried out experiments with *Tylenchulus semipenetrans*, *Anguina tritici*, and *Pellodera* sp. It was found that, whereas water and the nematocides ethylene dibromide (EDB) and 1,2-dibromo-3-chloropropane (DBCP) are readily taken up and released, glucose, sodium acetate, and glycine are not. This selectivity is lost after the nematodes are killed at 70°C. These workers have shown, for these nematodes, that the idea that nematocides act by dissolving the outermost thin lipid layer of the cuticle, thus making it more permeable, is erroneous. They have found that water enters more rapidly than DBCP and that exposure to EDB does not affect the subsequent permeability of the nematode to either water or sodium acetate.

Ellenby (1968b) has shown, by means of the interference microscope, that the ensheathed larva of *Haemonchus contortus* survives desiccation far better than the exsheathed form. The reason for this is that, although the sheath is at first freely permeable to water, it becomes less permeable as it dries and acts as a survival mechanism, slowing down the water loss and protecting the enclosed larva against desiccation. However, as Ellenby (1968b) points out, factors other than rate of water loss through the cuticle are involved in desiccation survival, since the infective larva of *Ditylenchus dipsaci*, which loses water more rapidly (Ellenby, 1968a) than the ensheathed larva of *Haemonchus contortus*, is, nevertheless, far better at surviving desiccation.

The marine nematode *Deontostoma (Thoracostoma) californicum* differs from those soil-inhabiting forms mentioned above in that there is no indication that an exit of ions occurs either in hypotonic media or following overosmoregulation in hypertonic solutions (Croll and Viglierchio, 1969). This nematode is adapted to intertidal life and can tolerate exposure and high salinity. As in *Panagrellus redivivus* and *Aphelenchus avenae* (Myers, 1966), this nematode takes up ions in hypertonic solutions until osmotic equilibrium is reached with the environment. It differs from these forms in having an isotonicity that is about four times greater, i.e., 0.6 M NaCl as compared with 0.15 M NaCl.

Generally, it seems that nematode cuticles are permeable to many chemicals and that the nature of this permeability is controlled by the living nematode. Environmental adaptations influence this pattern just as they can influence the structure of the cuticle itself.

B. Movement

So far, two hypotheses have been advanced for the role that the cuticle plays in the movement of nematodes.

1. *The Turgor Pressure System* (Harris and Crofton, 1957; Inglis, 1964)

In this system the muscles are opposed by the hydrostatic pressure of the body contents and the elasticity of the cuticle. When the muscles relax, this pressure brings the muscles back to their resting shape and so restores the body shape. The success of this system is thought by Harris and Crofton to be dependent on the presence of spiral fiber layers which form a lattice capable of extension. However, Inglis points out that a system of spiral fibers is not found in the majority of nematodes and is not essential for a turgor pressure system since all that is required is an anisometric skeleton which has been developed round a system of alternate rigid and flexible transverse cuticular rings or annuli.

2. *The Antagonistic Action System* (Wisse and Daems, 1968)

In this system the cuticle offers progressive resistance to deformation during bending of the body. Shortening of the cuticle above the contracted muscle leads to a compression of the striated layer which, in turn, leads to a bending of the cortical layers so that the transverse annulations become very pronounced and this is inhibited by components in the median layer. The net result is that an antideformation force is built up within the cuticle which is antagonistic to muscular action. In this hypothesis the cuticle is likened to a coiled spring covered on the inner side with a layer of muscle.

It seems that these hypotheses complement each other and that in nematodes without either crossed fiber layers or perpendicular rodlike striations in their basal layers, turgor pressure, cuticle elasticity, and the antideformation properties of layers common to these forms, for example, the transverse annulations of the cortical layer, are involved in varying degrees.

C. GROWTH

The fact that the cuticle is capable of considerable growth between molts and after the last molt has been shown in those parasitic nematodes in which this has been measured (Bird and Rogers, 1965; Watson, 1965b). This type of growth is probably common to most nematodes whether they be parasitic or free-living. It is one of the reasons for suggesting that the cuticle is not just an inert skeletal structure but is living and can respond to environmental changes. An example of this has been noted in the cuticles of adult females of *Tylenchorhynchus martini* in which this structure in swarming nematodes is different from that in those which are not swarming (Ibrahim, 1967).

I suggested some time ago (Bird, 1958a), when working with some of the larger nematodes parasitic in mammals, that an examination of cuticle response to artificial injury could provide the answer to this problem. A serious technical disadvantage of this method is, of course, that the nematode would have to be removed from its environment in order to injure the cuticle and would then have to be replaced in its host or maintained under artificial conditions. Perhaps because of these drawbacks, this technique has, as far as I know, never been used. However, an observation by Cleland and Johnston (1912) on the reaction of *Ascaris* cuticles to damage by acanthocephalans in the pig's intestine indicates that the hypodermis (cutis) does not repair the cuticle by producing layers similar to those that already exist, but instead produces a structure which resembles the hypodermis under the light microscope. However, this structure does not contain any nuclei and is separated from the hypodermis by a "well-defined line," presumably a thick membrane. It is clear from the accompanying diagram that, although these layers were only observed under the low power of the light microscope, the new structure is not part of the hypodermis and is formed below the basal (fiber) layers.

Further experimental work is needed in order to answer such questions as "Can the cuticle regenerate itself or part of itself at any stage of its growth?," "If regeneration occurs, does it occur more easily in forms with simple cuticles?," "What is the relationship between extent of injury and ability to regenerate?" It would be particularly interesting to have information on the ultrastructure of this "repair tissue" produced by *Ascaris*.

V. Summary

The cuticle is a multilayered flexible protective exoskeleton. Externally it is marked by punctations and transverse and longitudinal markings. Transverse annulations appear to be present in most, if not all, nematodes and are associated with their characteristic dorsoventral undulatory movement. The distance between these annulations is usually $1–2\,\mu$ although it can be much greater in some forms parasitic in animals.

Cuticles vary in thickness but the average ratio between thickness of cuticle and diameter of nematode is about 1:30–1:40.

The nematode cuticle consists of three layers: cortical, median, and basal. In some forms the median layer is missing and in others these three layers are themselves subdivided into layers.

The average thickness of the cuticle varies. In larvae it is about $0.4\,\mu$ thick; in those free-living adults in which it has been measured it is about $2\,\mu$ thick, and in the adults of parasitic forms it varies from 3 to $50\,\mu$ in thickness.

The cortical layer is divided into external and internal cortical layers. The external cortical layer consists of a triple-layered membrane which ranges from 25 to 40 mμ in thickness. The outermost layer is about 7 mμ thick and corresponds with a triple-layered plasma membrane; the middle non-osmiophilic layer is about 10–20 mμ thick, and the innermost osmiophilic layer is also 10–20 mμ thick. This innermost layer becomes thicker in some parasitic nematodes so that the external cortical layer can become 0.1–1 μ thick.

Apart from a thin layer of lipid and traces of carbohydrate, the external cortical layer is made up of proteins which are peculiar in that in some respects they resemble keratins and in others collagens. It differs from other layers of the cuticle in its resistance to various chemicals and this is presumably due to disulfide and/or quinone bonding of its proteins.

The internal cortical layer varies considerably in thickness from 0.15 to 0.25 μ in larval forms to 10 μ in adult nematodes parasitic in animals. It has a fibrous structure and there is no clear line of demarcation between it and the median layer. This layer appears to be biochemically active in some nematodes as both enzymes and ribonucleic acid have been detected in it.

The median layer is thought to be fluid-filled in many nematodes. It may be homogeneous or be traversed by rods, plates, or collagen fibrils. It may contain electron-dense spheres or be completely fibrillar. Morphologically it is the most variable of the three main layers. It ranges in thickness from 0.1 μ in larval forms to about 20 μ in the large ascarids. Chemically it is made up of proteins which resemble collagens.

The basal layer varies from 0.1 to 0.5 μ in thickness in free-living and larval nematodes, but in the adults of some of the forms parasitic in animals it can be as thick as 25 μ. In soil-inhabiting nematodes this layer is remarkably constant and consists of a latticework made up of parallel rows of rodlike structures crossing each other at right angles. The average distance between these rods is about 20 mμ. These regular periodicities may represent closely linked proteins which would make the cuticle more resistant to fluctuations in the environment.

The basal layer in many adult nematodes parasitic in animals is made up of fibers which cross each other to form a spiral mobile lattice which permits some elongation of the cuticle. The chemical composition of this layer is similar in many respects to that of the collagens.

The nematode cuticle is best described as being made up of unique proteins resembling secreted collagens stabilized at their surfaces by disulfide groups and quinone bonds. Its metabolic activity under the control of the hypodermis has been shown in both growth and permeability studies and its structure is closely associated with the characteristic dorsoventral undulatory movement of the Nematoda.

REFERENCES

Anya, A. O. (1966a). *Parasitology* **56**, 179.
Anya, A. O. (1966b). *Nature (London)* **209**, 827.
Beams, H. W., and Sekhon, S. S. (1967). *J. Ultrastruct. Res.* **18**, 580.
Beckett, E. B., and Boothroyd, B. (1961). *Ann. Trop. Med. Parasitol.* **55**, 116.
Bird, A. F. (1957). *Exp. Parasitol* **6**, 383.
Bird, A. F. (1958a). *Parasitology* **48**, 32.
Bird, A. F. (1958b). *Nematologica* **3**, 205.
Bird, A. F. (1967). *J. Parasitol* **53**, 768.
Bird, A. F. (1968). *J. Parasitol* **54**, 475.
Bird, A. F., and Bird, J. (1969). In "Chemical Zoology" (M. Florkin and B. T. Scheer, eds.), Vol. III, pp. 253–288. Academic Press, New York.
Bird, A. F., and Deutsch, K. (1957). *Parasitology* **47**, 319.
Bird, A. F., and Rogers, G. E. (1965). *Nematologica* **11**, 224.
Bird, A. F., and Rogers, W. P. (1956). *Exp. Parasitol* **5**, 449.
Bogiavlenskii, I. K. (1958). *Biophysics (USSR)* **3**, 449.
Bonner, T. P., Menefee, M. G., and Etges, F. J. (1970). *Z. Zellforsch Mikrosk. Anat.* **104**, 193.
Brown, C. H. (1950). *Nature (London)* **165**, 275.
Carbonell, L. M., and Apitz, C. R. (1961). *Exp. Parasitol.* **10**, 263.
Chitwood, B. G. (1936). *Proc. Helminthol. Soc. Wash.* **3**, 39.
Chitwood, B. G., and Chitwood, M. B., eds. (1950). "An Introduction to Nematology," 213 pp. Monumental Printing Co., Baltimore, Maryland.
Cleland, J. B., and Johnston, T. H. (1912). *Rep. Meet. Australas Ass. Advan. Sci.* **13**, 299.
Crewther, W. G., Fraser, R. D. B., Lennox, F. G., and Lindley, H. (1965). *Advan. Protein Chem.* **20**, 191.
Croll, N. A., and Viglierchio, D. R. (1969). *Proc. Helminthol. Soc. Wash.* **36**, 1.
Czermak, J. (1852). *Sitzungsber Kaiserl. Akad. Weiss. Wien, Math. Naturwiss. Kl.* **9**, 755.
Dawson, B. (1960). *Nature (London)* **187**, 799.
de Coninck, L. (1965). "Traité de Zoologie. IV (2): Nemathelminthes." Masson, Paris.
Durette-Desset, M. C. (1966). *Cah. Maboke.* **4**, 120.
Eckert, J., and Schwarz, R. (1965). *Z. Parasitenk.* **26**, 116.
Ellenby, C. (1946). *Nature (London)* **157**, 302.
Ellenby, C. (1963). *Experientia* **19**, 256.
Ellenby, C. (1968a). *Proc. Roy. Soc., Ser. B* **169**, 203.
Ellenby, C. (1968b). *J. Exp. Biol.* **49**, 469.
Ellenby, C., and Smith, L. (1967). *Comp. Biochem. Physiol.* **21**, 51.
Fairbairn, D. (1957). *Exp. Parasitol.* **6**, 491.
Fauré-Fremiet, E., and Garrault, H. (1944). *Bull. Biol. Fr. Belg.* **78**, 206.
Ferris, V. R., and Siegel, B. M. (1957). *Nematologica* **2**, 16.
Flury, F. (1912). *Arch. Exp. Pathol. Pharmakol.* **67**, 275.
Goldschmidt, R. (1904). *Zool. Anz.* **28**, 259.
Günther, B., and Kämpfe, L. (1966). *Verh. Deut. Ges. Goettingen* **30**, Suppl. 152.
Harris, J. E., and Crofton, H. D. (1957). *J. Exp. Biol.* **34**, 116.
Hinz, E. (1963). *Protoplasma* **56**, 202.
Ibrahim, I. K. A. (1967). *Proc. Helminthol. Soc. Wash.* **34**, 18.
Ibrahim, I. K. A., and Hollis, J. P. (1967). *Proc. Helminthol. Soc. Wash.* **34**, 137.
Inatomi, S., Sakumoto, D., Hano, K., and Tanaka, H. (1963). *Kiseichugaku Zasshi* **12**, 16.
Inglis, W. G. (1963). *Nature (London)* **197**, 618.
Inglis, W. G. (1964). *Proc. Zool. Soc. London* **143**, 465.

Inglis, W. G. (1969). *Bull. Brit. Mus. (Natur. Hist.)*, *Zool* **17**, 151.
Jamuar, M. P. (1966). *J. Parasitol.* **52**, 209.
Johnson, P. W., Van Gundy, S. D., and Thomson, W. W. (1970). *J. Nematol.* **2**, 42.
Kämpfe, L. (1966). *Mitt. Biol. Bundesanst. Land-Forstwirt. Berlin-Dahlem* **118**, 54.
Kan, S. P., and Davey, K. G. (1968). *Can. J. Zool.* **46**, 235.
Lee, D. L. (1961). *Nature (London)* **192**, 282.
Lee, D. L. (1962). *Parasitology* **52**, 241.
Lee, D. L. (1965a). "The Physiology of Nematodes," 154 pp. Oliver & Boyd, Edinburgh and London.
Lee, D. L. (1965b). *Parasitology* **55**, 173.
Lee, D. L. (1966a). *Parasitology* **56**, 127.
Lee, D. L. (1966b). *Advan. Parasitol.* **4**, 187.
Lee, D. L. (1970). *J. Zool.* **161**, 513.
Locke, M. (1966). *J. Morphol.* **118**, 461.
Looss, A. (1905). *Rec. Egypt. Govt. Sch. Med.* **3**, 1.
López-Abella, D., Jiménez-Millán, F., and Garcia-Hidalgo, F. (1967). *Nematologica* **13**, 283.
Marks, C. F., Thomason, I. J., and Castro, C. E. (1968). *Exp. Parasitol.* **22**, 321.
Monné, L. (1960). *Ark Zool.* **13**, 287.
Moore, S., and Stein, W. H. (1951). *J. Biol. Chem.* **192**, 663.
Myers, R. F. (1966). *Nematologica* **12**, 579.
Novelli, A. (1961). *Riv. Biol.* **54**, 139.
Peebles, C. R. (1957). *J. Parasitol.* **43**, Suppl., 45.
Picken, L. E. A., Pryor, M. G. M., and Swann, M. M. (1947). *Nature (London)* **159**, 434.
Poinar, G. O., and Leutenegger, R. (1968). *J. Parasitol.* **54**, 340.
Poinar, G. O., Leutenegger, R., and Gotz, P. (1968). *J. Ultrastruct. Res.* **25**, 293.
Raski, D. J., Jones, N. O., and Roggen, D. R. (1969). *Proc. Helminthol. Soc. Wash.* **36**, 106.
Riding, I. L. (1970). *Nature (London)* **226**, 179.
Robertson, J. D. (1959). *Biochem. Soc. Symp.* **16**, 3.
Rogers, W. P. (1962). "The Nature of Parasitism," 287 pp. Academic Press, New York.
Rogers, W. P. (1968). *Parasitology* **58**, 657.
Roggen, D. R., Raski, D. J., and Jones, N. O. (1967). *Nematologica* **13**, 1.
Samoiloff, M. R., and Pasternak, J. (1968). *Can. J. Zool.* **46**, 1019.
Savel, J. (1955). *Rev. Pathol. Comp. Hyg. Gen.* **55**, 213.
Sheffield, H. G. (1963). *J. Parasitol.* **49**, 998.
Simmonds, R. A. (1958). *Exp. Parasitol.* **7**, 14.
Stein, W. H., and Moore, S. (1950). *Cold Spring Harbor Symp. Quant. Biol.* **14**, 179.
Thust, R. (1966). *Zool. Anz.* **177**, 411.
Thust, R. (1967). *Z. Weiss. Zool., Abt. A* **178**, 1.
Toldt, K. (1899). *Arb. Zool. Inst. Univ. Wien* **11**, 289.
Trim, A. R. (1949). *Parasitology* **39**, 281.
Tsubota, T. (1966). *Kiseichugaku Zasshi* **15**, 58.
van Bömmel, A. (1895). *Arb. Zool. Inst. Wurzburg* **10**, 191.
Van Gundy, S. D., Bird, A. F., and Wallace, H. R. (1967). *Phytopathology* **57**, 559.
von Brand, T. (1966). "Biochemistry of Parasites," 429 pp. Academic Press, New York.
von Siebold, C. T. (1845). Wirbellose Thiere. *Lehrbuch der Vergleichenden Anatomie* pp. 114–115. Berlin.
Watson, B. D. (1962). Ph.D. Thesis, Univ. of Cambridge, Cambridge, England.
Watson, B. D. (1965a). *Quart. J. Microsc. Sci.* **106**, 75.
Watson, B. D. (1965b). *Quart. J. Microsc. Sci.* **106**, 83.
Watson, M. R., and Silvester, N. R. (1959). *Biochem. J.* **71**, 579.

Wieser, W. (1953), *Medd. Vaxtskyddanst. Stockholm* **65**, 1.
Wisse, E., and Daems, W. T. (1968). *J. Ultrastruct. Res.* **24**, 210.
Wright, K. A. (1965). *Can. J. Zool.* **43**, 689.
Wright, K. A. (1968). *Can. J. Zool.* **46**, 173.
Wright, K. A., and Hope, W. D. (1968). *Can. J. Zool.* **46**, 1005.
Wu, L.-Y. (1967). *Can. J. Zool.* **45**, 1003.
Yuen, P. H. (1967). *Can. J. Zool.* **45**, 1019.
Yuen, P. H. (1968a). *Nematologica* **14**, 385.
Yuen, P. H. (1968b). *Nematologica* **14**, 554.

4

MOLTING

I. Introduction

Growth in nematodes is associated with molting which normally occurs four times before the adult stage is reached.

Growth curves have been drawn for either a part or the whole of development in a number of different species of nematodes including *Turbatrix aceti* (Pai, 1928), *Ancylostoma caninum* (Scott, 1929; McCoy, 1930), *Ascaridea lineata* (Ackert, 1931), *Litomosoides carinii* (Scott, 1946), *Ascaris columnaris* (Tiner, 1953), *Angiostrongylus cantonensis* (Mackerras and Sandars, 1955), *Meloidogyne javanica* (Bird, 1959; Burdett *et al.*, 1963), *Cooperia curticei* (Sommerville, 1960), *Ditylenchus dipsaci* (Blake, 1962), *Caenorhabditis briggsae* (Jantunen, 1964), *Panagrellus silusiae* (Gysels and Bracke, 1964), *Ascaris lumbricoides* (Watson, 1965), *Nippostrongylus muris* (Twohy, 1956), *Blatticola blattae* (Cali and Mai, 1965), *Labiostrongylus longispicularis* (Mykytowycz and Dudzinski, 1965), *Aspiculuris tetraptera* (Anya, 1966), *Trichostrongylus retortaeformis* (Bailey, 1967), *Panagrellus silusiae* (Samoiloff and Pasternak, 1969), and *Aphelenchus avenae* (Fisher, 1970). These growth curves are usually sigmoidal in shape and the four steps of the hypothetical curve for nematode growth (Rogers, 1962; Lee, 1965) are not pronounced. In species of *Cylindrocorpus* (Chin and Taylor, 1970), however, the four molts do occur as distinct steps. In the majority of nematodes that have been studied, however, this is not the case. The reasons for this, assuming that frequent measurements have been made, are either that growth, as in *Caenorhabditis briggsae*, is scarcely interrupted by molting or that, as in *Meloidogyne*, growth does not occur between parasitic molts. In most parasitic forms greatest growth occurs after the last molt and molting tends to occur in the earlier half of the growth curve. An exception to this is *Cephalobus ciliatus* whose growth has been described by Nigon (1965).

The chemical aspects of growth and development in nematodes have recently been reviewed by Rogers and Sommerville (1969) and these workers point out that more information is needed on the relation between molting and the cessation of growth in nematodes before any generalization can be made.

In this chapter, I propose to deal primarily with the morphological aspects of molting but in order that this be properly understood, it is necessary to consider briefly the work that has been done so far on the physiology of this process.

II. The Stimulus

It has been suggested (Rogers and Sommerville, 1963), that the process of molting in nematodes may be analogous to that of the Insecta in that, for instance, neurosecretory cells are stimulated to produce secretions which activate glands that produce hormones or enzymes which, in turn, initiate molting. As a result of their experiments on exsheathment in trichostrongyles, Rogers and Sommerville have been able to provide some evidence to support their hypothesis on the nature of molting itself.

For various reasons, mostly technical, experiments on molting have been restricted to a few parasitic forms. The initial stimulus which comes from the host is varied and, for the larvae of *Haemonchus contortus*, *Trichostrongylus colubriformis*, and *T. retortaeformis*, includes dissolved gaseous carbon dioxide and (or) undissociated carbonic acid at 38° C (Rogers, 1966; Bailey, 1968). For the infective larvae of *Nematodirus battus*, it is hydrochloric acid (Christie and Charleston, 1965) and for the infective larvae of *Dictyocaulus viviparus*, it is the enzyme pepsin at a pH of 1–2 (Silverman and Podger, 1964). In the plant parasitic nematode *Paratylenchus nanus*, root exudations will act as a stimulus to the 4th-stage larval molt (Rhoades and Linford, 1959; Fisher, 1966). In other endoparasitic nematodes of plants in which molting does not occur until some growth has occurred within the host (Bird and Rogers, 1965), this stimulus may be more complex and may be closely associated with an actual increase in size of the nematode. Thus, the stimulus may come from within the parasite rather than directly from its host and the receptor may function here as a stretch receptor. Molting in nematodes parasitic in animals, which is induced as a result of a direct stimulus from the host, appears to be associated with development in a new and different environment. This type of molt usually bridges the gap that exists between the free-living and parasitic environments and permits the nematode to start to feed and grow in its new environment.

It is clear, from what has been done so far, that a molting stimulus occurs in some parasitic nematodes, although this type of stimulus varies considerably in different species. However, the response of nematodes to these stimuli appears to be more uniform throughout the group.

III. The Receptor

In the infective larvae of some nematodes parasitic in animals, molting is separated into two distinct phases. First the new cuticle is laid down and second the old cuticle is shed. The latter process is known as exsheathment and normally takes place in the host. These larvae respond to the stimuli described above by producing an exsheathing fluid which has been shown by Rogers (1965) to contain specific leucine aminopeptidase in infective larvae of *Haemonchus contortus* and *Trichostrongylus colubriformis*. These enzymes are, in some cases, only active in the species from which they have been isolated. Thus, the enzyme from *H. contortus* will only hydrolyze the inner parts of sheaths of this species and not those of *T. colubriformis* and vice versa. However, the enzyme from *H. contortus* is equally active on sheaths dissected from *Trichostrongylus axei* (Rogers and Sommerville, 1960) as on those dissected from *H. contortus*. This enzyme has been associated with molting in the nematodes *Phocanema decipiens* (Davey and Kan, 1967) and *Xiphinema index* (Roggen et al., 1967). However, Ozerol and Silverman (1969), who also worked on the exsheathing fluid of infective larvae of *H. contortus*, disagree with Rogers (1965) and conclude that "leucine amino-peptidase is not the enzyme responsible for exsheathment in *H. contortus*" and that the exsheathing principle, which is not totally destroyed by boiling for 10 min at 100°C, is either a small protein or a polypeptide. Further-more, Slocombe and Whitlock (1969) question whether analysis of exsheathing fluid can "tell anything about substances relating to ecdysis."

However, Rogers (1970) in answer to these criticisms, describes in detail his methods for obtaining exsheathing fluid and for detecting and estimating its leucine aminopeptidase content under physiological conditions. He considers that the methods employed by Ozerol and Silverman (1969) would have resulted in the destruction of this enzyme. In his discussion, Rogers lists considerable support for his hypothesis.

It seems likely that enzymes may be associated with true molting in nematodes and that, as techniques become more sensitive, their presence will be detected.

There is more agreement on the localization of the area responsible for the production of exsheathing fluid. As a result of ligaturing experiments (Sommerville, 1957; Fisher, 1966), UV irradiation (Rogers and Sommerville, 1960) and a histochemical technique (Davey and Kan, 1967) the site has been located in the anterior region of the nematode near the excretory gland. Experiments by Davey (1966) on *Phocanema decipiens* show that the histochemical appearance of leucine aminopeptidase in the excretory glands can be correlated with the (histochemical) detection of neurosecretory activity in the dorsal and ventral ganglia of this nematode. Recently, Rogers (1968) has detected granules similar to neurosecretory granules in a region just posterior to the excretory pore in infective larvae of *Haemonchus contortus*. These granules are associated with a diffusely granular region just posterior to the excretory pore lying under a part of the cuticle which is different from the rest of the cuticle in that its annular striations are only 0.3μ apart in contrast to the normal distance of 0.9μ for these larvae.

It has been suggested (Bird, 1968) that the receptor for certain types of stimuli in nematodes may be the hemizonid and that, in some cases, as in infective larvae parasitic in mammals, this structure may be associated with neurosecretion. The hemizonid is a ventrolateral commissure of the nervous system which appears to be universally distributed throughout the Nematoda (Goodey, 1951, 1959; Timm, 1960; Caveness, 1961). It is situated on the ventral aspect of the nematode body, usually in the region of the excretory pore, and is about $2\frac{1}{2}$ normal annular striations in width, which corresponds with the dimensions of the modified cuticle overlying the diffuse granular area described by Rogers (1968).

IV. Molting

The nematode cuticle may be shed in one piece, as in *Paratylenchus nanus* or *Seinura oxura* (Fisher, 1966; Hechler and Taylor, 1966), or the anterior part may be shed separately as a cap, as in trichostrongyle larvae and *Caenorhabditis briggsae* (Sommerville, 1957; Jantunen, 1964). The linings of the amphids, esophagus, excretory duct, phasmids, and rectum are shed at each molt. Some of these structures are shown very clearly in a photograph of a molted dauer larva cuticle of *Caenorhabditis briggsae* (Yarwood and Hansen, 1969).

Because of technical difficulties, the actual process of molting has been studied at the level of resolution of the electron microscope in only a few genera. This process may be similar in most nematodes, irrespective of whether they are free-living or parasitic.

So far, molting and the changes in fine structure associated with it have been described in only eight species, namely, *Meloidogyne javanica* (Bird and G. E. Rogers, 1965), *Heterodera schachtii* (Günther and Kämpfe, 1966), *Ascaris lumbricoides* (Thust, 1968), *Panagrellus silusiae* (Samoiloff and Pasternak, 1969), *Hemicycliophora arenaria, Aphelenchus avenae, Hirschmanniella gracilis* (Johnson *et al.*, 1970b), and *Nippostrongylus brasiliensis* (Lee, 1970).

Morphological changes in the hypodermis prior to molting have been observed in a number of nematodes, both under the light and electron microscopes. The onset of molting in *Meloidogyne javanica*, for instance, is heralded by a clear demarcation and increase in width of the hypodermis (Bird, 1959). This morphological change is readily observed under the light microscope. Under the electron microscope, it can be seen that this obvious structural change is brought about by an accumulation of ribosomelike granules and chemical tests show, not unexpectedly, that nucleic acids and proteins are present. A similar state of affairs exists in *Ascaris lumbricoides* (Watson, 1965) and *Phocanema decipiens* (Davey, 1965; Kan and Davey, 1968a,b). In *Phocanema*, there is a cycle of cytoplasmic RNA synthesis which is closely correlated with cuticle secretion and changes in cytoplasmic and nuclear morphology. Furthermore, Kan and Davey (1968b) report that the muscle cells are involved in molting and are actively synthesizing protein at the time the cuticle is being formed. The onset of molting in *Hemicycliophora arenaria* is preceded by the appearance of globular structures (0.2–1.2 μ in diamter) in the hypodermal cords. These globular structures disappear shortly after molting has been completed (Johnson *et al.*, 1970b).

The genus *Hemicycliophora* is atypical in that its species are characterized by having an outer sheath as well as a cuticle. Obervations with the aid of the electron microscope (Johnson *et al.*, 1970a,b) have revealed that both of these structures, which are complex and multilayered, are produced together at each molt so that the sheath is an integral part of the new cuticle and not a remnant of the old.

The first larval molt in *H. schachtii*, which occurs in the egg, has been described by Günther and Kämpfe (1966). It is initiated by strong contractions of the first larva. These lead to the detachment of a very thin cuticle at the anterior and posterior ends. The shed cuticle is apparently completely hydrolyzed, as it cannot be detected after molting. This does not appear to be true of molting in the later stages. The process (Fig. 12), first

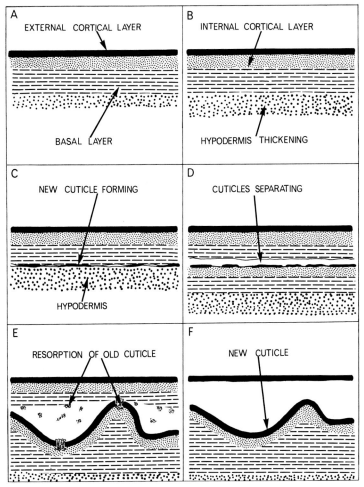

Fig. 12. Diagram of the changes which take place in the cuticle of *Meloidogyne javanica* during molting. (A) Normal cuticle; (B) thickening of hypodermis; (C) start of formation of new external cortical layer on top of the hypodermis; (D) new and old cuticle of similar dimensions and starting to separate; (E) inner layers of old cuticle being resorbed and new cuticle becoming convoluted; (F) completion of molt with only the external cortical layer of the old cuticle remaining (After Bird and Rogers, 1965.)

described at the level of resolution of the electron microscope in *Meloidogyne javanica* (Bird and Rogers, 1965), appears to take place as follows. The basal layer (fiber layer) starts to come away from the hypodermis and, beneath it, the hypodermis starts to form the external cortical layer of the new cuticle. The new, partially formed external cortical layer (Fig. 12C and D) takes the form, when sections are viewed under the electron microscope, of an interrupted osmiophilic line. The new cuticle grows beneath the old one and a stage is reached when both cuticles are of similar thickness with spaces in between (Fig. 12D). The new cuticle becomes highly convoluted (Fig. 12E) to allow for rapid growth of the nematode after molting and the spaces between the cuticles become filled with particles which appear to be associated with the breakdown and absorption of the innermost layers of the outer cuticle. The absorption of the old cuticle appears to take place through regions in the newly formed cuticle where the external cortical layer has not been formed. Finally, a stage is reached (Fig. 12F) when all that remains of the old cuticle is the external cortical layer. As the adult cuticle increases in thickness during the growth of the nematode, this thin remnant of the old cuticle becomes dislodged and broken.

Thust's (1968) observations on molting in *Ascaris lumbricoides* are similar to those for *M. javanica*. He states that "the molting process begins at the base of the cuticle" and that partial resorption of the shed cuticle takes place. He has also observed large numbers of multivesicular bodies in the hypodermis but is uncertain of their origin and function. Resorption of the shed cuticle and the outer sheath also takes place in *Hemicycliophora arenaria* (Johnson et al., 1970b).

It is worth noting here that resorption of the shed cuticle is not found in the specialized 3rd stage infective larvae of some forms parasitic in animals. In these larvae, as has been mentioned in the preceding chapter, the outermost cuticle or sheath is thicker than the new cuticle (Inatomi et al., 1963; Eckert and Schwarz, 1965). This is possibly an adaptation associated with the ability of the larvae to resist desiccation (Ellenby, 1968). Similarly, the shed cuticle of the fourth molt of *Trichinella spiralis* grown *in vitro* (Lee, 1966) does not appear to have undergone much resorption and resorption of the old cuticle was never observed during molting in *Panagrellus silusiae* by Samoiloff and Pasternak (1969). Similarly, resorption of the old cuticle during molting has not been observed in either *Aphelenchus avenae* or *Hirschmanniella gracilis* (Johnson et al., 1970b). In the final molt of *Nippostrongylus brasiliensis* (Lee, 1970) the old cuticle is cast without any digestion or resorption of its layers (Fig. 13). In the early stages of molting in this nematode (Fig. 13B) the hypodermis separates from the old cuticle, leaving a space which contains clumps of granular material. The new cuticle becomes folded into regular annuli (Fig. 13C) which, as they become more extensive, include folds of the hypodermis (Fig. 13D) which are eventually withdrawn (Fig. 13E) leaving characteristic membranous M-shaped structures (Figs. 13E and F). These gradually flatten out and disappear as the new cuticle matures. The area above the "M" in the annuli develops into the characteristic cuticular struts of this nematode by aggregation of granular

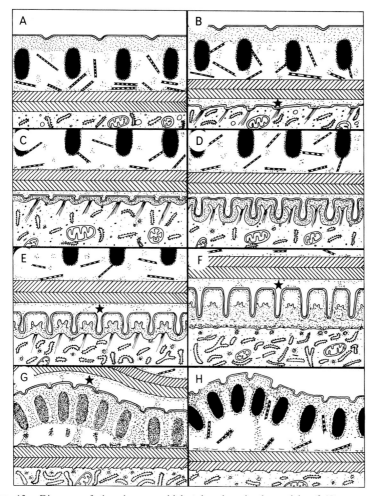

FIG. 13. Diagram of the changes which take place in the cuticle of *Nippostrongylus brasiliensis* during molting. (A) Normal cuticle; (B) separation of hypodermis from old cuticle and formation of external cortical layer; (C) formation of annuli; (D) infolding of hypodermis into annuli; (E) and (F) formation of M-shaped structures; (G) and (H) formation of cuticular struts. Note that in this sequence of events no part of the shed cuticle is resorbed. (Courtesy of Dr D. L. Lee; after Lee, 1970.)

material (Fig. 13G). These gradually become more distinct and move from the cortex to the fluid-filled median layer where they become associated with collagenlike fibers (Fig. 13H). The adult nematode emerges through an opening at the anterior end of the old cuticle.

As a result of electron microscope studies on the cuticle and molting of the free-living nematode *Panagrellus silusiae* (Samoiloff and Pasternak, 1968, 1969), it would appear that, typically, the shed cuticle is not resorbed in nematodes. It would be interesting to know the nature of this process in the free-living marine forms.

Progress on the physiological aspects of molting in nematodes has been slow because, unlike insects, they do not lend themselves to microsurgical operations involving the extirpation of organs. This is due to the high turgor pressure and the small size of the nematodes during molting.

The analogy between molting in *Meloidogyne javanica* and the ameta-bolous insect *Podura aquatica* (Noble-Nesbitt, 1963) has already been made (Bird and Bird, 1969). Here it is suggested that the particles (Fig. 12E) be-tween the cuticles of molting *M. javanica* may have a similar function to the granules between the cuticles of molting *P. aquatica*. A similar analogy can, perhaps, be made between *Ascaris lumbricoides* (Thust, 1968) and *Calpodes ethlius* (Locke, 1966; Locke and Collins, 1967) on the role of multivesicular bodies which occur in both forms in the hypodermis. These structures appear to be associated with protein synthesis and cuticle deposition in the insect and may have a similar function in *A. lumbricoides*. It is clear that many aspects of molting in both insects and nematodes may be similar, but it is, perhaps, rash to assume too many similarities in these two widely divergent groups. The observations that have been made so far on the pro-cesses of molting serve to emphasize the need for and the scope of further research of this nature with a wider variety of nematodes.

V. Summary

Molting normally occurs four times in nematodes. Growth curves for a number of different species of nematodes have been drawn and are usually sigmoidal in shape.

The stimulus which initiates molting varies in different species. Work on exsheathment of trichostrongyle larvae has helped toward understanding the processes of molting as a whole. Broadly speaking, an external stimulus triggers off a response within the nematode, eventually leading to the pro-duction of substances within the nematode which initiate molting. The nature of the stimulus in free-living nematodes is unknown. It may be as-sociated with growth, and molting may be a response to stretch receptors in the cuticle. This may also be true of nematodes parasitic in plants, although root exudations can act as stimuli to molting in some forms. In cases where a direct stimulus from the host, such as CO_2, pH, temperature, Eh, or enzymes, is involved, the molt usually initiates parasitic development.

The receptor in all cases may be a cuticular and hypodermal structure of universal occurrence in nematodes, such as the hemizonid. The receptor appears to be associated with neurosecretory activity which leads to the production of an enzyme or enzymes which initiate molting. Experimental evidence is sparse at the moment and much more is needed to establish the hypothesis.

Prior to molting, the hypodermis increases in thickness due to the accumulation of ribosomelike granules which contain nucleic acid and protein.

Parts of the external cortical layer are first laid down on the surface of the hypodermis at the base of the old cuticle. The new cuticle is formed beneath the new external cortical layer and, in some species, the old cuticle is partially resorbed through the new cuticle before it is shed, while in others, it is shed intact.

REFERENCES

Ackert, J. E. (1931). *Parasitology* **23**, 360.
Anya, A. O. (1966). *J. Helminthol.* **40**, 261.
Bailey, M. A. (1967). Ph. D. Thesis, Univ. of Adelaide, South Australia.
Bailey, M. A. (1968). *Comp. Biochem. Physiol.* **26**, 897.
Bird, A. F. (1959). *Nematologica* **4**, 31.
Bird, A. F. (1968). *J. Parasitol* **54**, 475.
Bird, A. F., and Bird, J. (1969). *In* "Chemical Zoology" (M. Florkin and B. T. Scheer, eds.), Vol. III, pp. 253–288. Academic Press, New York.
Bird, A. F., and Rogers, G. E. (1965). *Nematologica* **11**, 224.
Blake, C. D., (1962). *Ann. Appl. Biol.* **50**, 703.
Burdett, J. F., Bird, A. F., and Fisher, J. M. (1963). *Nematologica* **9**, 542.
Cali, C. T., and Mai, W. F. (1965). *Proc. Helminthol. Soc. Wash.* **32**, 164.
Caveness, F. E. (1961). *Proc. Helminthol. Soc. Wash.* **28**, 169.
Chin, D. A., and Taylor, D. P. (1970). *Nematologica* **16**, 1.
Christie, M. G., and Charleston, W. A. G. (1965). *Exp. Parasitol.* **17**, 46.
Davey, K. G. (1965). *Can. J. Zool.* **43**, 997.
Davey, K. G. (1966). *Amer. Zool.* **6**, 243.
Davey, K. G., and Kan, S. P. (1967). *Nature (London)* **214**, 737.
Eckert, J., and Schwarz, R. (1965). *Z. Parasitenk.* **26**, 116.
Ellenby, C. (1968). *J. Exp. Biol.* **49**, 469.
Fisher, J. M. (1966). *Aust. J. Biol. Sci.* **19**, 1073.
Fisher, J. M. (1970). *Aust. J. Biol. Sci.* **23**, 411.
Goodey, J. B. (1951). *J. Helminthol.* **25**, 33.
Goodey, J. B. (1959). *Nematologica* **4**, 157.
Günther, B., and Kämpfe, L. (1966). *Verh. Deut. Ges. Goettingen* **30**, Suppl. 152.
Gysels, H., and Bracke, E. (1964). *Natuurwetensch. Tijdschr. (Ghent)* **46**, 17.
Hechler, H. C., and Taylor, D. P. (1966). *Proc. Helminthol. Soc. Wash.* **33**, 90.
Inatomi, S., Sakumoto, D., Hano, K., and Tanaka, H. (1963). *Kiseichugaku Zasshi* **12**, 16.
Jantunen, R. (1964). *Nematologica* **10**, 419.
Johnson. P. W., Van Gundy, S. D., and Thomson, W. W. (1970a). *J. Nematol.* **2**, 42.
Johnson, P. W., Van Gundy, S. D., and Thomson, W. W. (1970b). *J. Nematol.* **2**, 59.
Kan, S. P., and Davey, K. G. (1968a). *Can. J. Zool.* **46**, 235.

Kan, S. P., and Davey, K. G. (1968b). *Can. J. Zool.* **46**, 723.
Lee, D. L. (1965). "The Physiology of Nematodes," 154 pp. Oliver & Boyd, Edinburgh and London.
Lee, D. L. (1966). *Advan. Parasitol.* **4**, 187.
Lee, D. L. (1970). *Tissue Cell* **2**, 139.
Locke, M. (1966). *J. Morphol.* **118**, 461.
Locke, M., and Collins, J. V. (1967). *Science* **155**, 467.
McCoy, O. R. (1930). *Amer. J. Hyg.* **11**, 413.
Mackerras, M. J., and Sandars, D. F. (1955). *Aust. J. Zool.* **3**, 1.
Mykytowycz, R., and Dudzinski, M. L. (1965). *Parasitology* **55**, 527.
Nigon, V. (1965). *In* "Traité de Zoologie" (P. P. Grassé, ed.), Vol. IV, pp. 218–386. Masson, Paris.
Noble-Nesbitt, J. (1963). *Quart. J. Microsc. Sci.* **104**, 369.
Ozerol, N. H., and Silverman, P. H. (1969). *J. Parasitol.* **55**, 79.
Pai, S. (1928). *Z. Wiss. Zool.* **131**, 293.
Rhoades, H. L., and Linford, M. B. (1959). *Science* **130**, 1476.
Rogers, W. P. (1962). "The Nature of Parasitism: The Relationship of Some Metazoan Parasites to their Hosts." Academic Press, New York.
Rogers, W. P. (1965). *Comp. Biochem. Physiol.* **14**, 311.
Rogers, W. P. (1966). *In* "Biology of Parasites" (E. J. L. Soulsby, ed.) pp. 33–40. Academic Press, New York.
Rogers, W. P. (1968). *Parasitology* **58**, 657.
Rogers, W. P. (1970). *J. Parasitol.* **56**, 138.
Rogers, W. P., and Sommerville, R. I. (1960). *Parasitology* **50**, 329.
Rogers. W. P., and Sommerville, R. I. (1963). *Advan. Parasitol.* **1**, 109.
Rogers, W. P., and Sommerville, R. I. (1969). *In* "Chemical Zoology" (M. Florkin and B. T. Scheer, eds.), Vol. III, pp. 465–499. Academic Press, New York.
Roggen, D. R., Raski, D. J., and Jones, N. O. (1967). *Nematologica* **13**, 1.
Samoiloff, M. R., and Pasternak, J. (1968). *Can. J. Zool.* **46**, 1019.
Samoiloff, M. R., and Pasternak, J. (1969). *Can. J. Zool.* **47**, 639.
Scott, J. A. (1929). *Amer. J. Hyg.* **10**, 125.
Scott, J. A. (1946). *J. Parasitol.* **32**, 570.
Silverman, P. H., and Podger, K. R. (1964). *Exp. Parasitol.* **15**, 314.
Slocombe, J. O. D., and Whitlock, J. H. (1969). *J. Parasitol.* **55**, 1102.
Sommerville, R. I. (1957). *Exp. Parasitol.* **6**, 18.
Sommerville, R. I. (1960). *Parasitology* **50**, 261.
Thust, R. (1968). *Z. Wiss. Zool., Abt. A* **178**, 1.
Timm, R. W. (1960). *Nematologica* **5**, 150.
Tiner, J. D. (1953). *J. Infec. Dis.* **92**, 105.
Twohy, D. W. (1956). *Amer. J. Hyg.* **63**, 165.
Watson, B. D. (1965). *Quart. J. Microsc. Sci.* **106**, 83.
Yarwood, E. A., and Hansen, E. L. (1969). *J. Nematol.* **1**, 184.

5
THE HYPODERMIS

I. Introduction

The hypodermis lies between the cuticle and the somatic muscle. It is a particularly important and metabolically active part of a nematode, being responsible, among other things, for the secretion and maintenance of the cuticle. Despite its importance, it has received scant attention from the authors of the dozen or so books that have appeared on various aspects of nematology over the last thirty years; apart from the works of Chitwood and Chitwood (1950), Hyman (1951), Hirschmann (1960), de Coninck (1965), Crofton (1966), and Bird and Bird (1969), the hypodermis has rarely had more than a paragraph allotted to it.

The reasons for this are probably due to its small size and inaccessibility to fixatives and stains. The intercordal hypodermis in small larval forms is less than $0.5\ \mu$ thick, although in the largest nematodes it is up to $20\ \mu$ thick; the relatively impermeable cuticle, acting as a barrier on the external surface of the hypodermis, makes this layer one of the most difficult to fix and stain.

The hypodermis, which is occasionally called the epidermis or subcuticle, is a thin layer that is characteristically thickened in the dorsal, ventral, and lateral positions to form four hypodermal cords. These protrude into the pseudocoelomic cavity between the somatic muscles and divide them into four quadrants. In some nematodes, such as the Mermithidae, subsidiary cords occur between the four main cords.

The two largest projections are the lateral cords which commonly run the whole length of the body. Their position is often demarcated externally by cuticular structures known as lateral alae, which have been described in Chapter 3, and which are seen most clearly in transverse sections (Fig. 14A). The lateral cords are visible in the larger nematodes as pale lateral lines on the surface of the body. In many forms the dorsal and ventral cords tend

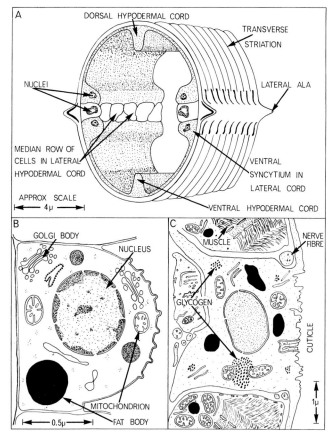

Fig. 14.   Diagrams of hypodermal cords in larvae and adult stages. (A) 3rd-stage parasitic larva of *Ascaris lumbricoides*. (After Thust, 1968.) (B) Hypodermal cell of a 1st-stage larva of *Ascaris lumbricoides*. (After Thust, 1968.) (C) Transverse section through lateral hypodermal cord of a 3rd-stage larva of *Nippostrongylus brasiliensis*. (After Lee, 1966.)

to disappear posteriorly, but in some species either or both may be more prominent in the tail region.

The hypodermis in some nematodes is cellular and presumably both cuticle and hypodermis and muscle and hypodermis are separated by cell membranes. The hypodermis may be surrounded by a cell membrane in all types of nematodes, since membranes separating hypodermis from cuticle and hypodermis from muscle have been observed in *Xiphinema index* (Wright, 1965; Roggen *et al.*, 1967) and *Ascaris lumbricoides* (Watson, 1965b) in which the hypodermis is syncytial. There is some disagreement, however, as Hinz (1963), working with *Parascaris equorum*, could not detect an outer plasma membrane separating the cuticle from the hypodermis by means of the electron microscope, although the inner membrane separating the hypodermis from the muscle could be seen.

It is clear that further research using the electron microscope to resolve these hypodermal membranes in a variety of nematodes is needed in order to clarify a number of conflicting reports. The fact that there is disagreement as to the nature of these structures in closely related species suggests either that these results are obtained by variability in techniques or that the membranes themselves are a reflection of the high metabolic activity of the hypodermis and are constantly being broken down and re-formed.

It appears from the work of Thust (1968) on the morphogenesis of *Ascaris lumbricoides* cuticle that the cellular hypodermis in this nematode is the primitive type. It is derived from six longitudinal rows of dorsal ectodermal blastomeres that eventually give rise to a cellular hypodermis, which does not start to become syncytial until about 3 days after the nematode has become parasitic, i.e., it is a 3rd-stage parasitic larva. Before this time, Thust (1968) was unable to observe more than a single nucleus within a plasmalemma. With the aid of the electron microscope, Thust has shown that after this period of time, both nuclei and cells multiply. The median rows of cells in the lateral hypodermal cords remain cellular, whereas the dorsal and ventral rows become syncytial (Fig. 14A). These syncytia differ from the median hypodermal cells in that they contain much glycogen and multivesicular bodies whose function, as mentioned in Chapter 4, remains obscure.

The hypodermis in the large, adult, parasitic ascarids, as mentioned above, is completely syncytial. This observation has been stated by numerous light microscopists and has been confirmed by electron microscopists (Watson, 1965b; Hinz, 1963).

Nuclei are always found in the lateral cords of nematodes, irrespective of the species or particular stage of development or whether they occur in other parts of the hypodermis or not (Fig. 14).

In some groups, lateral canals of the excretory system lie embedded in the lateral hypodermal cords. The relationship between the excretory system and the hypodermis is discussed in greater detail in Chapter 9 on the excretory system. Similarly, the relationships between the longitudinal nerves of nematodes and their hypodermal cords are considered in greater detail in Chapter 7 on the nervous system.

II. Types of Hypodermis

The hypodermis of nematodes is perhaps best considered as belonging to one of three principal types.

A. CELLULAR HYPODERMIS

As mentioned above, this may be, at least in some forms, the most primitive type. It is found in widely divergent species, such as the free-living marine nematode *Euchromadora vulgaris* (Watson, 1965a), the soil-inhabiting *Rhabditis pellio* (Beams and Sekhon, 1967), and the parasitic *Trichuris myocastoris* (Wright, 1968a). In *Euchromadora vulgaris*, the intercordal hypodermis is about 1 μ thick, the nuclei of the hypodermal cells are large, and the cytoplasm contains mitochondria and glycogen granules. The intercordal hypodermis in *T. myocastoris* is about 2.5 μ thick and, as in *E. vulgaris*, is divided into cells. In *T. myocastoris* the cytoplasm of the intercordal hypodermal cells contains abundant mitochondria as well as a few glycogen granules, lipid droplets, and rough endoplasmic reticulum. Thus, these cells are similar to those depicted in the preparasitic larval stage (Fig. 14B) which develops within the egg (Thust, 1968).

B. PARTIALLY CELLULAR HYPODERMIS

In these forms, cells are present in the cordal hypodermis but are absent from the intercordal hypodermis. In the cosmopolitan free-living genus *Plectus*, whose members are bacterial feeders, the number of cells in the cords varies from species to species (Maggenti, 1961). In *P. parietinus* the dorsal hypodermal cord has a single row of nuclei in the area anterior to the esophagus but posterior to this it is anucleate. However, in the ventral cord there is a single row of cells and nuclei which persists throughout the length of the worm. The lateral cords of this nematode are composed of three rows of cells, two sublateral and one lateral. The nuclei of the cells of the lateral cord are of equal size and each cell is uninucleate.

This configuration in the lateral cords occurs frequently in small free-living nematodes.

Other nematodes whose hypodermis consists of cellular cordal areas interspersed with noncellular intercordal areas include *Capillaria hepatica* (Wright, 1968a) which is parasitic in animals and *Panagrellus silusiae* (Yuen, 1968) which is free-living. In *C. hepatica* the intercordal hypodermis is formed of cell processes from cells of the lateral and median hypodermal cords.

In *P. silusiae* there are six hypodermal cords, a dorsal, a ventral, two laterals, and two subventrals. The cords have thin membranes which lie closely parallel to those of the neighboring somatic muscle cells. In the anterior region of this nematode the cords contain well-defined laminated structures of unknown function. The lateral cords in this region are cellular while the dorsal and ventral cords are not. Further electron microscope studies of these areas in many other species of nematodes will doubtless show that at least the lateral cords are cellular in many forms.

The cell walls are obviously difficult to resolve in the hypodermis and, although nuclei are often described, it is not always clear as to whether they were observed in syncytia or in cells. Similarly, difficulties in distinguishing between hypodermal membranes and pseudocoelomic membranes have been reported (Yuen, 1967) and there is also difficulty at times in distinguishing between membranes of the endoplasmic reticulum and cell membranes in the hypodermis (Wright, 1965; Roggen *et al.*, 1967). These are technical problems and will doubtless be resolved as methods are improved. At the moment, however, there are a number of nematodes in which the hypodermal cords appear to be syncytial but some of these may prove to be cellular when examined under higher resolution. These nematodes include *Helicotylenchus vulgaris* (Yuen, 1965), *Ditylenchus dipsaci* (Yuen, 1967), and *Xiphinema index* (Wright, 1965; Roggen *et al.*, 1967). In *H. vulgaris* all of the four hypodermal cords contain nuclei from the base of the buccal stylet to the dorsal esophageal gland where the dorsal cord becomes anucleate.

In *D. dipsaci* the intercordal hypodermis is seen under the electron microscope as a narrow electron-dense anucleate band between the cuticle and the somatic musculature. The four hypodermal cords project into the pseudocoelom where it becomes difficult to distinguish their boundaries from the pseudocoelomic membranes.

In *X. index* the hypodermis is poorly developed in the anterior region and nuclei are absent from the four cords. Posterior to the nerve ring the cords contain nuclei but cellular boundaries have not been clearly delineated. Thus, these nematodes may belong to the group with the third type of hypodermis.

C. Syncytial Hypodermis

This group includes many of the large parasitic forms that have been described. It includes forms such as *Phocanema decipiens* (Davey, 1965) where all the nuclei making up the syncytium are located in the lateral cords, *Ancylostoma duodenale* (Looss, 1905) where a few nuclei are found in the dorsal and ventral cords and are very numerous in the lateral cords, particularly behind the nerve ring, and *Ascaris lumbricoides* (Watson, 1965b) and *Parascaris equorum* (Hinz, 1963) where the intercordal hypodermis is about 20 μ thick and where electron micrographs have failed to show cell walls between the numerous nuclei. The syncytial cytoplasm of these forms is rich in glycogen granules and mitochondria. The hypodermal nuclei of these ascarids may be 5–8 μ in diameter. Not only are they much larger than the nuclei of the smaller forms but they are also more numerous and tend to occur close together in clusters in the cytoplasm of the syncytium.

In the head region of nematodes, the cuticle lining the stoma is surrounded by a thin layer of hypodermis. Electron microscope studies of the head of *X. index* (Wright, 1965) have revealed that there are connections between the stomatic hypodermis and the somatic hypodermis. It is probable that these types of connections are found throughout the Nematoda and they may be associated with the arcade described and illustrated diagrammatically in *Rhabditis strongyloides* by Chitwood and Chitwood (1950). The arcade consists of a circular band of tissue which usually surrounds the esophagus at the base of the lips. It appears to contain nine cells and has been reported from observations with the light microscope in various ascarids and oxyurids by earlier workers (Hoeppli, 1925; Martini, 1916) and by Chitwood and Chitwood (1933) in *Cephalobellus papilliger* and by Elsea (1951) in female *Meloidogyne hapla*. Although Chitwood and Chitwood (1933) consider the arcade cells to be the formative cells of the wall of the buccal cavity, their physiological significance has yet to be determined.

III. Hypodermal Glands

Hypodermal glands occur in many different species of nematodes and differ considerably both functionally and morphologically. The earlier literature has been reviewed by Chitwood and Chitwood (1950). Since this time, both light and electron microscope studies have provided further information on the morphology of some of these glands although very little is known about their function.

In the free-living *Plectus parietinus* the hypodermal glands are unicellular and are found in the lateral cords. They open through sublateral pores in the cuticle. These hypodermal glands begin in the esophageal region and extend posteriorly as far as the tail.

Sections through a lateral hypodermal gland cell in a lateral cord of the free-living nematode *Acanthonchus duplicatus* have been examined and photographed under the electron microscope by Wright and Hope (1968). They appear to be large cells, almost 10 μ in depth, contain a prominent nucleus, and have what appears to be a vacuolated cytoplasm. Their function is unknown, although it has been suggested (Wright, 1963) that they may be either osmotic or ionic regulators.

In at least two genera of the superfamily Trichuroidea, specialized regions of the cuticle and the underlying hypodermis occur. These structures, known as bacillary bands, are confined to the lateral esophageal region in the genus *Trichuris* but extend the length of the body in the ventral and lateral regions of the genus *Capillaria*.

The structure of the bacillary band had been variously interpreted by earlier workers, until electron microscope studies of this region (Wright, 1963, 1968b; Sheffield, 1963) showed that it is a modified hypodermal cord containing hypodermal gland cells which open to the exterior through cuticular pores. It has been shown (Wright, 1963, 1968b) that two types of cells occur in both genera. These are known respectively as hypodermal gland cells and nonglandular hypodermal cells and are illustrated diagrammatically in Fig. 15.

In *Trichuris* the nonglandular cells of the bacillary band are fewer in number and are harder to see than those in *Capillaria* and their cytoplasm is frequently seen only as fine processes between the hypodermal gland cells. However, their cytoplasmic complement of organelles is similar although they possess less glycogen. A striking difference between these cells in the two genera is that in *T. myocastoris* there are numerous infoldings of the basal cell membrane to form β-cytomembranes (Sjöstrand, 1956) which extend into the cells to the level of the nuclei (Wright, 1968b), whereas in *C. hepatica* they have not been detected.

The bacillary bands are one cell thick in both genera. The nonglandular cells in *C. hepatica* (Fig. 15) ensheath the hypodermal gland cells except, of course, in the vicinity of the pore in the cuticle. The cell membrane of the gland cell beneath the pore is highly infolded and is called the lamellar apparatus. Stretching across the pore at the top is the boundary layer and between this and the lamellar apparatus is an area known as the pore chamber. The fine structure of this gland cell is almost uniform throughout the length of the worm.

The nonglandular cells are in direct contact with the cuticle (Fig. 15). They contain large quantities of glycogen which is located in the innermost

98   5. THE HYPODERMIS

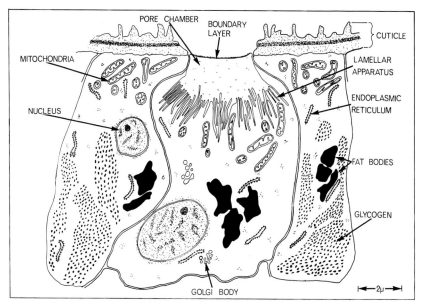

FIG. 15. Diagram of a bacillary band or modified hypodermal cord of *Capillaria hepatica* showing a glandular cell flanked by two nonglandular cells. (After Wright, 1963.)

two thirds of the cell together with lipid droplets. The outermost third of the cell contains mitochondria and endoplasmic reticulum.

The function of the cells of the bacillary bands of the two genera described above is still a matter for conjecture. Wright (1968b) suggests that the development of β-cytomembranes in *Trichuris* may be a reflection of the environmental osmotic stresses to which this nematode is subjected in its host's cecum because these β-cytomembranes resemble those in tissues which function in water control in other organisms. On the other hand, *C. hepatica*, which inhabits the liver of its host, may not have this complex of β-cytomembranes because it is not subjected to osmotic stress in its environment.

Other modifications of the hypodermis found in some free-living forms are the caudal glands. These consist of three unicellular glands, each with a duct uniting posteriorly with the others to form a common duct which opens to the exterior through an ampulla bearing a fine terminal tube. This structure, which is called the spinneret, apparently functions like a needle valve (Cobb, 1915). It consists of a small cone which blocks the pore of the terminal tube. This cone has muscles attached to it and, when they contract, the cone is withdrawn from the aperture that it is blocking and the caudal gland secretion is emitted. This secretion hardens in water to form a thread of material which serves to anchor the nematode. The caudal glands of nematodes are considered by Hyman (1951) to be identical with the pedal glands of rotifers.

IV. Composition

Information on the chemical composition of the hypodermis of nematodes is sparse. It has largely been obtained through the use of histological or histochemical techniques because of the difficulty in separating hypodermal tissue from either cuticle or muscle. As mentioned above, both fat and glycogen are common constituents of the hypodermis and have been identified both histochemically and morphologically in the fixed state by means of the electron microscope in a variety of different nematodes (von Kemnitz, 1912; Fairbairn, 1957; Hinz, 1963; Wright, 1963; Anya, 1964). The histochemical and ultrastructural changes in the hypodermis preceding and associated with molting have been described in Chapter 4. Hemaglobin is found in the lateral hypodermal cords in *Ascaris lumbricoides* (Smith and Lee, 1963) and in the lateral and ventral cords of *Mermis subnigrescens* and *Enoplus brevis* (Ellenby and Smith, 1966). Enzymes such as leucine aminopeptidase, esterase, and acid phosphatase have been identified in the hypodermis of nematodes (Lee, 1962a,b; Roggen *et al.*, 1967; Probert, 1969); as techniques improve, doubtless various other enzymes will be identified in this region which appears to be an area of intense metabolic activity throughout the life of the nematode.

V. Summary

The hypodermis lies between the cuticle and muscle and projects into the pseudocoelomic cavity in the dorsal, ventral, and lateral regions to form four hypodermal cords.

The hypodermis is cellular in larval and some adult forms but becomes syncytial in some of the larger parasitic forms. However, improved methods of electron microscopy may reveal that some of these larger forms may have a cellular hypodermis whose membranes may be difficult to locate, owing either to their tenuosity or to alterations in their structure caused by intense metabolic activity.

Glands occur in the hypodermis of many different species of nematodes, both free-living and parasitic. Little is known about their function, although it has been suggested that they act as either osmotic or ionic regulators

100   5. THE HYPODERMIS

because of the similarity of some of their cytoplasmic components to structures which have this function in other organisms. The function of the caudal glands of the hypodermis, which are found in some free-living nematodes, is more obvious as they produce an adhesive secretion. Information on the chemical composition of the hypodermis has been obtained largely through the use of histochemical and cytological techniques. At times, such as just before the onset of molting, there is an accumulation of protein and nucleic acids. The hypodermis is at all times rich in glycogen and lipid and a number of enzymes have been identified. This number is doubtless restricted by the paucity of techniques available, as this region is clearly one of the most metabolically active in the nematode body.

REFERENCES

Anya, A. O. (1964). *Parasitology* **54**, 555.
Beams, H. W., and Sekhon, S. S. (1967). *J. Ultrastruct. Res.* **18**, 580.
Bird, A. F., and Bird, J. (1969). *In* "Chemical Zoology" (M. Florkin and B. T. Scheer, eds.), Vol. III, pp. 253–288. Academic Press, New York.
Chitwood, B. G., and Chitwood, M. B. (1933). *Z. Zellforsch. Mikrosk. Anat.* **19**, 309.
Chitwood, B. G., and Chitwood, M. B., eds. (1950). "An Introduction to Nematology," 213 pp. Monumental Printing Co., Baltimore, Maryland.
Cobb, N. A. (1915). *J. Parasitol.* **2**, 95.
Crofton, H. D. (1966). "Nematodes," 160 pp. Hutchinson, London.
Davey, K. G. (1965). *Can. J. Zool.* **43**, 997.
de Coninck, L. (1965). *In* "Traité de Zoologie" (P. P. Grassé, ed.), Vol. IV, pp. 1–217. Masson, Paris.
Ellenby, C., and Smith, L. (1966). *Comp. Biochem. Physiol.* **19**, 871.
Elsea, J. R. (1951). *Proc. Helminthol. Soc. Wash.* **18**, 53.
Fairbairn, D. (1957). *Exp. Parasitol.* **6**, 491.
Hinz, E. (1963). *Protoplasma* **56**, 202.
Hirschmann, H. (1960). *In* "Nematology" (J. N. Sasser and W. R. Jenkins, eds.), pp. 130–135. Univ. of North Carolina Press, Chapel Hill, North Carolina.
Hoeppli, R. (1925). *Z. Zellforsch. Mikrosk. Anat.* **2**, 1.
Hyman, L. H. (1951). "The Invertebrates," Vol. III, 572 pp. McGraw-Hill, New York.
Lee, D. L. (1962a). *Parasitology* **52**, 241.
Lee, D. L. (1962b). *Parasitology* **52**, 533.
Lee, D. L. (1966) *Parasitology* **56**, 127.
Looss, A. (1905). *Rec. Egypt. Govt. Sch. Med.* **3**, 1.
Maggenti, A. R. (1961). *Proc. Helminthol. Soc. Wash.* **28**, 118.
Martini, E. (1916). *Z. Wiss. Zool.* **116**, 137.
Probert, A. J. (1969). *Parasitology* **59**, 269.
Roggen, D. R., Raski, D. J., and Jones, N. O. (1967). *Nematologica* **13**, 1.
Sheffield, H. G. (1963). *J. Parasitol.* **49**, 998.
Sjöstrand, F. S. (1956). *In* "Physical Techniques in Biological Research" (G. Oster and A. W. Pollister, eds.), Vol. III, pp. 241–298. Academic Press, New York.

Smith, M. H., and Lee, D. L. (1963). *Proc. Roy. Soc., Ser. B* **157**, 234.
Thust, R. (1968). *Z. Wiss. Zool., Abt. A* **178**, 1.
von Kemnitz, G. (1912). *Arch. Zellforsch.* **7**, 463.
Watson, B. D. (1965a). *Quart. J. Microsc. Sci.* **106**, 75.
Watson, B. D. (1965b). *Quart. J. Microsc. Sci.* **106**, 83.
Wright, K. A. (1963). *J. Morphol.* **112**, 233.
Wright, K. A. (1965). *Can. J. Zool.* **43**, 689.
Wright, K. A. (1968a). *Can. J. Zool.* **46**, 173.
Wright, K. A. (1968b). *J. Parasitol.* **54**, 1106.
Wright, K. A., and Hope, W. D. (1968). *Can. J. Zool.* **46**, 1005.
Yuen, P. H. (1965). *Nematologica* **11**, 623.
Yuen, P. H. (1967). *Can. J. Zool.* **45**, 1019.
Yuen, P. H. (1968). *Nematologica* **14**, 554.

6

MUSCULATURE

I. Introduction

The history of investigation into the structure of nematode muscle has recently been comprehensively reviewed by Debell (1965) in an article on neuromuscular junctions in nematodes. This review is well worth reading because it illustrates how the modern techniques of electrophysiology and electron microscopy have helped to solve a controversy which started over a hundred years ago when Schneider (1860, 1863) stated that "the nerves do not branch out to the muscles, instead, branches of the muscle cells reach the nerves." He observed that the muscle cell consists of a contractile striated portion and a noncontractile vesicular portion from which an arm makes contact with the nervous system. Schneider found that these two components of the muscle were histologically distinct.

This concept that muscle in nematodes is made up of contractile and noncontractile parts was not accepted by such subsequent workers as Bastian (1866), Leuckart (1876), Joseph (1882), Deineka (1908), and Plenk (1924), who could not conceive of noncontractile muscle tissue.

The relationship between some muscle cells and a longitudinal nerve cord in ascarids is shown in the three-dimensional scale diagram (Fig. 16). The fine structure of this neuromuscular relationship has been established by a

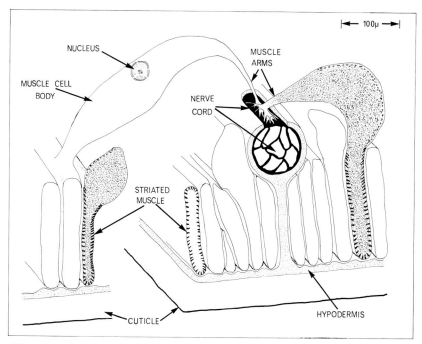

FIG. 16.   Diagram showing the spindle-shaped somatic muscle cells of *Ascaris lumbricoides* and their connection with the nervous system. Note the coelomyarian type of cell and the polymyarian muscle arrangement. (After Debell, 1965.)

number of workers using the electron microscope, notably by Hinz (1963) and Rosenbluth (1965b), and will be discussed in greater detail in Chapter 7 on the nervous system. Figure 16 depicts the somatic musculature as a single layer of spindle-shaped fibers running longitudinally beneath the hypodermis and consisting of muscle showing striations. Each of these fibers is connected to a noncontractile muscle cell body which projects into the pseudocoelom and contains the nucleus of the muscle cell. A muscle arm is sent to a nerve cord from the muscle cell body.

The muscles of nematodes may, perhaps, be best considered under two broad headings—somatic and specialized. The specialized muscles have the same origin as the somatic but are limited to a particular part of the body for some specific purpose. Both will be considered in greater detail later in this chapter.

Information on the neuromuscular physiology of nematodes has been restricted to the large ascarids for obvious reasons. It is only comparatively recently (Jarman, 1959) that recording microelectrodes have been used to measure transmembrane potentials in the somatic muscles of these animals.

Thanks to improved staining techniques and the electron microscope, information on the ultrastructure and chemical composition of somatic muscles of many different species of nematodes, including small free-living and larval forms, is accumulating. Similarly, information on muscle function is slowly accumulating due to the use of various techniques such as the intracellular microelectrode.

In this chapter I shall consider the types of muscle found in nematodes, their fine structure and composition, and various aspects of muscle function. I shall attempt to deal primarily with anatomy and morphology of nematode musculature but shall include some information on physiology and function in an effort to complement and clarify the principle theme.

II. Types of Muscle

As mentioned above, muscle may be broadly considered under the headings somatic muscle and specialized muscle.

A. SOMATIC MUSCLE

Schneider's terminology for nematode muscles, because of its convenience, is still used. It refers to (a) the shape of the muscle, and (b) its arrangement in the nematode as a whole and has recently been discussed by Hope (1969) in a paper on the somatic muscles of the free-living marine nematode *Deontostoma californicum*. Hope's illustrations (Fig. 17) show that the striated part of the muscle cell is shaped like a trough. This trough varies from wide and shallow to narrow and deep. Where it is wide and shallow, the striated part lies next to the hypodermis and is perpendicular to it (Fig. 17A). Under these conditions, the sarcoplasm is exposed on three sides. This type of muscle cell is known as platymyarian. In the other types of muscle cells, the sarcoplasm is either partially or wholly enclosed by the striated muscle fibers. In coelomyarian muscle cells, the sarcoplasm bulges into the pseudocoel and the fibers extend up its sides for varying distances (Figs. 16, 17B, and E), whereas in circomyarian cells, a term introduced by Chitwood and Chitwood (1950), the sarcoplasm is completely surrounded by striated fibers (Fig. 17C). This latter type of cell is usually associated with specialized muscles, although it has been reported instead of coelomyarian cells in the distal somatic muscle of *Ascaris*.

The form, number, and arrangement of muscle cells are no longer considered to be of much taxonomic value as they may differ in different

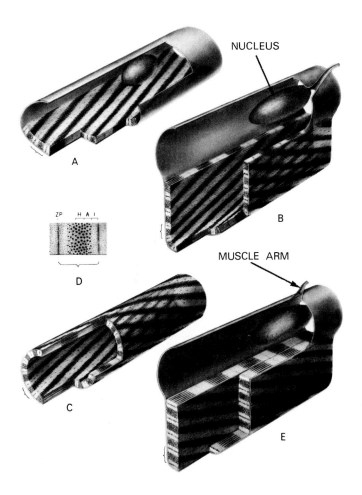

FIG. 17. Diagrams showing different types of muscle cells. (A) Platymyarian; (B) coelomyarian; (C) circomyarian; (D) enlarged portion of the bracketed region shown on each diagram; (E) coelomyarian muscle cell of *Deontostoma californicum*. (Courtesy of Dr. W. D. Hope; Hope, 1969.)

parts of the same nematode and, while being different from closely related genera, may be similar in totally unrelated species.

The longitudinal somatic muscle cells are usually grouped into rows between the cords and may be classified (Schneider, 1866) according to the number of rows. There may be no rows or only two, in which case the cell is classified as holomyarian. Usually, there are two to five rows of muscle

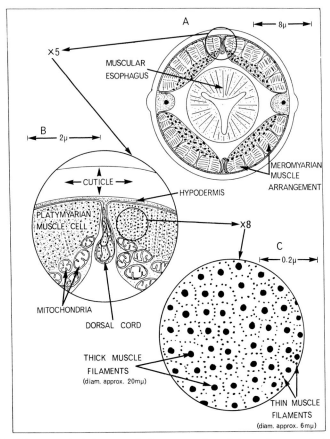

FIG. 18. Diagrams depicting a typical meromyarian–platymyarian muscle type at different levels of magnification. (A) Whole transverse section; (B) portion of muscle cells on either side of dorsal nerve cord; (C) two types of muscle filaments as seen at high resolution with the aid of the electron microscope.

cells between the cords and this type is called meromyarian (Figs. 17A, 18). If there is a large number of muscle rows in each sector (Fig. 16), as is the case with the large ascarids, the condition is known as polymyarian. Again, there is no hard and fast rule and some nematodes may be holomyarian in one part and meromyarian in the other.

Generally speaking, platymyarian cells are grouped into a meromyarian arrangement and this seems to be the most common configuration. It appears to be the basic type from which the more complex coelomyarian and polymyarian types have evolved, as it is found in the larval stages of adults with these forms. This had been noted by Martini at the turn of the century (Chitwood and Chitwood, 1950) and has more recently been demonstrated by means of electron microscope studies on the larval stages of *Ascaris lumbricoides* (Thust, 1968).

Generally, types of muscle cells and their arrangements are associated with particular taxonomic groups but this is not always so. In fact, there are so many exceptions that it is clear that form and number of muscle cells are not important taxonomic criteria. Furthermore, some genera may have more than one muscle type and arrangement. Thus, in the genus *Haemonchus*, muscle form and arrangement may be meromyarian–platymyarian in the anterior part of the body and polymyarian–coelomyarian in the median part (Chitwood and Chitwood, 1950).

Nematodes with the meromyarian type of musculature have very few cells and thse have been counted in two of the larger parasitic forms of this type. Thus, *Oxyurius equi* has 65 muscle cells and *Strongylus* sp. has 87.

The number of muscle cells visible in a transverse section varies throughout the length of the nematode (Chitwood and Chitwood, 1933). These workers noticed that the muscle cells of *Cephalobellus papilliger*, a nematode with a typical meromyarian–platymyarian musculature, were united in each sector by anastomoses of their extremities. Intercellular connections between nematode muscle cells had been noted in the meromyarian nematode *Ancylostoma duodenale* many years before by Looss (1905). Looss, referring to the sarcoplasmic processes running from the muscle cells to the longitudinal nerves stated: "The most remarkable peculiarity is that each muscle cell may have several such transverse processes (I have counted as many as five or six); further, that the processes themselves are branched and anastomose with one another; not only do the processes of one and the same cell fuse but those of different cells also."

Several years after these detailed observations of Looss, connections between muscle cells were observed in *Ascaris* by de Baillon (1911); more recently, Wright (1966), using glycerin-cleared dissections, a technique also used to great advantage by Looss (1905), has examined the cytoplasmic connections between the muscles of eight genera of polymyarian nematodes and a meromyarian nematode of the genus *Dermatoxys*. He was unable to detect connections between the muscles in *Dermatoxys* but was able to observe them in all of the polymyarian genera. These were *Contracaecum*, *Toxascaris*, *Toxocara*, *Porrocaecum*, *Cystidicola*, *Amplicaecum*, *Physaloptera*, and *Deontostoma*. These cytoplasmic bridges connecting the muscle cells occurred more frequently in the anterior ends of these nematodes. They are thought to be the pathway by which an electrical stimulus applied to one muscle cell spreads to other muscle cells and so leads to coordinated muscular contraction.

By observing photomicrographs of serial sections of *Toxascaris leonina*, Wright (1966) has been able to trace interconnections between muscle cells just posterior to the esophagus; this is shown diagrammatically in Fig. 19. This figure shows the muscle cells (in black) which are connected in the particular section under observation and also those (shaded) which had been connected in previous sections. In the eight sections (A–H) shown, five of the cells (3, 4, 6, 7, and 8) are interconnected while three (1, 2, and 5) are not, although apparently, within the thickness of another four sections, all of the eight cells were found to be linked (Wright, 1966).

Thus, it is clear that, in this nematode, the muscle cells within a quadrant are all interconnected; Wright (1966) has described a connection between

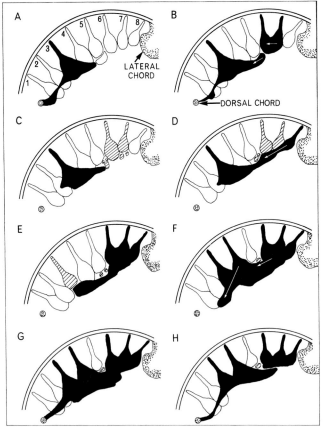

FIG. 19. Diagrams showing muscle cell connections observed in serial sections of *Toxascaris leonina*. (After Wright, 1966.)

cells in different quadrants on either side of the ventral cord. Furthermore, the same muscle cell may send processes to different structures (Looss, 1905) and so a muscle cell can connect both to the sublateral nerve and to the dorsal cord (Wright, 1966).

It is quite clear that the muscle cells of nematodes are interconnected in a complex manner, and it seems reasonable to postulate that this arrangement is necessary for efficient muscular coordination, particularly in the larger nematodes.

B. Specialized Muscle

Broadly speaking, these muscles are, perhaps, best considered under two major headings. First, those muscles associated with the alimentary tract which are involved in processes such as feeding, digestion, and defecation, and second, those muscles associated with various aspects of reproduction.

1. Muscles Associated with the Alimentary Tract

a. Cephalic Muscles. The somatic musculature at the anterior end of the body has been examined in a variety of nematodes. In the marine Enoplida (Inglis, 1964) these muscles are arranged similarly as seven muscles (three anterior and four posterior) in each of the three sectors of the esophagus. All these muscles are inserted on the onchial area and all have their origins on the outer surface of the esophagus. In most cases there are no special labial muscles, the mouth being controlled by either the somatic musculature or the esophageal musculature or both (Inglis, 1966).

In *Ancylostoma duodenale*, Looss (1905) has described eight cephaloeso-phageal muscles, four anterior and four posterior. These muscles are inserted into the esophagus below the nerve ring and run anteriorly, where they are inserted both on the wall of the mouth capsule and the cuticle. Looss (1905) observed that these muscles become distinguished from the ordinary somatic muscles of this worm in that their fibrillar substance passes from a "grooved form to that of a closed cylinder" and "as cylinders of fibrillae filled with sarcoplasm, the muscles then run freely through the body cavity" to the point where they are inserted into the esophagus. These muscles are interesting in that they are platymyarian at their origin on the cuticle and mouth capsule, but become coelomyarian and finally, of course, circomyarian as they run through the body cavity.

Recently, the cephalic musculature of a number of plant parasitic nematodes has been examined with the aid of both the light and electron microscopes. These include *Xiphinema index* (Wright, 1965; Roggen *et al.*, 1967), *Xiphinema americanum* (López-Abella *et al.*, 1967), *Ditylenchus dipsaci* (Yuen, 1967), *Trichodorus christiei* (Hirumi *et al.*, 1968), and *Trichodorus allius* (Raski *et al.*, 1969). In these stylet-bearing plant parasitic nematodes, the cephaloesophageal muscles have become modified into stylet protractor muscles. In the Tylenchida these appear to have a basic number of three. These muscle cells are trifid and form nine muscle slips (Yuen, 1967). Yuen has compared the diagrams of protractor muscle configuration in *Heterodera glycines* (Hirschmann, 1959), *Rotylenchus goodeyi* (Coomans, 1962), and *Ditylenchus dipsaci* (Yuen, 1967) and concludes that there is "no doubt as to their basic similarity" as, in all three cases, "the protractors are shown to be divided into a ventral and dorsal group." The observations by Coomans and Hirschmann that the protractors are subdivided into six bands instead of nine were caused by the limited resolution imposed by the light microscope, as the three primary divisions are hard to perceive since their cell membranes lie so close together.

Furthermore, Yuen found that the anterior end of the stylet protractor muscles of *D. dipsaci* originated at the body wall just below the basal plate of the head skeleton and so are not attached to the labial framework. The relationship between these muscles and the somatic muscles is shown diagrammatically (Fig. 20A).

In the Dorylaimida more muscles are associated with stylet movement than in the Tylenchida. Coomans (1963) has studied the cephalic (stomatal) muscles of several members of this group and has reported that there are three sets of specialized stomatal muscles. The first set are the four dilator buccae muscles which originate posteriorly in the body wall just below the level of the amphidial pouches and extend anteriorly into the stomatal hypodermis in the vicinity of the guide ring. They are thought to function in widening the cheilostom of *Discolaimus* prior to protrusion of the stylet into its prey (Coomans, 1963); hence their name. The second set of muscles, the stylet protractors, are eight in number, four sublateral, two subdorsal, and two subventral. These muscles are attached posteriorly to the flanges of the stylet and anteriorly to the body wall. It is clear that when they contract the stylet is protruded. Only these two types of cephalic musculature have been observed in the genus *Xiphinema*. Their relationship to each other in *X. index*, as seen through the electron microscope, has been depicted diagrammatically by Roggen *et al.* (1967).

The third set of muscles, which are found in forms such as *Discolaimus*, are the stylet retractor muscles; they have an obvious function and extend anteriorly from the body wall to the lower middle part of the stoma.

The relationship between these three sets of cephalic muscles in *Discolaimus* is illustrated diagrammatically (Fig. 20B).

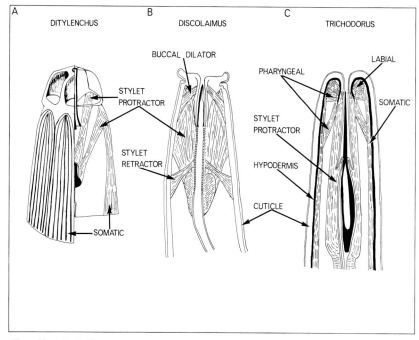

Fig. 20. Cephalic musculature in different species of nematodes. (A) *Ditylenchus dipsaci.* (After Yuen, 1967.) (B) *Discolaimus* sp. (After Coomans, 1963.) (C) *Trichodorus allius.* (After Raski *et al.*, 1969.)

The cephalic musculature of *Trichodorus allius* has recently been investigated by Raski and his co-workers (1969), who divide the muscles roughly into labial, pharyngeal, and protractor muscles (Fig. 20C). The four labial muscles connect the outer stomatal cuticular lining to the body wall and they are almost as broad as they are long (Fig. 20C). Three perpendicular pharyngeal muscles run from a perpendicular line adjacent to the basement membrane of the hypodermal tissue surrounding the pharynx, to the body wall, passing between the somatic muscles in the process.

Four longitudinal pharyngeal muscles occur which resemble the stylet retractors described above, both in number and approximate morphological position (Fig. 20B and C).

The stylet protractor muscles in *T. allius* are strongly developed muscles, basically three in number, consisting of a dorsal and two subventrals. The two latter bifurcate as they move to the outer edge of the pharyngeal tissue, resulting in five large, irregularly shaped muscles.

b. Esophageal Muscles. The muscles of the esophagus will be considered, together with other parts of the digestive system, in Chapter 10 on the alimentary tract. Although there is considerable functional and anatomical diversity in the esophagi of nematodes, they have a number of characteristics in common. For instance, they consist of a syncytium with an anterior muscular portion and a posterior globular portion arranged in a triradiate manner with a dorsal and two subventral sectors. The structure of the esophageal muscle cells will be considered later in this chapter.

   c. Intestinal Muscles. These are muscles which run from the body wall to the intestine. At the time of writing their book, Chitwood and Chitwood (1950) mentioned that these structures had received little attention. Unfortunately, this statement is as true now as it was twenty years ago. The intestinal muscles are thought (Chitwood and Chitwood, 1950) to play an important role in the movement of the contents of the intestine and have been observed in the genera *Eustrongylides*, *Oxyuris*, *Blatticola*, *Enoplus*, and *Metoncholaimus*. In *Eustrongylides* these somatointestinal muscles, extending from the body wall to the gut, are almost perpendicular; consequently their connections may be observed in transverse sections (Chitwood and Chitwood, 1950). Also, their action in bringing about peristaltic movement of the gut has been observed in living specimens.

   Cytoplasmic connections running across the pseudocoelom and connecting the somatic muscle to the intestine are probably found in most nematodes. I have observed them in frozen sections of *Ascaris lumbricoides* but never in wax sections and feel that their apparent absence in many forms may be due to the method of preparation of the tissue. However, Looss (1905) has shown these muscles (Fig. 21A) in his beautiful drawings of *Ancylostoma duodenale*.

   d. Anal Muscles. The most commonly described and most characteristic of the anal muscles in nematodes is the H-shaped depressor ani. This muscle has been described by various authors in numerous genera including *Ascaris* (Voltzenlogel, 1902), *Ancylostoma* (Looss, 1905), *Oxyuris* (Martini, 1916), *Plectus* (Maggenti, 1961), and *Eudorylaimus* (Das, 1962). It consists of two vertical groups of fibers which join the dorsal surface of the rectum or cloaca to the dorsal body wall and are connected by a horizontal band of sarcoplasm containing a single nucleus (Fig. 21B). It clearly functions normally to dilate the rectum and permit defecation, although in forms such as the female of *Meloidogyne*, which have no connection between the anus and the alimentary tract, it functions as a type of pump which brings about the extrusion of the gelatinous matrix from the rectal glands (Maggenti and Allen, 1960). These workers noticed that during this process, the depressor ani muscle contracted once every 10 sec at a constant rate throughout the period of observation (4 hr at a temperature of 70° F).

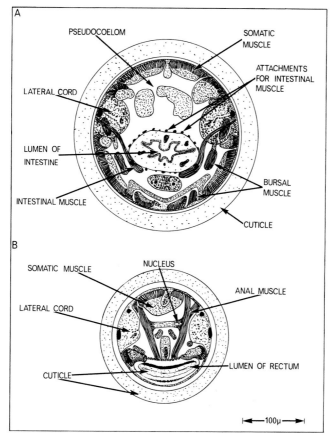

FIG 21. Diagrams of transverse sections through different regions of *Ancylostoma duodenale*. (A) A section cut through the body of a male showing the muscle connections between somatic muscles and the intestine; (B) a section cut through the posterior end of the body of a female showing the H-shaped depressor ani muscle. (After Looss, 1905.)

Muscles known as dilator ani have also been described in some nematodes. These muscles extend from the ventral body wall to the ventral surface of the cloaca or anus and are thought to function in opening these apertures.

2. Muscles Associated with Reproduction

a. The Female. The vulvar muscles function either as dilators or constrictors. The former, known as dilator vulvae muscles, are better known. They connect the ventral wall of the vulva with the body wall ventrolaterally. These muscles are illustrated in a diagram which depicts a cross section through the vulva and vagina of *Plectus parietinus* (Maggenti, 1961). The cuticle of the vagina near the vulva of this nematode is marked by striae and punctations. Maggenti states that "there are four dilator vulval muscles, two anterior and two posterior. Each muscle contains four cells which are attached to the base of the vagina. From the vagina the muscles run obliquely, anteriorly, and posteriorly, respectively, to the lateral chords."

b. The Male. Muscles associated with reproduction in the male may be divided into four major groups: the spicular muscles, the gubernacular muscles, the copulatory muscles, and the bursal muscles. These structures will be dealt with in more detail in Chapter 11, which deals with the nematode reproductive system.

The spicules serve to open and dilate the vagina of the female; these movements are brought about by the spicular muscles which usually consist of a pair of retractor muscles and a pair of protractor muscles per spicule, both pairs being attached to the proximal end of the spicule. The former extend anteriorly to the hypodermis in the region of the lateral cord and the latter extend posteriorly to the ventral body wall.

The gubernaculum is defined by Chitwood and Chitwood (1950) as a plate, formed from the walls of the spicular pouch, in the groove of which the spicules move. Its muscles may be retractor and extend to the dorsal wall of the body, protractor and extend to the ventral wall of the body, or seductor which extend to the lateral walls of the body.

During copulation in nematodes the male coils its tail around the female's vulval region. This ventral flexing of the tail in males is brought about by the copulatory muscles which extend from the lateral cords to the subventral body wall and vary in number from forty to fifty pairs to three or four pairs.

Firm attachment during copulation is achieved in some forms by a modification of the male tail to form a copulatory bursa. This is a modification of the cuticle which results in a marked increase in its surface area and which is most pronounced in members of the Strongyloidea. Its structure has been described in *Ancylostoma duodenale* by Looss (1905). There are a number of specialized muscles in this region which are responsible for the bending and opening and closing of the bursa. These muscles have been examined and drawn in great detail by Looss, whose work in this field remains unsurpassed and to which the reader is referred for further information.

Whereas information on the anatomy of whole muscles and their attachments to various organs is sparse, particularly in the smaller nematodes, there have been some significant contributions to our knowledge of the fine structure of nematode muscles in recent years, thanks to the electron microscope; I shall now consider this subject.

III. Structure

As I have mentioned above, the most common and perhaps basic type of musculature in nematodes is that in which the cells are of the platymyarian type grouped into a meromyarian arrangement. Most small nematodes have this type of musculature. Its fine structure has been examined, with the aid of the electron microscope, in a number of different species in recent years. These observations include the following species: *Euchromadora vulgaris* (Watson, 1965a), *Nippostrongylus brasiliensis* (Lee, 1966; Jamuar, 1966), *Xiphinema index* (Wright, 1965; Roggen *et al.*, 1967), *Enterobius vermicularis* (Tsubota, 1966), *Ditylenchus dipsaci* (Yuen, 1967), *Panagrellus silusiae* (Yuen, 1968), *Meloidogyne javanica* (Bird, 1968), *Heterodera rostochiensis* (Wisse and Daems, 1968), and *Trichodorus christiei* (Hirumi *et al.*, 1968; Hirumi *et al.* in press).

The noncontractile portion of the platymyarian muscle cell (Figs. 7A, 17A, and 18) contains a nucleus which lies in a cytoplasm full of large mitochondria with numerous cristae and containing, in addition, glycogen granules, lipid bodies, endoplasmic reticulum, and ribosomes.

The contractile portion is made up of myofilaments and the relative position of these structures at three different levels of magnification in a typical platymyarian muscle cell is shown in the scale diagram (Fig. 18).

When viewed at the limit of resolution of the electron microscope, the structures in the contractile portion show a remarkable similarity throughout the Nematoda, irrespective of whether they are part of a platymyarian muscle cell or a coelomyarian muscle cell or whether they are associated with the pharynx or the body wall. Some of the measurements of myofilaments from different sources are given in Table V. These measurements are largely a reflection of the variability in techniques used by different workers because variability within the same species of nematode is as great as that between different genera in different families.

The round figure of 20 mμ for the large filaments and 6 mμ for the smaller filaments (Fig. 18) probably represents a reasonable average diameter.

In the work published so far in which these structures have been photographed at the highest resolutions, notably in *Ascaris lumbricoides* (Rosenbluth, 1965a, 1967) and in *Trichodorus christiei* (Hirumi *et al.*, 1968), there is very close agreement on the dimensions and anatomy of these structures. Thus, both groups of workers consider that the thick filaments (230 Å in diameter in *Ascaris* and 220 Å in *Trichodorus*) are not homogeneous, but are made up of subunits which are 50 Å in diameter. In both cases, the thin filaments which surround the thick ones are 80 Å in diameter. They vary in number in the A zone (Fig. 18) from 10 to 12 per thick filament, as in *Nippo-*

TABLE V

MUSCLE TYPES AND DIAMETERS OF FILAMENTS IN VARIOUS SPECIES OF NEMATODES

Species (adults unless stated)	Muscle type[a]	Average diameter thick filaments (Å)	Average diameter thin filaments (Å)	Author
Parascaris equorum	Somatic (C)	150	—	Hinz (1963)
Parascaris equorum	Somatic (C)	120	40	Auber-Thomay (1964)
Ascaris lumbricoides	Somatic (C)	175	90	Reger (1964)
Ascaris lumbricoides	Somatic (C)	230	80	Rosenbluth (1965a)
Capillaria hepatica	Somatic (C)	250	—	Wright (1964)
Euchromadora vulgaris	Somatic (P)	230	60	Watson (1965a)
Nippostrongylus brasiliensis (larva and adult)	Somatic (P)	240	90	Jamuar (1966)
Nippostrongylus brasiliensis (larva)	Somatic (P)	220	60	Lee (1966)
Enterobius vermicularis	Somatic (P)	300	150	Tsubota (1966)
Dirofilaria immitis	Somatic (C)	170	70	Lee and Miller (1967)
Xiphinema index	Somatic (P)	260	55	Roggen *et al.* (1967)
Trichodorus christiei	Pharyngeal	220	80	Hirumi *et al.* (1968)
Ascaris lumbricoides	Esophageal	160	55	Reger (1964)
Heterodera rostochiensis	Somatic (P)	250	—	Wisse and Daems (1968)
Deontostoma californicum	Somatic (C)	200	60	Hope (1969)
Meloidogyne javanica	Somatic (P)	220	60	Bird (unpublished)

[a]P, Platymyarian; C, coelomyarian.

strongylus brasiliensis (Lee, 1966) and *Ascaris lumbricoides* (Rosenbluth, 1965a), to situations in which they appear to be absent, as only the thick filaments have been detected (Table V). This has been reported in *Capillaria hepatica* (Wright, 1964) and *Heterodera rostochiensis* (Wisse and Daems, 1968). Identification of thin filaments may be dependent on the techniques used, as these structures are clearly visible in the closely related *Meloidogyne javanica* (Bird, 1968).

As mentioned above, large nematodes such as the ascaridoids have coelomyarian-type cells. The structure of this type of cell is, perhaps, best illustrated in three-dimensional diagrams (Figs. 16, 17B and E). Electron microscope studies of the fine structure of these muscle cells have been done with *Capillaria hepatica* (Wright, 1964), *Parascaris equorum* (Hinz, 1963; Auber-Thomay, 1964), *Ascaris lumbricoides* (Reger, 1964; Watson, 1965b; Rosenbluth, 1965a,b, 1967), *Deontostoma californicum* (Wright, 1966; Hope, 1969), and *Dirofilaria immitis* (Lee and Miller, 1967).

Recently, Hirumi and his co-workers (Hirumi *et al.*, in press) have examined the ultrastructure of muscle cells of *Longidorus elongatus* which they have termed shallow coelomyarian. These muscles appear to be inter-mediate in a suggested evolutionary scale of nematode muscle development, being more advanced than the platymyarian type and more primitive than the true coelomyarian type.

The coelomyarian muscle cell (Fig. 16) which, together with other longi-tudinally orientated cells of this type, makes up the single-layered body musculature of the large nematodes, consists of three principal parts. These are, first, the striated or fiber part which is contractile; second, the cell body or belly, which is essentially a sac of glycogen and which contains the nucleus; and third, the arm which extends to the nerve cord and estab-lishes a myoneural junction. This is achieved (Fig. 16) by the arm breaking up into several fingerlike processes and these make synaptic contact with nerve fibers. These neuromuscular junctions will be dealt with in more detail in Chapter 7 on the nervous system.

One of the differences between coelomyarian cells and platymyarian cells is that in the latter the mitochondria lie in the noncontractile part of the cell (Fig. 18), whereas in the coelomyarian cell they are located in the sarcoplasmic core which lies between the U-shaped contractile fibers (Figs. 22–24). However, the sarcoplasmic core continues into the muscle body and a few mitochondria are found there, together with the nucleus and glycogen granules mentioned above.

Rosenbluth (1965a) considers that the two types of myofilaments in the muscle fibers interdigitate and form H, A, and I bands (Fig. 24), as has been described in the myofilaments of vertebrate striated muscle (Hanson and Huxley, 1955).

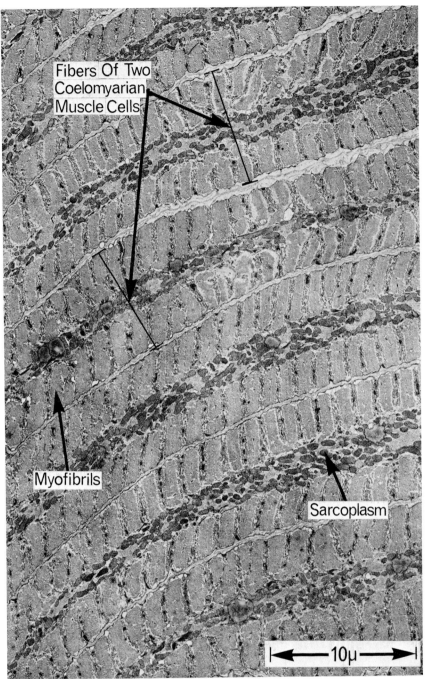

Fibers Of Two
Coelomyarian
Muscle Cells

Myofibrils

Sarcoplasm

|◄———10μ———►|

FIG. 22.   Low-power electron micrograph of a transverse section cut through the oblique straited muscle fibers of *Ascaris lumbricoides*. × 4000. (Courtesy of Dr. J. Rosenbluth; Rosenbluth, 1965a.)

118

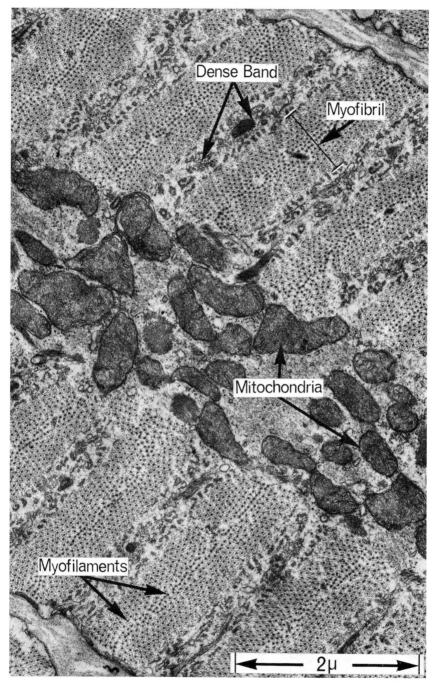

FIG. 23.   Similar to Fig. 22 but at higher magnification. × 25,000. (Courtesy of Dr. J. Rosenbluth; Rosenbluth, 1965a.)

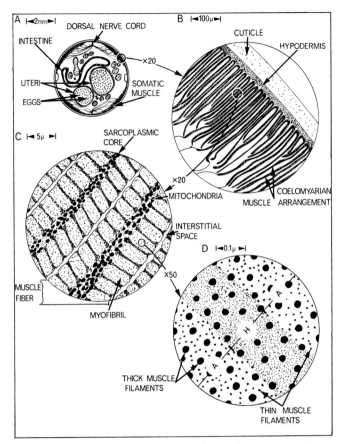

FIG. 24.   Diagrams depicting the typical polymyarian–coelomyarian muscle type of *Ascaris lumbricoides* over a wide range of magnifications. (A) Whole transverse section; (B) part of the muscle quadrant between the dorsal nerve and lateral hypodermal cord; (C) fibers of two muscle cells; (D) an H and two A bands and the two types of muscle filaments at high resolution.

Over the years, there has been considerable discussion as to whether the muscles of nematodes should be considered as smooth or striated. Rosenbluth (1965a) considers that, in the case of *Ascaris*, they are neither but have certain characteristics of both, although they more closely resemble striated. He calls them obliquely striated and, with the aid of diagrams, explains how the pronounced stagger of the myofilaments results in the obliquity of the striations. Some idea of the structure of the coelomyarian muscle cell may be obtained by examining Figs. 22, 23, and 24. The myofibrils (Figs. 22 and 23) alternate with dense bands. In the center of each myofibril (Figs. 23 and 24), there is a zone with only thick myofilaments, which is the H zone. On either side of the H zone are zones containing thick and thin myofilaments, the A zones, and outside these, on either side, is a narrow zone consisting only of thin myofilaments, the I zones. The outermost, or D, zones contain dense bands made up of filaments clumped together into Z bundles.

From his observations of transverse sections of *Ascaris* somatic muscle fibers showing this repeating pattern, Rosenbluth (1965a) has made a three-dimensional model, which corresponds, in essence, to the sliding filament model of Hanson and Huxley (1955). There are some differences, however. First of all, adjacent parallel filaments are not lined up with one another but are staggered, so that each thick filament is about 10% of its length ahead of its neighbor; and second, Z lines, as seen in striated vertebrate myofibrils, are absent, being replaced by miniature counterparts in the form of small bundles of thin filaments. By means of this model, it is possible to consider the controversy as to whether this muscle is smooth or striated. The contractile part clearly consists of two kinds of myofilaments which are grouped together in a regular sequence in which I, A, and H zones can be recognized. In one plane the bands are in register and the system clearly resembles that of classic striated muscle. On the other hand, typical Z lines are missing and in another plane the myofilaments are staggered. Thus, *Ascaris* muscle is neither smooth nor striated in the same sense as classic vertebrate muscle. It is, however, more closely related to striated muscle and is, perhaps, best referred to as "obliquely striated" (Rosenbluth, 1965a).

The coelomyarian somatic muscle of the free-living marine nematode *Deontostoma californicum* has also been examined with the electron microscope in some detail (Hope, 1969) and found to be essentially similar, in many respects, to that of other nematodes that have been studied at high magnification, as well as to that of some other invertebrates (Kawaguti and Ikemoto, 1957, 1958a,b,c). Thus, it has obliquely striated muscle with characteristic repeated patterns of H, A, and I bands and Z components. *Deontostoma* differs from other forms that have been described in that its Z components are barlike and do not have a well-developed T-system whereas its sarcoplasm reticulum is better developed than in *Ascaris*. In *Deontostoma*, as can be seen (Fig. 17E), the bands and Z planes are thought to be inclined in the same direction and at the same angle in both right and left sides of the fiber, whereas in *Ascaris* (Fig. 17B), the oblique bands form a partial helix when viewed through the opposing sides of the fiber (Hope, 1969), because the bands of one side are out of register with those of the other, whereas in *Deontostoma*, they are on the same level and so give the appearance of continuity the whole width of the fiber.

There is obviously a very close relationship in myofilament morphology in many widely divergent types of animals. In those nematodes in which the myofilaments have been observed and counted at high resolution in the A band, the relationship between thick and thin filaments is very similar to that described for the intersegmental abdominal muscles of the insect *Rhodnius prolixus* (Toselli and Pepe, 1968). These workers found that, in transverse sections through the A band region, each thick filament is surrounded by twelve thin filaments, two thin filaments being shared by two neighboring thick filaments so that the ratio of thin to thick filaments is 6:1. This configuration is probably common to many nematodes (Figs. 18 and 24) and Toselli and Pepe (1968) draw attention, by means of diagrams representing their arrangement, to the fact that this structure is related to that found in insect flight muscle and vertebrate skeletal muscle.

IV. Function

I propose to deal briefly with muscle function under a number of headings. First, its function as a glycogen storage depot; second, the morphology of muscle contraction at high resolution; and finally, some comments on the physiology of this process. The influence of muscle on movement of the whole intact nematode has already been mentioned in Chapter 3 on the exoskeleton.

A. GLYCOGEN STORAGE

Although nematode muscle cells are rich in numerous biochemical substances, perhaps the most obvious to the histochemist and biochemist is the large amount of glycogen that is stored in the body or belly of the co-elomyarian muscle cell. Rosenbluth (1965b) has shown that in unstarved *Ascaris lumbricoides*, the material in these bellies is intensely PAS-positive, stains brown with iodine, and exhibits metachromasia with toluidine blue. When viewed under the electron microscope, it can be shown that this material consists of large numbers of particles, each of which is several hundred angstrom units in diameter. On the basis of staining properties, size, configuration, and biochemistry, there seems to be no doubt that this material is glycogen. In starved nematodes the muscle bellies are shrunken, there is no positive result in histochemical tests for glycogen, and no sign of the particles described above when sections are viewed under the electron microscope.

Thus, the muscle belly appears to serve as a glycogen storage depot which may be utilized either by the muscle itself or by the whole nematode during starvation.

Glycogen loss from somatic muscle during starvation is rapid and has been estimated to be 27% of the initial value during the first day (Harpur, 1963) and appears to be about 60% of this value after 3 days.

The significance of the muscle cell body as the main storage site for glycogen in the large ascarids is well documented (von Kemnitz, 1912; Toryu, 1933; von Brand, 1937; Fairbairn, 1957). It seems likely, judging from histochemical and electron microscope observations of other nematodes, notably those of *Nippostrongylus*, *Dirofilaria*, *Phocanema*, and *Deontostoma* (Jamuar, 1966; Lee and Miller, 1967; Kan and Davey, 1968; Hope, 1969), that this may be one of the functions of somatic muscles in the Nematoda.

It has been suggested (von Brand, 1966) that the amount of glycogen stored in parasitic nematodes is related to the availability of oxygen in the parasite's environment. Thus, forms living in oxygen-deficient habitats or in habitats subject to periodic fluctuations in amounts of oxygen tend to store large amounts of glycogen.

B. CONTRACTION

It has been suggested (Lee, 1966) that the thick myofilaments contain myosin and the thin filaments contain actin. In this respect, then, nematode somatic muscle would resemble vertebrate striated muscle, about which a great deal is known (Hanson and Huxley, 1955) and in which the essential feature of contraction is the sliding of actin filaments past myosin filaments. This leads to an increase in their area of overlap, which corresponds to a decrease in width of the I bands, while the filaments themselves remain at constant length. The energy necessary for this mechanical work comes from that stored within the high-energy phosphate linkages of ATP which are split by myosin.

The most thorough study of the contraction mechanism of nematode somatic muscle is undoubtedly that of Rosenbluth (1967), who studied the process of contraction in the obliquely striated somatic muscles of *Ascaris*, under both the light and electron miscoscopes, using muscles fixed at both maximum expansion and contraction. Expansion was obtained by perfusion with piperazine citrate and contraction by perfusion with acetylcholine. Under the light microscope, the most obvious difference between expanded and contracted nematode muscle is seen in longitudinal section where the cuticle investing contracted muscle is highly corrugated whereas in an extended specimen it appears smooth at low magnification. The degree of buckling of the cuticle thus appears to be related to the degree of shortening of the muscle.

As a result of observations of these muscles in contracted and expanded states under the electron microscope, Rosenbluth (1967) has suggested that there are two mechanisms associated with somatic muscle contraction in *Ascaris*. First, a mechanism similar to that described for vertebrate striated muscle, in which there is a sliding of thin filaments past thick filaments; and second, an increase in the degree of overlap of thick filaments and a decrease in the extent of stagger.

C. Physiology

Work done on neuromuscular physiology has been reviewed by Rogers (1962) and, more recently, by Lee (1965) and Debell (1965).

Just as the use of the electron microscope has added and will, of course, continue to add, a great deal to our knowledge of muscle structure, so the intracellular microelectrode has added to our knowledge of its physiology. Prior to its use, however, some information was obtained by the use of a technique initiated by Toscano Rico (1926) and developed by various other workers, notably Baldwin and Moyle (1947, 1949), Norton and De Beer (1957), and Krotov (1956a,b), in which the movements of either whole nematodes, segments, or nerve-muscle strips under physiological conditions *in vitro* were measured and recorded by means of a kymograph. These workers showed that rhythmic contractions occur in the muscles of *Ascaris* and in *Phocanema* (Bradley, 1961a,b) which may be induced and modified by weights or electrical stimuli.

Harris and Crofton (1957) have shown that the weight necessary to start this rhythmic contraction produces a tension corresponding to that produced by the hydrostatic pressure changes in the intact nematode.

Ascaris somatic muscle responds to drugs which affect the cholinergic neuromuscular junctions of other animals. Thus, it contracts when exposed to acetylcholine and this response is blocked by tubocurarine (Baldwin and Moyle, 1949; Norton and De Beer, 1957).

Krotov (1956a,b) observed that the anterior and posterior ends of intact *Ascaris* were more sensitive to these pharmacologically active substances than were other parts of the nematode's body or the nerve-muscle strips used by Baldwin and Moyle (1949) in which the lowest concentration at which activity was obtained with acetylcholine was 10^{-6}, whereas Krotov obtained a response with as little as 10^{-11} of acetylcholine. Using various pharmacologically active substances, all these workers came to the conclusion that the somatic muscle of *Ascaris* responded in the same way to these substances as does vertebrate skeletal muscle.

Furthermore, by means of leech muscle bioassay, Mellanby (1955) has detected acetylcholine at various concentrations in the tissues of the nematodes *Litomosoides carinii*, *Dirofilaria repens*, and *Ascaris lumbricoides*.

Despite these observations, as well as those described above on the fine structure of nematode somatic muscle, there are still some functional similarities between this muscle and classic smooth muscle (Crofton, 1966). This type of muscle is usually arranged in sheets and acts against similar muscle or a hydrostatic skeleton, whereas striated muscles are arranged in blocks and act on rigid structures. Thus, functionally, nematode muscles resemble classic smooth muscles in some respects since they act on a non-rigid cuticle in a manner which can influence other muscle cells in the vicinity.

In order to reach a definite conclusion regarding the role of acetylcholine in nerve transmission in nematodes, information is needed on the role of nerves, in the responses described above, of *Ascaris* to pharmacologically active substances. We are now closer to getting this information thanks to the use of the recording microelectrode by a number of workers, notably Jarman (1959), Debell *et al.* (1963), Del Castillo *et al.* (1963, 1964a,b), and Goodwin and Vaughn Williams (1963). Briefly, the transmembrane potentials of the muscle cell bellies are rhythmically interrupted by transient depolarizations of about 15–40 mV. The repetitive spike potentials responsible for the contraction of *Ascaris* muscle are generated by pacemakers located in the region where the neural ends of the muscle arms interlace with those of other cells to form a longitudinal band along the inner surface of the median line. This band of finger tissue closely resembles vertebrate smooth muscle. The spike potentials responsible for muscle contraction generate within the fingers and spread along the arms to the bodies and contractile fibers of the cells. This activity is modulated by the nematode's nervous system by means of two different neurohumors liberated from the longitudinal nerves which lie adjacent to the finger tissue (Fig. 16) within a trough of hypodermal tissue, the median line. One of these neurohumors, probably acetylcholine, accelerates membrane activity whereas the other, unidentified, but which may be γ-aminobutyric acid (GABA), inhibits it. Thus, despite the great dissimilarity between nematode somatic muscle cells and mammalian visceral muscle cells in structure, there is, nevertheless, a striking electrophysiological similarity.

Muscle activity is modified through the pacemakers which are thought to be influenced by internal changes in the nematode or by the nervous system's responding to external stimuli impinging on sense receptors (Arthur, 1968).

In conclusion, although detailed information on the structure and physiology of nematode muscle is still somewhat sparse, particularly in the smaller nematodes, it is clear that the last decade has yielded more information than all the preceding years, thanks to advances in technology. We may look forward to a considerable increase in our knowledge of this subject in the years ahead.

V. Summary

The somatic muscles of nematodes are grouped into rows between the cords. There may, in some cases, not be any rows or only two (holomyarian) or, more commonly, there may be two to five rows (meromyarian) or there may be a large number of rows (polymyarian).

There are three types of muscle cell, a flat type of cell (platymyarian), a U-shaped type of cell (coelomyarian) in which the fibers extend up the side of the cell and the sarcoplasm bulges into the pseudocoelom, and finally, cells in which the fibers encircle the sarcoplasm (circomyarian). This nomenclature is simply one of convenience and has no taxonomic significance, since the type of cell and its arrangement can vary within the same nematode.

The most common configuration is platymyarian cells grouped in meromyarian arrangement, a condition also found in the larval stages of some of the more complex coelomyarian–polymyarian types.

Muscle cells are connected to each other by means of cytoplasmic bridges in many nematodes and may have more than one nervous connection. These structures obviously assist greatly in coordinated muscular contraction.

In addition to somatic muscle, there are a number of specialized muscles which are associated with feeding, food movement, and defecation (cephalic, esophageal, intestinal, and anal muscles) as well as with reproduction (vulvar, spicular, gubernacular, copulatory, and bursal muscles).

At the limits of resolution of the electron microscope, it can be shown that the myofilaments of the contractile part of the nematode muscle cell are remarkably similar, irrespective of whether they are part of a platymyarian or a coelomyarian muscle cell. Furthermore, these similarities extend beyond the Nematoda, the arrangement of the myofilaments being related to that found in insect flight muscle and vertebrate skeletal muscle.

The myofilaments are of two kinds, thin (about 80 Å in diameter) and thick (about 230 Å in diameter and made up of 50 Å subunits) which are grouped together in a regular sequence in which I, A, and H zones can be recognized. In the A zone the thick filaments are surrounded by about twelve thin ones and the thin filaments are shared by neighboring thick filaments, so that the ratio of thick to thin is about 1:6.

The thick filaments are thought to contain myosin and the thin filaments actin. These actin filaments slide past the myosin filaments during contraction and resemble vertebrate striated muscle in this respect, except that there is also an increase in the degree of overlap of the thick filaments. The noncontractile part of the platymyarian muscle cell contains a nucleus, a cytoplasm full of mitochondria, and some glycogen granules and lipid bodies. In the coelomyarian muscle cell, however, the mitochondria lie in the sarcoplasmic core between the contractile fibers and only a few mitochondria, together with the nucleus, are found in the noncontractile body which is virtually a storage depot for glycogen. An arm extends from this body to the nerve cord, where it breaks up into fingerlike processes which interdigitate with processes from other arms and make contact with nerve fibers. It is in this region that pacemakers are located which are responsible for muscle contraction. This process is modulated by two different neurohumors which are liberated from the adjacent longitudinal nerves.

Thus, nematode muscle is peculiar in a number of respects. Structurally, the contractile portion is obliquely striated and resembles classic striated muscle more than it does smooth muscle, but physiologically the reverse is true. Furthermore, nematode muscles are unusual in that the muscle sends branches to the nerve rather than the nerve sending branches to the muscle.

REFERENCES

Arthur, E. J. (1968). *Diss. Abstr., B* **28**, 4427.
Auber-Thomay, M. (1964). *J. Microsc. (Paris)* **3**, 105.
Baldwin, E., and Moyle, V. (1947). *J. Exp. Biol.* **23**, 277.
Baldwin, E., and Moyle, V. (1949). *Brit. J. Pharmacol. Chemother.* **4**, 145.
Bastian, H. C. (1866). *Phil. Trans. Roy. Soc. London* **156**, 545.
Bird, A. F. (1968). *J. Parasitol.* **54**, 475.
Bradley, C. (1961a). *Can. J. Zool.* **39**, 35.
Bradley, C. (1961b). *Can. J. Zool.* **39**, 129.
Chitwood, B. G., and Chitwood, M. B. (1933). *Z. Zellforsch. Mikrosk. Anat.* **19**, 309.
Chitwood, B. G., and Chitwood, M. B., eds. (1950). "An Introduction to Nematology," 213 pp. Monumental Printing Co., Baltimore, Maryland.
Coomans, A. (1962). *Nematologica* **7**, 242.
Coomans, A. (1963). *Nematologica* **9**, 587.
Crofton, H. D. (1966). "Nematodes," 160 pp. Hutchinson, London.
Das, V. M. (1962). *Can. J. Zool.* **40**, 747.
de Baillon, P. C. (1911). *Cellule* **27**, 165.
Debell, J. T. (1965). *Quart. Rev. Biol.* **40**, 233.
Debell, J. T., Del Castillo, J., and Sánchez, V. (1963). *J. Cell. Comp. Physiol.* **62**, 159.
Deineka, D. (1908). *Z. Wiss. Zool.* **89**, 243.
Del Castillo, J., De Mello, W. C., and Morales, T. A. (1963). *Arch. Int. Physiol.* **71**, 741.
Del Castillo, J., De Mello, W. C., and Morales, T. A. (1964a). *Brit. J. Pharmacol. Chemother.* **22**, 463.

Del Castillo, J., De Mello, W. C., and Morales, T. A. (1964b). *Experientia* **20**, 141.
Fairbairn, D. (1957). *Exp. Parasitol.* **6**, 491.
Goodwin, L. G., and Vaughn Williams, E. M. (1963). *J. Physiol. (London)* **168**, 857.
Hanson, J., and Huxley, H. E. (1955). *Symp. Soc. Exp. Biol.* **9**, 228.
Harpur, R. P. (1963). *Can. J. Biochem. Physiol.* **41**, 1673.
Harris, J. E., and Crofton, H. D. (1957). *J. Exp. Biol.* **34**, 116.
Hinz, E. (1963). *Protoplasma* **56**, 202.
Hirschmann, H. (1959). *Proc. Helminthol. Soc. Wash.* **26**, 73.
Hirumi, H., Chen, T. A., Lee, K. J., and Maramorosch, K. (1968). *J. Ultrastruct. Res.* **24**, 434.
Hirmui, H., Raski, D. J., and Jones, N. O. (1971). *J. Ultrastruct. Res.* (in press).
Hope, W. D. (1969). *Proc. Helminthol. Soc. Wash.* **36**, 10.
Inglis, W. G. (1964). *Bull. Brit. Mus. (Natur. Hist.), Ser. D, Brit. Natur.* **11**, 265.
Inglis, W. G. (1966). *Proc. Linn. Soc. London* **177**, 55.
Jamuar, M. P. (1966). *J. Parasitol.* **52**, 209.
Jarman, M. (1959). *Nature (London)* **184**, 1244.
Joseph, G. (1882). *Zool. Anz.* **5**, 603.
Kan, S. P., and Davey, K. G. (1968). *Can. J. Zool.* **46**, 723.
Kawaguti, S., and Ikemoto, N. (1957). *Biol. J. Okayama Univ.* **3**, 223.
Kawaguti, S., and Ikemoto, N. (1958a). *Biol. J. Okayama Univ.* **4**, 79.
Kawaguti, S., and Ikemoto, N. (1958b). *Biol. J. Okayama Univ.* **4**, 177.
Kawaguti, S., and Ikemoto, N. (1958c). *Biol. J. Okayama Univ.* **4**, 207.
Krotov, A. I. (1956a). *Med. Parazitol. Parazit. Bolez.* **25**, 58.
Krotov, A. I. (1956b). *Med. Parazitol. Parazit. Bolez.* **25**, 60.
Lee, C., and Miller, J. H. (1967). *Exp. Parasitol.* **20**, 334.
Lee, D. L. (1965). "The Physiology of Nematodes," 154 pp. Oliver & Boyd, Edinburgh and London.
Lee, D. L. (1966). *Parasitology.* **56**, 127.
Leuckart, R. (1876). "Die Menschlichen Parasiten," Vol. 2. Winter, Leipzig.
Looss, A. (1905). *Rec. Egypt. Govt. Sch. Med.* **3**, 1.
López-Abella, D., Jiménez-Millán, F., and Garcia-Hidalgo, F. (1967). *Nematologica* **13**, 283.
Maggenti, A. R. (1961). *Proc. Helminthol. Soc. Wash.* **28**, 118.
Maggenti, A. R., and Allen, M. W. (1960). *Proc Helminthol. Soc. Wash.* **27**, 4.
Martini, E. (1916). *Z. Wiss. Zool.* **116**, 137.
Mellanby, H. (1955). *Parasitology* **45**, 287.
Norton, S., and De Beer, E. J. (1957). *Amer. J. Trop. Med. Hyg.* **6**, 898.
Plenk, H. (1924). *Z. Mikrosk.-Anat. Forsch.* **4**, 163.
Raski, D. J., Jones, N. O., and Roggen, D. R. (1969). *Proc. Helminthol. Soc. Wash.* **36**, 106.
Reger, J. F. (1964). *J. Ultrastruct. Res.* **10**, 48.
Rogers, W. P. (1962). "The Nature of Parasitism: The Relationship of Some Metazoan Parasites to their Hosts," 287 pp. Academic Press, New York.
Roggen, D. R., Raski, D. J., and Jones, N. O. (1967). *Nematologica* **13**, 1.
Rosenbluth, J. (1965a) *J. Cell Biol.* **25**, 495.
Rosenbluth, J. (1965b) *J. Cell Biol.* **26**, 579.
Rosenbluth, J. (1967). *J. Cell Biol.* **34**, 15.
Schneider, A. (1860). *Arch. Anat. Physiol. Leipzig.* p. 224.
Schneider, A. (1863). *Arch. Anat. Physiol. Leipzig.* p. 1.
Schneider, A. (1866). "Monographie der Nematoden," 357 pp. Gregg, Berlin.
Thust, R. (1968). *Z. Wiss. Zool., Abt. A* **178**, 1.
Toryu, Y. (1933). *Sci. Rep. Tohoku Imp. Univ.* **4**, 65.
Toscano Rico, J. (1926). *C. R. Soc. Biol.* **94**, 921.

Toselli, P. A., and Pepe, F. A. (1968). *J. Cell Biol.* **37**, 445.

Tsubota, T. (1966). *Kiseichvgaku Zasshi* **15**, 64.

Voltzenlogel, E. (1902). *Zool. Jahrb. (Anat.).* **16**, 481.

von Brand, T. (1937). *J. Parasitol.* **23**, 68.

von Brand, T. (1966). "Biochemistry of Parasites," 429 pp. Academic Press, New York.

von Kemnitz, G. (1912). *Arch. Zellforsch.* **7**, 463.

Watson, B. D. (1965a). *Quart. J. Microsc. Sci.* **106**, 75.

Watson, B. D. (1965b). *Quart. J. Microsc. Sci.* **106**, 83.

Wisse, E., and Daems, W. T. (1968). *J. Ultrastruct. Res.* **24**, 210.

Wright, K. A. (1964). *Can. J. Zool.* **42**, 483.

Wright, K. A. (1965). *Can. J. Zool.* **43**, 689.

Wright, K. A. (1966). *Can. J. Zool.* **44**, 329.

Yuen, P. H. (1967). *Can. J. Zool.* **45**, 1019.

Yuen, P. H. (1968). *Nematologica* **14**, 554.

7
THE NERVOUS SYSTEM

I. Introduction

Information on the nervous system of nematodes has been reviewed by various authors over the last twenty years, notably by Chitwood and Chitwood (1950), Hyman (1951), Schuurmans Stekhoven (1959), Bullock and Horridge (1965), de Coninck (1965), Lee (1965), and Crofton (1966). As Crofton mentions in his concise chapter on the nervous system, much of the work done has been topographical and anatomical. Most of the detailed histological work has been done on the large ascarids and Goldschmidt's (1903, 1908, 1909, 1910) detailed work has been repeatedly quoted and his complex, numbered diagrams of fiber connections in the dorsal and ventral parts of the circumesophageal nerve ring have been published virtually unchanged in a number of books including one of the most recent reviews (Bullock and Horridge, 1965). I have avoided republishing these particular diagrams because they are so complex that I feel that their validity should first be established by at least one other worker making an equally detailed and thorough study of these fiber connections in the nerve ring of a nematode using modern techniques. However, as Bullock and Horridge (1965) have stated, Goldschmidt's papers still remain the most detailed available on the nervous system of nematodes and great credit must go to this worker for his tenacity and skill in cataloging every ganglion and cell in the nervous system of *Ascaris*. The more concise and beautifully illustrated work of Looss (1905) on *Ancylostoma duodenale* should not, however, be forgotten, as it must have been of considerable help to Gold-schmidt in his monumental work.

The large forms parasitic in animals were, because of their size, the only nematodes which could be dissected or sectioned for work with the light microscope and the sense organs and nervous systems of the myriads of smaller forms, which are much more typical representatives of the Nema-toda, are only now becoming known thanks to the use of the electron microscope.

As a result of the increased resolution now available, structures whose absence throughout the group had been assumed, have now been revealed. An example of these are cilia, whose presumed absence was included in all definitions of the Nematoda until quite recently, although Martini (Schuurmans Stekhoven, 1959) had described cilialike structures in amphids of *Oxyuris curvula*. Their presence was first thought to have been detected, by means of the electron microscope, in the intestinal wall of *Ancylostoma caninum* (Browne and Chowdhury, 1959) and in *Trichinella spiralis* (Beckett and Boothroyd, 1961). However, it is now known, as a result of later electron microscope studies on these nematodes (Browne *et al.*, 1965; Bruce, 1966; Miller, 1967), together with similar studies on various other species of nematodes, notably *Ascaris suum* (Kessel *et al.*, 1961; Sheffield, 1964), *Parascaris equorum* (Joyon and Collin, 1962), *Capillaria hepatica* (Wright, 1963), *Nippostrongylus brasiliensis* (Jamuar, 1966; Lee, 1968), *Trichuris suis* (Jenkins, 1967), *Aspiculuris tetraptera* (Lee and Anya, 1968), and a species of *Metastrongylus* (Jenkins and Erasmus, 1969), that these are really microvilli.

As a result of much of this work, Andreassen (1966) stated that "we must continue to say cilia have not yet been found in nematodes." He predicted that if they were to be found, they would be found in the sensory organs. In fact, unknown to Andreassen, they had already been found in a sense organ of the free-living marine nematode *Deontostoma californicum* by Hope (1965) and have subsequently been identified in sense organs in various nematodes including *Xiphinema index* (Roggen *et al.*, 1966), *Haemonchus contortus* (Ross, 1967), *Dirofilaria immitis* (Kozek, 1968), and *Trichodorus christiei* (Hirumi, personal communication). Clearly, cilia occur widely throughout the Nematoda in sensory organs and are discussed in greater detail below.

Sensory organs are either common to all nematodes, an example being the amphids, or occur in a large group of nematodes, an example being the phasmids, which are considered to be so important taxonomically that the division of the Nematoda into two major groups is dependent on the presence or absence of these structures.

In the area around the mouth, the sensory structures are arranged in a characteristic hexaradiate pattern which is common, although sometimes modified, to the whole group.

In this chapter I propose to deal first with the various sense organs and then to consider the structure of the nervous system, the relatively new subject of neurosecretion, the connections between nerve and muscle, and finally, to consider briefly the behavioral responses of nematodes to various physical and chemical stimuli.

II. Sense Organs

A. Cephalic Sense Organs

The symmetrical relationship between the sense organs of nematodes and their mouth structures has been reviewed in some detail (Chitwood and Chitwood, 1950; de Coninck, 1965) and I refer the reader to these books which depict the variability of cephalic sensory structures in many different species of nematodes. Basically, these are considered by most workers to consist of circles of structures arranged in a hexaradiate pattern. The general plan accepted by the majority of nematologists is that of de Coninck (1942). This consists (Fig. 25A) of a head with six lips which has a total complement of sixteen papillae arranged in three circles, an outer circle of four cephalic papillae, a middle circle of six outer labial papillae and an inner circle of six inner labial papillae (Fig. 25A). This complement of papillae is found in many marine forms, where they often occur as long, cuticular bristles, but their number is usually reduced in terrestrial and parasitic forms. In some forms, the lips may fuse to form three lips, as in the ascarids (Figs. 25B and 26B), or fuse completely to form a united ring around the mouth, as can be seen in many of the filarioid nematodes (Anderson, 1968). Until the advent of the electron microscope, there was no information available on this structure of the cephalic sense organs except in the case of the large ascarids (Goldschmidt, 1903).

In *Ascaris* the six inner labial papillae are missing (Fig. 25B) although their nerves are still present. The three lips possess among them a total of twelve sensory structures consisting of ten papillae and two amphids. The cephalic papillae and the outer labial papillae are located in four instances under a thin, oval-shaped portion of the cuticle and these structures, two

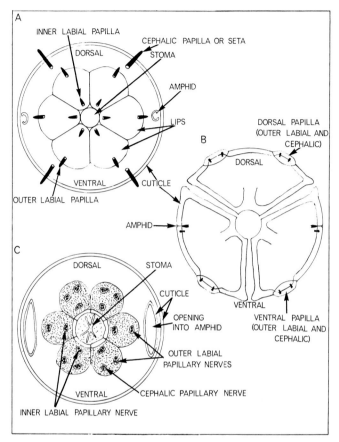

FIG. 25.   Diagrams of frontal views of nematodes. (A) A generalized nematode showing the sensory organs. (After de Coninck, 1942). (B) *En face* view of *Ascaris* showing lips and sensory organs. (After Lee, 1962.) (C) Section through tip of head of *Xiphinema* showing sensory structures.

on the dorsal lip and one on each of the subventrals, are termed dorsal and ventral papillae, respectively (Lee, 1962, 1965). The remaining two outer labial papillae are located close to the amphids (Fig. 25B).

  These papillae of *Ascaris* are readily observed if the tip of the head is cut in transverse section with a sharp scalpel or razor blade and immediately placed in a drop of body fluid or normal saline and examined under the microscope (Fig. 26A,B, and C) although all the papillae may not be visible in the same focal plane. The outer labial and cephalic papillae can be seen, provided the biopsy is done rapidly, as stalked structures which appear to

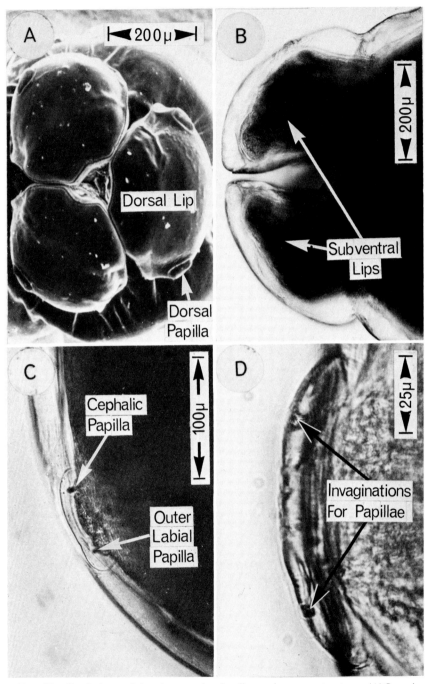

FIG. 26. Head views of *Ascaris suum* showing lips and sensory structures. (A) Scanning electron micrograph of an *en face* view. × 120. (Courtesy of Dr. P. A. Madden; Madden *et al.*, 1970.) (B) Light photomicrograph of a lateral view. ×126. (C) Light photomicrograph of part of an *en face* view showing labial and cephalic papillae. ×320. (D) As for C. ×800.

be capable of some movement (Fig. 26B). In fixed or dead material they apparently retract and the cuticular canals which they occupy when extended are seen more easily (Fig. 26C). Sections through these papillae (Goldschmidt, 1903, 1908) reveal that they are not structurally similar. In the cephalic papillae, the papillary nerve terminates as a nerve fiber which projects through a canal in the cuticle and is associated with a lens-like thickening at its base, whereas in the outer labial papillae it terminates as a bulb under the cuticle (Goldschmidt, 1903).

Cephalic sense organs have now been described in the head region of a number of small nematodes including *Xiphinema index* (Wright, 1965; Roggen *et al.*, 1967), *Ditylenchus dipsaci* (Yuen, 1967), *Xiphinema americanum* (López-Abella *et al.*, 1967), *Neoaplectana carpocapsae* (Poinar and Leute-negger, 1968), *Panagrellus silusiae* (Yuen, 1968), *Trichodorus christiei* (Hirumi *et al.*, 1968), and *T. allius* (Raski *et al.*, 1969). These structures have also been observed in larval and adult stages of *Meloidogyne javanica* (Bird, unpublished observations) and doubtless are similar in a wide variety of both free-living and parasitic nematodes.

The electron micrographs of Wright (1965), Roggen *et al.* (1967) and López-Abella *et al.* (1967) showing sections cut through the tip of the head of the genus *Xiphinema*, depict the morphology of the nerves supplying the sensory papillae perhaps a little more clearly than those of other workers on various other genera of nematodes (Fig. 25C).

The ring of six inner labial papillary nerves is always the first to be cut through in transverse sections of material cut head on. In the genus *Meloidogyne* their morphology is similar in both males and females and they are readily detected, particularly in transverse sections (Fig. 27), together with the cuticle-lined openings of the amphids. As anteroposterior sectioning continues, the outer labial papillary and the cephalic papillary nerves are recognized.

Generally, this arrangement of sixteen papillary sense organs and two amphids seems to be similar in all plant parasitic and free-living nematodes which have so far been examined with the aid of the electron micro-scope.

Yuen (1968) has observed that in both *Ditylenchus dipsaci* and *Panagrellus silusiae* the sensillae of the amphids are modified endings of axons from part of the lateral cephalic nerves. She considers that the amphids may thus be specially modified dorsolateral papillae of the lateral lips and that this conclusion invalidates Chabaud's (1955) objection to the Chitwood and Wehr (1934) hypothesis on the generalized distribution of the cephalic sense organs of nematodes. Chitwood and Wehr (1934) considered that the papillae occur in two circles, an inner one of six and an outer one of twelve, two outer and an inner on each lip. Chabaud (1955) pointed out that the dorsolateral papillae were hypothetical. Hirumi *et al.* (1968) indicate that the amphidial nerves are independent of the papillary nerve

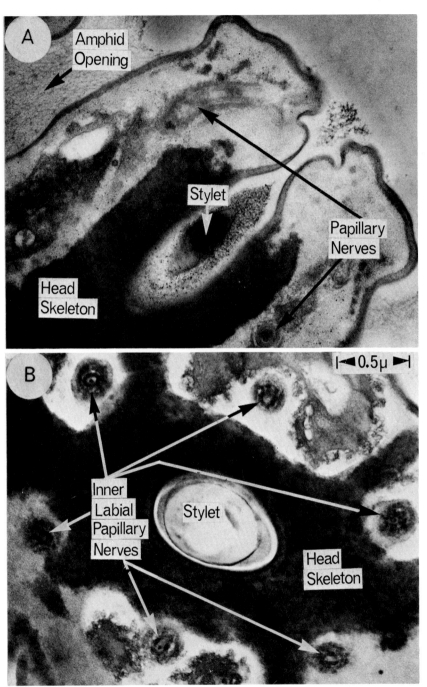

FIG. 27. Electron micrographs of sections cut through the tip of the head region of male specimens of *Meloidogyne javanica*. (A) Longitudinal section. × 40,000. (B) Cross section showing the six inner labial papillary nerves. × 40,000.

system in *Trichodorus christiei* and most workers prior to this have stressed that the amphidial nerves are discrete structures which run back to the lateral ganglia.

I am not concerned here with the phylogenetic aspects of the cephalic sensory structures and prefer, for convenience, to subscribe to de Coninck's (1942) hypothesis, particularly because the amphids differ so much in their fine structure from papillae.

Amphids, as has been mentioned above, are found in all nematodes. They are most conspicuous in marine forms and most reduced in forms parasitic in animals, although in plant parasitic nematodes they occupy quite a considerable area in the head region (Figs. 25 and 31). For a detailed account of their external morphology and phylogenetic relationships, I refer the reader to de Coninck (1965). Amphids, which were first called lateral organs (Bastian, 1865) and were later renamed amphids (Cobb, 1913) because of differing structures with similar names in fishes and amphibians, may be extremely large in relation to the size of the nematode, as in the marine nematode *Rhaptothyreus typicus*, which lives at great depth (1330 to 1470 meters) (Hope and Murphy, 1969), or very small in relation to the size of the nematode, as in *Ascaris*. In *R. typicus*, the amphids, which are oval in shape (Fig. 28), may be as large as $100\,\mu$ long and $40\,\mu$ wide and occupy much of the head region, whereas in most plant parasitic nematodes they are only a fraction of this in size. Nevertheless, even in these forms they occupy much of the head region. It is extremely difficult to detect these structures in small nematodes under the light microscope using traditional nonspecific staining methods, but advantage may be taken of the fact that they contain esterases (Fig. 29A) and may be shown in contrast to the rest of the head region by means of histochemical methods which are specific for these substances (Bird, 1966). Because of their prominence and morphological position, it is clear that they must have very important sensory functions. Probably they have a number of functions which would vary in different genera inhabiting different environments. It is generally thought that the papillae are touch or tactoreceptors, the ocelli, to be described below, photoreceptors, and the amphids chemoreceptors.

Steiner (1925) suggested that the amphids in plant parasitic nematodes are involved in the orientation of these nematodes toward plant roots in response to chemicals which the roots emit. The responses of nematodes to various stimuli will be discussed briefly later in the chapter. It has been suggested by various workers that the amphids respond to a number of chemicals, including gases such as carbon dioxide, as well as to physical stimuli such as electric currents and heat, and it has recently been suggested (El-Sherif and Mai, 1969) that "the anatomy of the nematode sensing organs should be examined to determine whether or not they have any infrared detector configuration." I am not sure whether sensory structures associated

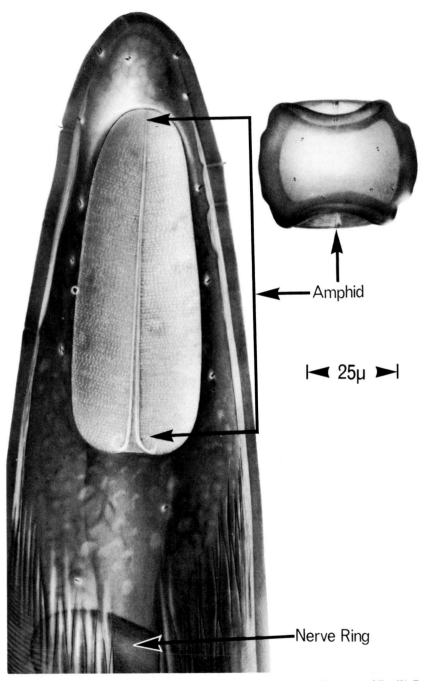

FIG. 28.   Diagram showing the amphids in *Rhaptothyreus typicus*. (Courtesy of Dr. W. D. Hope; Hope and Murphy, 1969.)

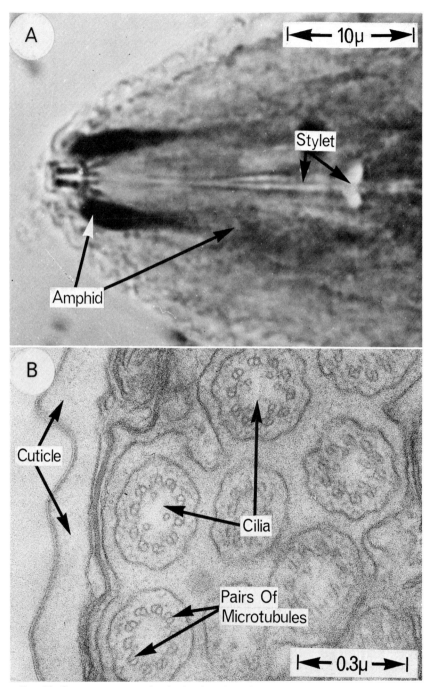

FIG. 29. Sensory structures in the head region of nematodes. (A) Photomicrograph of a longitudinal section through the head region of a young female specimen of *Meloidogyne javanica* showing the amphids stained for esterase. × 3500. (Bird, 1966.) (B) Electron micrograph of a section cut through part of an amphid in the 4th-stage larva of *Haemonchus contortus* showing cross section of cilia. × 100,000. (Courtesy of Mrs. M. M. R. Ross; Ross, 1967.)

with IR detection have any particular characteristics when viewed under the electron microscope but there is no doubt that much more work is needed on the fine structure of the amphids in a wide range of nematodes. It is, perhaps, worth noting at this stage that the pit organs of snakes such as the rattlesnake are IR-sensitive structures. They are located on either side of the face between eye and nose and consist of pits filled with vascular tissue containing numerous nerve endings (Bullock and Cowles, 1952; Bullock and Fox, 1957; Terashima *et al.*, 1970).

Knowledge on the form and function of sensory organs in nematodes is limited by the many technical problems which have yet to be overcome. The electron microscope may be used to solve the problems associated with structural size but no methods have so far been developed which permit extirpation or inactivation of the sensory structures under consideration without seriously affecting the physiology of the nematode.

Recent work by Hope (1965), Roggen *et al.* (1966), Ross (1967), Kozek (1968) and Hirumi (personal communication) has established, as mentioned above, that cilia are found in a wide range of different nematodes and probably occur universally in their sensory structures. Cilia, or structures similar to them, are found in the various papillae as well as in the amphids, although, in the papillae there may be only one or two cilialike structures, whereas in the amphids they are much more numerous (Fig. 29B). Thus, in *Trichodorus christiei* (Hirumi and Chen, 1968), although there are only two or three cilia in each cephalic papilla, there are as many as twenty-three cilia in each amphid.

The cilia that have so far been examined in nematodes lack a basal body and show much diversity in the number and arrangement of the microtubules (Figs. 29B and 32). Thus, Ross (1967) reports a $10 + 0–4$ configuration in *Haemonchus contortus*, Roggen *et al.* (1966) $9 + 4$, $8 + 4$, and $8 + 2$ in *Xiphinema index*, Poinar and Leutenegger (1968) $5 – 10 + 0 – 2$ in *Neoaplectana carpocapsae*, Kozek (1968) $1 + 11 + 4$ and $9 + 2$ in *Dirofilaria immitis* and Hirumi and Chen (1968) report $10 + 7$ and 20 single microtubules in *Trichodorus christiei*, depending on whether a section of the bottom or the top of the cilia is examined. A large number of single microtubules are also found in the modified amphidial cilia of *Meloidogyne javanica* (Figs. 30 and 32A) at its distal end. An amphid consists (Fig. 31) of a cuticular pit which ends in a pouch. The nerve endings of the amphidial nerve extend upward as dendritic processes which are more clearly defined as cilia at the bottom of the pit as they are more spread apart. As they approach the surface they become packed together and lose the characteristic cilialike configuration of microtubules. They end just below the aperture of the amphids and have slightly swollen tips (Figs. 30 and 31).

The appearance of receptors ending in modified cilia with supernumerary

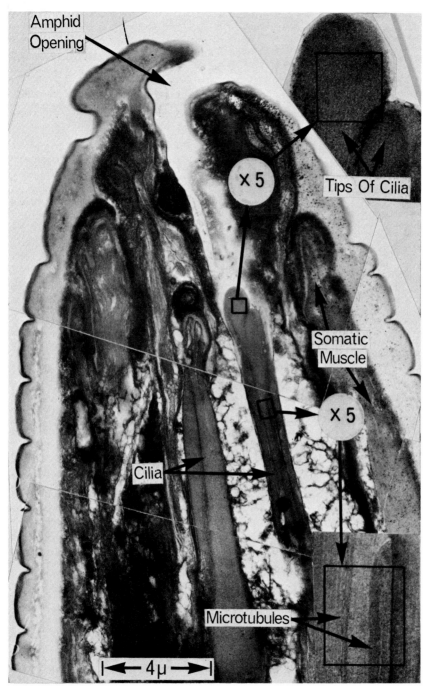

Amphid Opening

× 5

Tips Of Cilia

Somatic Muscle

× 5

Cilia

Microtubules

|◄— 4µ —►|

FIG. 30. Electron micrograph montage of a longitudinal section cur through the head of a male specimen of *Meloidogyne javanica*, showing cilia in the sensory structures. × 7500.

141

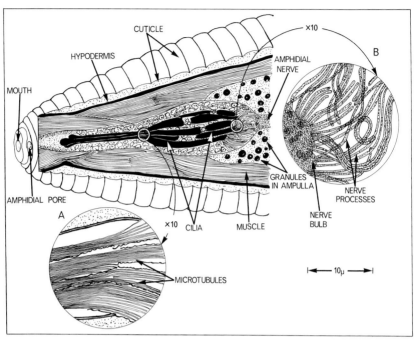

FIG. 31.   Scale diagram of part of the tip of the head of *Meloidogyne* cut open to reveal one of the two amphids.

microtubules is not rare and their occurence in a number of invertebrates has been reviewed by Lyons (1969a,b). As Lyons (1969b) points out, "many sensory cilia have a distal 9 + 0 or 9 + 2 'ciliary segment'" which is lost further up the cilium as it becomes filled with many microtubules.

In view of the reported variability in structure of cilia in nematodes, it is perhaps unwise to speculate on any specific function for receptor organs but preferable to consider that they may respond to a variety of environmental stimuli.

Information on the physiology of these receptors in the lower invertebrates will probably be obtained more readily from organisms such as turbellarians which take much more kindly to surgery than do nematodes.

B. CUTICULAR SENSE ORGANS

By cuticular sense organs is meant those sense organs found between the head and the tail whose structures are not so pronounced and whose functions are not so obvious.

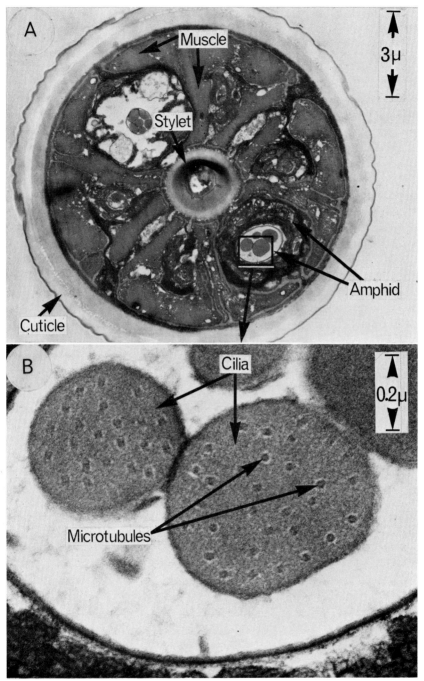

FIG. 32. Electron micrographs of a cross section through the tip of the head of a male specimen of *Meloidogyne javanica*. (A) Whole cross section showing the position of the two amphids. × 7500. (B) Cross sections through cilia showing the microtubules. × 100,000.

Hyman (1951) mentions that nematodes are abundantly supplied with free nerve endings. Lee (1962) has reported the presence of esterase in *Ascaris lumbricoides* cuticle, particularly in the head and tail regions. We now have evidence of a dermal light sense in the larvae of *Trichonema* sp. (Croll, 1965, 1966b) and in the infective larvae of *Haemonchus contortus* and *Nippostrongylus brasiliensis* (Wilson, 1966) and Croll and Maggenti (1968) have demonstrated a peripheral nervous system in *Deontostoma californicum*. Thus, it is not surprising to find in electron micrographs of longitudinal sections of the anterior region of a female *Meloidogyne javanica* and infective larvae of *Haemonchus contortus* (Rogers, 1968) that nerve endings are shown within the cuticle, having passed through both the muscle and hypodermis. (Fig. 33A and B). In *M. javanica* this particular structure is quite large and it probably represents a cephalid (Hirschmann, 1959). Cephalids are structures which Hirschmann (1959) has described in the plant parasitic nematodes *Hoplolaimus tylenchiformis* and *Heterodera glycines*. They are highly refractive and are bi-convex in longitudinal section, occurring in the cephalic region and extending around the nematode's body either in the same annule or running slightly obliquely.

It is possible that areas of the cuticle containing nerve endings may be found in various parasitic species, scattered throughout their body walls and corresponding to the somatic setae which have been described, under the light microscope, in free-living marine forms (Maggenti, 1964).

The observation that, in parasitic forms, sensory structures such as papillae may be reduced so that they do not rise above the level of the cuticle and their nerves do not pierce the cuticle was made many years ago in *Ancylostoma duodenale* (Looss, 1905), but so far as I know, sections have never been cut through these areas to ascertain the extent of nerve penetration into the body wall.

Nerve fibers have been detected (Goodey, 1959) in *Dolichodorus heterocephalus* running from the circumesophageal nerve ring into a structure known as the hemizonid (Goodey, 1951). This structure, which has been shown to be of widespread occurrence in nematodes (Timm, 1960), is a ventrolateral commissure of the nervous system. It is situated on the ventral surface of the body, usually just anterior to the excretory pore, although it may be posterior (Caveness, 1961), and lies between the cuticle and the hypodermis. It has been suggested, as mentioned in Chapter 4 on molting, that the hemizonid may be a receptor organ (Bird, 1968) and that, in infective larvae parasitic in mammals, it may be associated with neurosecretion. This is purely speculative as we have no information at present on the function of the hemizonid. However, it is interesting to note (Fig. 33C) that neurosecretory granules have been found (Rogers, 1968) associated with a structure which is not unlike the cuticle receptor shown in Fig. 33A and B, in that the axons tend to merge into the cuticle without limiting membranes. As mentioned in Chapter 4, I think that this may be the hemi-

above (Schulz, 1931b) in that they too consist of two anterior dorsolaterally placed structures, each consisting of a lens resting on chromatic material in a spindle-shaped pit. There appears also to be a pigment cell located posteriorly to the chromatic unit. Recent studies on the ultrastructure of the photoreceptors of *Deontostoma californicum* (Siddiqui and Viglierchio, 1970) and the eye spots of *Oncholaimium vesicarium* (Burr, 1970) show that the pigmented areas are made up of numerous electron-dense granules located in the esophageal cells.

It is clear that further research into the fine structure of ocelli in nematodes is needed together with physiological work on the function of these receptor organs.

D. CAUDAL SENSE ORGANS

The tail region of nematodes contains both papillae and, in many cases, a pair of postanal lateral sensory organs similar to the amphids, which are known as the phasmids (Cobb, 1923). Their principle claim to fame has been their role in taxonomy. Nematodes have been divided into two major groups depending on whether they have phasmids or not, namely, the Phasmidia and the Aphasmidia (Chitwood and Chitwood, 1950) or whether they have lateral canals opening into the excretory system or not, namely, the Secernentea and the Adenophorea (von Linstow, 1909); generally, the Phasmidia are Secernentea and the Aphasmidia are Adenophorea. Goodey (1963) has pointed out that there are nematodes belonging to the Aphasmidia which have phasmids; as our knowledge of the excretory system is limited, this basic primary division of the Nematoda is unsatisfactory. Despite superficial observations of phasmids in a large number of nematodes, there is at the moment, as far as I know, only one paper which deals with the fine structure of sensory organs in the tail region of nematodes. Kozek (1968) describes the ultrastructure of paired cuticular channels, each containing a single cilium, in the postanal region of the microfilaria of *Dirofilaria immitis*. Kozek considers that these structures, which are clearly shown in an electron micrograph of an oblique section through the tail region, may be the precursors of the phasmids. It has been shown by means of histochemical techniques that the phasmids contain esterases; Ramisz (1966) has demonstrated this quite clearly in a photomicrograph of the tail region of a female *Oesophagostomum dentatum*. These structures have also been clearly shown by Sanwal (1957) in the tail region of female *Radopholus gracilis* by a silver impregnation technique.

The superficial structure of various papillae occurring in the caudal region of both male and female nematodes has been described in a number of texts (Chitwood and Chitwood, 1950; Hyman, 1951; de Coninck, 1965) and structures such as the bursal papillae in some males are obviously associated with the process of copulation (Jones, 1966). Unfortunately, as is often the case in new areas of research, new structures are observed and named without their relationship with other structures being realized and they are frequently given different names which often leads to some confusion. Thus, structures such as cephalids, hemizonids, and hemizonions may, perhaps, be better considered as cuticular sense organs, the amphids and phasmids as lateral sense organs, and the deirids and postdeirids, together with the various other types of papillae, as papillary sense organs. In fact, all these organs contain dendritic structures, part of which often resembles a cilium so that they all appear to be modifications of a basic pattern.

III. The Nervous System

I shall consider the nervous system in three parts. First of all the peripheral nervous system, second the central nervous system, and third the enteric or sympathetic nervous system:

A. The Peripheral Nervous System

It is not surprising that a peripheral nervous system has now been shown to exist in the Nematoda (Croll and Maggenti, 1968) because of the demonstration, by the various techniques mentioned above, that nerve endings penetrate at least some parts of the cuticle.

Gustaf Retzius (1906) was the first person to notice that a "fine, characteristic, remarkably regular mosaic pattern" could be observed under the cuticles of several free-living nematodes after silver staining. He came to the conclusion that the stained pattern represented the cell walls of the hypodermis and his illustrations of these structures have appeared in many texts under this designation. Retzius did not completely misinterpret the nature of the structures stained by his silver technique. He noticed that scattered sporadically in the mosaic were heavily stained round knobs which he concluded were the peripheral ends of sensory nerve cells. These neurons appear in the camera lucida illustrations and the diagrams of Maggenti (1964) and Croll and Maggenti (1968).

The general pattern of the peripheral nervous system in *Deontostoma californicum* (Fig. 34) has been worked out by Croll and Maggenti (1968) using a novel technique which can only be applied to the living nematode because it relies on the nematode's response to changes in osmotic pressure by flushing dilute silver nitrate through its cuticle. Briefly, the method consists of transferring living *Deontostoma californicum* from seawater into 10% sodium nitrate for 5 min, which causes the nematode to shrink, placing it in 0.5% silver nitrate for 15 sec, and finally transferring it to distilled water.

The peripheral nervous system of this nematode, which becomes apparent through the deposition of colloidal silver, consists of a latticework of nerves which is more elaborate in some areas because of the formation of plexuses. The papillae and setae are all connected to this peripheral mesh-

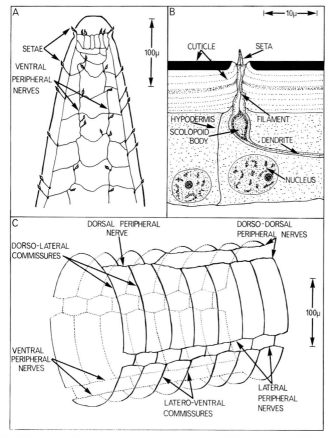

Fig. 34.   Diagrams of the peripheral nervous system of *Deontostoma californicum*. (A) A ventral view of the anterior region. (After Croll and Maggenti, 1968.) (B) Longitudinal section through the body wall, showing a seta. (After Maggenti, 1964.) (C) Arrangement of peripheral nerves throughout the body. (After Croll and Maggenti, 1968.)

work (Fig. 34A) and there is also connection with the underlying central nervous system through structures known as scolopoid bodies (Fig. 34B) which are associated with sensory neurons. This system (Fig. 34C) consists of a single dorsal peripheral nerve which divides into two peripheral dorso-dorsal nerves about 1 mm from the anterior end of the nematode. These are connected to each other by dorsodorsal commissures. There are two lateral peripheral nerves, the dorsolateral and the ventrolateral, and they are connected by laterolateral commissures. These two lateral nerves may unite anteriorly to form a single nerve. There are two longitudinal ventroventral peripheral nerves (Fig. 34C) which are joined by transverse ventroventral commissures.

The frequency of occurrence of the various intraneural commissures, other than that of the laterolateral commissures, is not constant, but inter-neural commissures consisting of single nerves linking two different longitudinal peripheral nerves occur at relatively constant intervals of 25–35 μ.

It is thought (Croll and Maggenti, 1968) that the peripheral nerve network acts to coordinate impulses from sensory organs, such as setae or papillae, with each other and with the central nervous system.

B. The Central Nervous System

In microscopic nematodes, the most obvious part of the central nervous system is the circumesophageal commissure or nerve ring and this itself is often hard to see, especially in living specimens.

The nerve ring in these small nematodes is not easy to stain and is best seen when the nuclei on either side of it are stained with a nuclear stain such as gallocyanin or, better still, these areas may be thrown into greater contrast by observing living specimens under UV light. Under these conditions (Fig. 35 A), the nuclei absorb the ultraviolet and so appear dark on the photo-graphic print and the nerve ring appears as a relatively clear space between them (Bird and Saurer, 1967). The photograph in Fig. 35A was taken with a low-pressure mercury arc lamp at 254 mμ. The specimen, which was an infective larva of *Meloidogyne javanica*, was immobilized by means of an anesthetic.

Detailed information on the structure of the nerve ring in these micro-scopic larvae can only be obtained with the aid of the electron microscope. A longitudinal section cut through the nerve ring of an infective larva of *Meloidogyne javanica* is shown in Fig. 35B. Several nuclei are shown on either side of the nerve ring which consists, in section, of two lobes on either side of the esophagus and the two ducts of the subventral esophageal glands. At still higher magnification (Fig. 35C), the close packing of the nerve cell

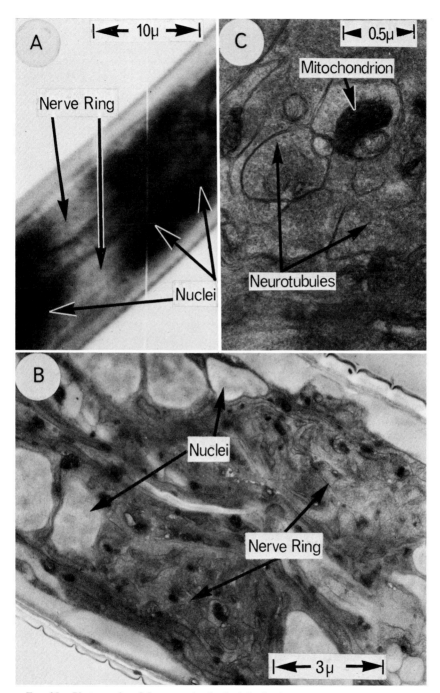

FIG. 35.   Photographs of the nerve ring in the infective larva of *Meloidogyne javanica*. (A) Photomicrograph of a living larva taken under UV light and showing the nerve ring in contrast to the nuclei on each side of it. × 3000. (B) Electron micrograph of a longitudinal section showing nerve ring and nuclei. × 10,000. (C) Electron micrograph of part of the nerve ring. × 40,000.

processes, together with their internal neurotubular structure, becomes apparent.

In some genera, as in *Xiphinema* and *Longidorus*, there are two nerve rings (Goodey and Hooper, 1963) and "a second large aggregation of the nervous tissue" has been found behind the nerve ring in *Trichinella spiralis* and *Syphacia obvelata* (Ramisz, 1965) which may have similar functions.

Ramisz (1965, 1966, 1967) has, in addition to the two species mentioned above, examined the nervous system of the following genera: *Oesophagostomum*, *Metastrongylus*, *Protostrongylus*, and *Capillaria*. She used a histochemical technique for the detection of acetylcholinesterase which has subsequently been described (Bueding *et al.*, 1967). I have used this method on various plant parasitic nematodes without achieving the degree of success obtained by Bueding and his co-workers on the trematode *Schistosoma mansoni*. Ramisz (1966) has, however, obtained some quite good results with strongyloid nematodes, as can be seen in her photomicrographs of nerve rings and the bursal region of males.

Most nematologists have favored drawings of their stained preparations of the nervous system rather than photographing them. Based on my own efforts, my conclusion is that normally these preparations are not very clear and, at best, only show a small portion of the nervous system. An exception to this and, so far as I know, one of the best set of photomicrographs of the nematode nervous system, is that of R. V. Anderson (1966) shown in Fig. 36. These photomicrographs help to show that, generally speaking, there are two main areas in which the nervous system is concentrated. First in the esophageal region (Fig. 36A) and second in the anal region (Fig. 36B and C). Both of these two major centers of nervous coordination are, of course, connected by longitudinal nerves (Fig. 36D).

As mentioned at the start of this chapter, information on the nervous system of nematodes has been reviewed by various authors, some very recently. The Chitwoods (1950) have compiled the most comprehensive review and I refer the reader to the relevant chapter in their book for background reading on much of the early work done in this field.

1. The Anterior Region

I propose to consider this region in some detail and will refer to diagrams of four species from widely divergent environments. These are *Ascaris* (Goldschmidt, 1903, 1908, 1909, 1910; Davey, 1964, 1966) representing the large parasitic forms found in warm-blooded animals (Fig. 37A), *Rhabditis* (Chitwood and Wehr, 1934) (Fig. 37B) representing the soil-inhabiting types, and *Thelastoma* (Lee, 1959) and *Cephalobellus* (Chitwood and Chitwood, 1933) (Fig. 37C and D) representing forms parasitic in insects.

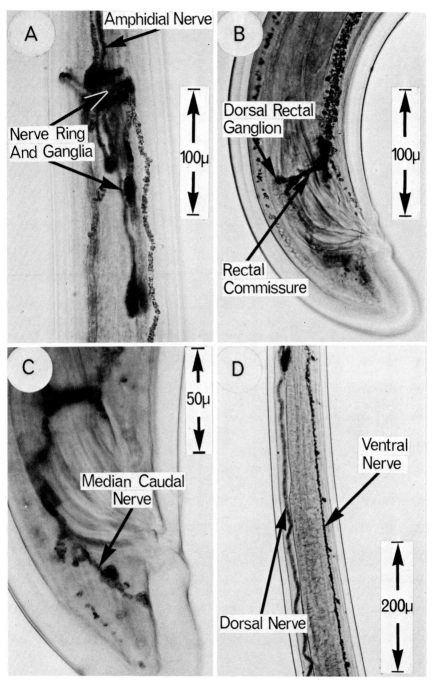

FIG. 36. Photomicrographs of the nervous system of *Aporcelaimus amphidysis*. (Courtesy of Dr. R. V. Anderson; R. V. Anderson, 1966.) (A) Laterodorsal view of the central nervous system. × 336. (B) Posterior view showing rectosympathetic nervous system. × 336. (C) As for B. × 560. (D) Low power shot of the nervous system in the middle region. × 168.

153

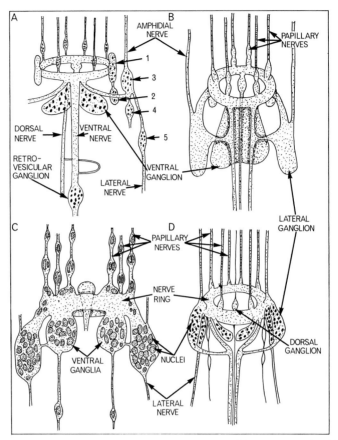

FIG. 37.   Diagrams of the anterior nervous systems in different nematodes. (A) *Ascaris*. (After Goldschmidt, 1908.) (B) *Rhabditis*. (After Chitwood and Wehr, 1934.) (C) *Thelastoma*. (After Lee, 1959.) (D) *Cephalobellus*. (After Chitwood and Chitwood, 1933.)

Because of their size, the ascarids are readily sectioned serially using wax embedding techniques, which are still the most satisfactory for this type of work, and they may also be dissected and the nervous system exposed in this way, thus removing the barrier imposed by the cuticle to fixatives and, in particular, to stains, which makes a thorough study of the nervous system of microscopic nematodes so difficult.

The method used by Goldschmidt (1908) to study the anterior part of the nervous system *in toto* is briefly as follows. A lateral or dorsal incision is made 1 cm from the anterior end and continued to the lips. The esophagus is gently pulled forward with fine forceps so that the nerve ring is exposed.

The preparation is then stained in methylene blue (concentration not given) at 60° C for 6–8 hr, rinsed (presumably in water) and then dehydrated in a series of alcohols and cleared for 2–3 days in clove oil. This method results in the nerve cells being colored blue in contrast to the yellow-colored muscles. The nerve ring or *commissura cephalica* (Looss, 1905) surrounds the esophagus and lies close to it. Associated with the nerve ring are a number of ganglionic masses, notably the ventral ganglion which, in *Ascaris* and *Rhabditis* (Fig. 37A and B), is a symmetrically bilobed structure lying ventrally on the esophagus, whereas in *Thelastoma* and *Cephalobellus* (Fig. 37C and D) it is definitely a paired structure. In all cases the ventral nerve(s) arise from these ganglia and run posteriorly.

The ventral ganglion (ganglia) contain(s) 33 cells in *Ascaris* (Goldschmidt, 1908), 26 (13 in each) in *Thelastoma* (Lee, 1959), 16 (8 in each) in *Cephalobellus* (Chitwood and Chitwood, 1933) and *Oxyuris* (Martini, 1916), and 25 in *Ancylostoma* (Looss, 1905).

Two important ganglionic masses associated with the nerve ring are the lateral ganglia (Figs. 37 and 38) whose cell content varies a little in different genera. Thus, each ganglion contains 19 cells in *Thelastoma*, 21 in *Oxyuris*, 26 in *Cephalobellus*, 42 in *Spironoura* and *Rhabditis*, 41 in *Oesophagostomum*, and 35 in *Ascaris*.

The lateral ganglia occur in the lateral line adjacent to the nerve ring (Fig. 38A) and have been further divided by Goldschmidt (1908) in *Ascaris* into six groups of ganglia. I do not propose to name these groups because they are not easy to locate even in an ascarid and I feel that the inclusion of a large number of Latin names is confusing. I have listed the five largest of these as Nos. 1–5 in Fig. 37A. The reason for this is to draw attention to group No. 3, which constitutes the *ganglia nervi papillaris lateralis majoris* (Goldschmidt, 1908) in which Gersch and Scheffel (1958) have discovered neurosecretory substances by means of the paraldehyde—fuchsin technique in a bipolar cell; it is one of eleven cells in this ganglion described by Goldschmidt (1908, 1910) which contained small, grainlike cytoplasmic inclusions in the neighborhood of the nucleus. I shall deal collectively with neurosecretion in a later part of this chapter. Commissures connect the ventral and lateral ganglia (Fig. 37C) and are known as the *commissura cephalica ventrolateralis*. In *Ascaris*, these have also been shown to contain neurosecretory substances (Gersch and Scheffel, 1958).

The dorsal ganglion, in contrast to the ventral ganglion, is small and contains few cells (Figs. 37 and 38A). In *Ascaris*, it is made up of two cells and in *Thelastoma* and *Cephalobellus*, there is only one cell. In *Ascaris* there is also a pair of subdorsal ganglia which each contain two cells.

In addition to the four major ganglionic masses associated with the

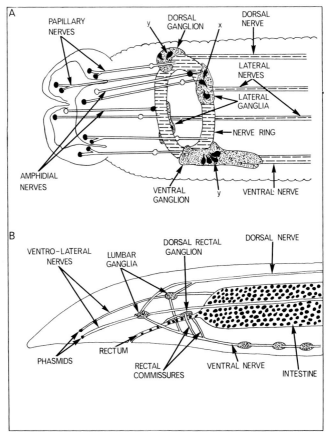

FIG. 38.   Diagrams of a generalized nervous system in the head and tail regions. (A) Head region of *Ascaris*. (After Davey, 1966.) (B) Tail region of a typical nematode. (After Crofton, 1966.)

nerve ring that are mentioned above, there are the ganglia of the papillary nerves which lie just in front of the nerve ring in the tissue surrounding the esophagus. These are the paired subdorsal, subventral, and lateral papillary ganglia (Figs. 37 and 38A). In *Ascaris* the subdorsal and subventral papillary ganglia each contain seven cells and the lateral four cells, whereas each ganglion appears to contain five cells in *Thelastoma*.

Running forward from the papillary ganglia are the six papillary nerves (Figs. 37 and 38A) which proceed directly forward to the head papillae. Sixteen of the thirty-six nerve cells of the papillary ganglia send their processes to the head papillae; the others have not been traced to special sense organs and may end freely in the lips (Bullock and Horridge, 1965).

It is highly likely that they are associated with cuticular sensory structures such as the cephalids which have been described above (Fig. 33A and B).

Also running anteriorly is a pair of amphidial nerves (Figs. 37 and 38A) which, although closely associated with the lateral papillary nerves, nevertheless have very different origins, as mentioned earlier in this chapter. The neuron bodies of the papillary nerves are situated in the papillary ganglia and their axons enter the nerve ring directly, whereas the eleven neuron bodies of each of the amphidial nerves occur in the lateral ganglia and their axons reach the nerve ring via the lateroventral commissure, ventral ganglion, and subventral nerve trunks.

A series of longitudinal nerves runs posteriorly from the nerve ring and these vary in number from four to twelve. The four most obvious (Fig. 37) are a ventral, a dorsal, and a pair of laterals. Most species also have a pair of subventrals and a pair of subdorsals. These nerves are all connected at irregular intervals by commissures.

The ventral nerve is the largest of these nerves. It runs obliquely outward from the esophagus and becomes embedded in the ventral hypodermal cord. It is composed of a large number of nerve fibers, the actual number depending on the region through which the section is cut. In *Ascaris*, just behind the nerve ring, there are fifty-five fibers but, further back, this number is considerably reduced. Thus, sixteen fibers are visible in the low-power electronmicrograph of a transverse section through the ventral nerve cord shown in Fig. 39. The ventral nerve is a paired structure in forms such as *Ascaris, Oxyuris*, and *Cephalobellus*. On the posterior side of the excretory pore in these genera, the nerves fuse in the retrovesicular ganglion which is composed of thirteen cells and is the first of the chain of ganglia of which the ventral nerve is made up. The posterior ramifications of the ventral nerve will be discussed below in the section on the posterior region.

The dorsal nerve is much smaller than the ventral and, in *Ascaris*, at its source at the dorsal ganglion on the posterior margin of the nerve ring, it consists of only three fibers. Further back there are four fibers; after the first dorsolateral commissure there are seven, between the first and second dorsolateral commissures there are nine, and behind this there are thirteen (Goldschmidt, 1908). The dorsal nerve runs obliquely out from the esophagus, becomes embedded in the dorsal hypodermal cord and runs posteriorly.

The lateral nerves contain four fibers in *Ascaris*, two coming from the nerve ring and two from the lateral ganglion of that side. The subventral and the subdorsal nerves also each contain four fibers in this genus.

All these nerves running posteriorly are connected to each other by means of commissures. When viewed under the electron microscope, the nerve fibers of these longitudinal nerves are clearly distinguishable from the surrounding tissue by their low uptake of electron dense stains (Figs. 35 and 39). These fibers (Hinz, 1963; Rosenbluth, 1965; Debell, 1965) usually measure approximately 5–15 μ in diameter, although their diameter may vary from 2.5 to 40 μ in *Parascaris equorum* (Hinz, 1963).

The nerve fibers contain mitochondria which are scattered irregularly throughout their length and so may or may not appear in cross sections. At high resolution (Fig. 35C), their internal neurotubular structure becomes visible. Thus, the ultrastructure of the nerve cell processes of nematodes appears to be similar to that of the axons of other animals that have been described.

It has been shown by means of the electron microscope that nerve cords in *Trichuris myocastoris* are composed of several groups of neurons separated by processes from hypodermal cells (Wright, 1970). Nerve cell bodies were found within the ventral nerve cord in this nematode. It was observed that neurons emerging from the cords entered the intercordal region where they became invaginated in hypodermal tissue and could be seen deeply in the hypodermis ensheathed by the membrane of the hypodermal cell.

2. *The Posterior Region*

The ventral nerve consists posteriorly of a chain of ganglia of which the last one is known as the preanal ganglion (Fig. 38B). Posterior to this ganglion, two branches are given off from the ventral nerve to form the rectal commissures, a structure which is sometimes referred to as the posterior nerve ring. These commissures enter the pseudocoelom and fuse with the dorsorectal ganglion on the dorsal surface of the rectum which is part of the enteric nervous system considered later in this chapter.

Prominent paired lumbar ganglia are located at the posterior end of nematodes. These structures (Fig. 38B) lie in the path of the lateral nerves and are connected to the ventral nerve by the ventrolateral connectives or anolumbar commissures which arise from behind the preanal ganglion and run through the hypodermis to the lumbar ganglia. Similarly, the dorsal nerve branches in the anal region to give rise to two dorsolateral commissures which connect it to the lumbar ganglia (Fig. 38B). Running posteriorly from the lumbar ganglia into the tail are the paired ventrolateral nerves which link the phasmids (if present) to these ganglia.

The posterior nervous system in bursate males of nematodes such as *Ancylostoma* (Looss, 1905), *Haemonchus* (Veglia, 1915), *Oesophagostomum, Metastrongylus,* and *Protostrongylus* (Ramisz, 1966) is more innervated than in females. In additon to the general description given above for the nerves and ganglia of the posterior region, there are collections of fibers known

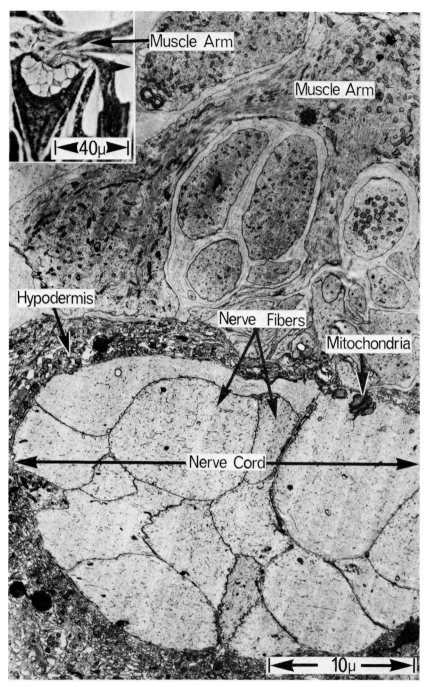

FIG. 39. Electronicrograph of neuromuscular connections in *Ascaris*. × 4000. (Courtesy of Dr. J. Rosenbluth; Debell, 1965.)

as bursal nerves. These are paired nerves which arise from the lateral nerves and also connect to the ventral nerves by means of the ventrolateral commissures. The increase in both size and complexity of the ganglia and nerves of the male tail when compared with that of the female has been clearly illustrated by Looss (1905) in *Ancylostoma duodenale*. In this species, the ganglia in males and females are similar except that, in males, the preanal ganglia are each subdivided into two parts, the antero- and posteroanal ganglia and the lumbar ganglia are each subdivided into three parts, the lumbar, postlumbar and, last of all, the costal ganglia. These various ganglia are interconnected by commissures which increase the complexity of the nervous system in this region. Despite the morphological differences, the only difference in numbers of nerve cells in the sexes in *Ascaris* (Goldschmidt, 1910) is that the males possess an extra cell in each lateral ganglion.

There are ten pairs of sensory papillae in male strongyloids and, apart from the prebursal papillae, all of these are situated in the bursa and terminate its rays. The reader is referred to Chitwood and Chitwood (1950) for a more detailed account of this rather specialized structure which, so far as I am aware, has yet to be carefully examined with the aid of the electron microscope.

The extent of the posterior nervous system in relation to that of the anterior nervous system is shown in the photomicrograph of these structures (Fig. 36).

3. *Nerve Cells*

The nerve cells vary in shape and size. In *Ascaris* they range from about 15 to 70 μ in diameter and appear to be similar in their cytology throughout the group, although practically all the information available has been obtained from the large ascarids. In the specimens that have been studied, cell constancy has been observed, at least for various parts of the nervous system, in *Anguilla, Ascaridia, Cephalobellus, Haemonchus, Oesophagostomum, Oxyuris, Rhabditis*, and *Thelastoma*. Generally speaking, there appear to be about 250 nerve cells, although, judging from the number of nuclei associated with the nerve ring in the infective larvae of forms such as *Meloidogyne javanica*, I suspect that this number could be much lower in some forms. Yuen (1968), working on the ultrastructure of *Panagrellus*, has, for instance, suggested that there is considerable variation in the distribution of the cephalic nerves; she found less than the number found in other nematodes. However, it has also been suggested (Bullock and Horridge, 1965) that the marine free-living species have a much larger number of nerve cells. Thus, at the moment, the position remains rather speculative and a great deal of detailed and painstaking work is needed to clarify the position.

Goldschmidt (1908) has been the only person so far to determine the position of practically every nerve cell in a nematode; his counts of these structures in *Ascaris* are listed in Table VI. It can be seen that there is almost complete bilateral symmetry.

Goldschmidt (1910) has described the cytological features of many of these cells which vary with the method used, so, as Bullock and Horridge (1965) have already suggested, it is perhaps best, at this stage, to refer to these descriptions and await the results of electron microscope work. I feel also that advantage may be taken of the size of some of the nerve cells in *Ascaris* to examine them freshly extirpated under the phase and interference contrast microscopes.

Hinz (1963) points out that only scanty information is available on observations on the nerve sheaths. In his observations on the fine structure of the nerve cell processes in *Parascaris equorum*, he found it impossible to distinguish dendrites and axons clearly and was only able to identify ganglial cells in ultrathin sections a few times. Because of this and because of the different morphological types of nerve cells that have been described by the earlier workers using the light microscope, he has wisely limited himself to describing the structure of nerve cell processes. These, as mentioned above, consist in transverse section (Fig. 39) of irregularly shaped structures of variable diameter surrounded by a single, continuous membrane which, at times, is interrupted by acute-angled indentations. Hinz is uncertain whether these represent synapses or sections through a folded membrane. He has also observed that sheaths, in the form of fine concentric membranes, about 12 mμ in diameter, surround either a single nerve process or several of them. This has also been shown in published electron micrographs (Yuen, 1968) of cross sections through the anterior end of *Panagrellus silusiae* where they surround the nerve processes of the amphid. The structures depicted by Yuen (1968) are much farther apart than the lamellated sheaths of typical mammalian myelinated axons. These concentric membranes surrounding nerve processes in nematodes are much less regular than the lamellae of the myelinated nerve and Hinz (1963) concludes that it is not feasible to homologize these structures with the medullary sheath structure of the vertebrate axon.

4. *The Nerve Ring*

Goldschmidt (1909) points out that it is difficult to observe the contents of the nerve ring in *Ascaris* because the fibers are packed so close to each other into a bundle that individual tracing of these fibers becomes impossible by examination of the whole structure. Accordingly, he laboriously reconstructed this complex part of the nervous system by means of serial sections, a task which, at that time, could only be achieved with a large nematode such as *Ascaris* and which, today, could only be achieved with the microscopic nematodes by means of serial ultramicrotome sections observed under the electronmicroscope, an even more arduous task. Goldschmidt (1909) cut both serial cross sections and serial oblique sections, the latter so that the entry of fibers close together could be studied with less confusion.

The nerve ring lies close to the outer wall of the esophagus and is bounded by a sheath. Swellings occur where nerves enter the ring and, in *Ascaris*, the ventral part of the nerve ring is four times thicker than the dorsal. A cross section of the nerve ring in an area free from nerve entry shows a large number of irregularly shaped fibers between which there is no connective tissue apart from the thin fiber membranes. In small nematodes, such as the soil-inhabiting, free-living forms and the infective larvae of parasitic forms, the number of fibers in the nerve ring appears (Fig. 35B) to be much less than that depicted by Goldschmidt (1909) in his drawings. This observation is in accordance with the lower number of nuclei observed in longitudinal sections of *Meloidogyne javanica* in the region of the nerve ring. However, serial longitudinal and transverse sections have not been cut and, even though this larva is only about 17 μ in diameter, a true assessment of the number of nuclei in this region cannot be made until this has been done.

I have already mentioned the detailed diagrams drawn by Goldschmidt (1909) on the basis of observations of hundreds of serial sections, which illustrate the fiber composition and connections in the dorsal and ventral parts of the nerve ring; the reader is referred to the various texts in which these diagrams have been reproduced. I suspect that, when similar "wiring" diagrams become available for the microscopic nematodes, they will be somewhat simpler, although the investigator will require even more patience and tenacity when mapping these structures using serial ultramicrotome sections.

In *Ascaris* the nerve ring is surrounded by a mass of lamellated connective tissue which is more than twice as wide as the ring itself and which is continuous with the lateral ganglia. Similar tissue encases the main nerves and has been mentioned above. Beneath these lamellae the nerve ring is surrounded by a dense capsule. The degree of thickness of the connective tissue surrounding the nerve ring probably varies considerably in different nematodes. In the 2nd-stage infective larva of *Meloidogyne javanica* it is much less obvious (Fig. 35B).

In *Ascaris* eight cells may be classified as cells of the nerve ring. Four of these are associated with the covering of the nerve ring; they are known as glia cells and are connected to the submedian papillary nerves. The other four consist of a dorsal cell, a ventral cell, and a pair of laterals and these communicate with each other and with various other nerve processes and ganglia. A similar arrangement of cells in the nerve ring has been observed in *Spironoura* and *Oesophagostomum* (Chitwood and Chitwood, 1950), while approximately twice this number has been recorded in *Oxyuris* (Martini, 1916).

Nuclei do not appear to be present in the nerve ring of *Meloidogyne* (Fig. 35A and B) and may also be absent in many other microscopic nematodes.

C. The Enteric Nervous System

This part of the nervous system in nematodes has received very little attention. What little is known has been reviewed by Chitwood and Chitwood (1950) and Bullock and Horridge (1965).

The esophageal enteric or sympathetic system in *Ascaris* (Goldschmidt, 1910) consists of a nerve ring in the posterior third of the esophagus. Adhering to this ring dorsally and subventrally are three large ganglial cells. From the ring, running anteriorly, are three nerves. The dorsal nerve contains about 13 fibers at its origin and the laterals 6 each. These nerves are associated with various nerve cells along their paths. In *Ascaris* there is a total of about 17 (Table VI) altogether, whereas in *Angusticaceum* it is 27, in *Oxyuris* it is 20, and in *Spironoura* it is 29. This system in *Ascaris* is connected to the central nervous system by a nerve fiber from the anterior lateral nerve.

The rectal enteric or sympathetic system consists of a total of eight cells (Table VI) which are associated with the rectal commissures (Fig. 38B) and their associated ganglia and nerves. The dorsal rectal ganglion gives rise to a median caudal nerve which extends posteriorly into the tail. In males a nerve is given off laterally to a ganglion associated with each spicule.

IV. Neurosecretion

Neurosecretory activity has been detected in nearly all groups of animals having a central nervous system.

A true neurosecretory system, such as has been recorded in some arthropod and vertebrate systems, consists of neurosecretory cells which are connected by axons to neurohemal structures which release hormones in response to the neurosecretions.

Nerve cells which, by means of cytological stains, can be shown to secrete granules or globules are possibly neurosecretory; most of the evidence for neurosecretion in nematodes is based on the results of such cytological

TABLE VI

NERVE CELLS OF ASCARIS LUMBRICOIDES

Ganglia or sensory structures	Anterior nervous system	Posterior nervous system	Enteric nervous system	No. of cells in each
1	Ventral ganglion			33
2	Lateral ganglia			$35 \times 2 = 70$
3	Dorsal ganglion			2
4	Subdorsal ganglia			$2 \times 2 = 4$
5	Subdorsal papillary ganglia			$7 \times 2 = 14$
6	Subventral papillary ganglia			$7 \times 2 = 14$
7	Lateral papillary ganglia			$4 \times 2 = 8$
8	Retro-vesicular ganglion			13
9	Nerve ring			4
10		Preanal ganglion		11
11		Preanal sensory cells		$15 \times 2 = 30$
12		Lumbar ganglion		6
13		Postanal sensory cells		$7 \times 2 = 14$
14		Latero-caudal nerves		$3 \times 2 = 6$
15			Esophageal sympathetic	17
16			Rectal sympathetic	$2 \times 2 + 4 = 8$
Total				254

staining tests which are often most unspecific. It is important to realize (Bern, 1966) that these cytochemical reactions must be related to both ultrastructure and physiological function before the presence or absence of neurosecretory activity can be established.

Gersch (1957) and Gersch and Scheffel (1958) were the first workers to draw attention to the possibility of neurosecretion in the nervous system of nematodes. Working with *Ascaris*, they found first that nerve extracts from this nematode influenced the heart beats of a snail in a manner some-what similar to extracts from snails' cerebral ganglia and also that a bipolar cell in each of the *ganglia nervi papillaris lateralis majoris* (Fig. 37A, No. 3) gave a positive reaction with the paraldehyde-fuchsin staining technique, as did axons in the ventrolateral commissures. Following these observa-tions, Ishikawa (1961) found granules which stained with Gomori's chrome–hematoxylin in the dorsal, ventral, and lateral ganglia of *Ascaris* and Messner and Günther (1966), using a paraldehyde–fuchsin staining technique, have reported the presence of a neurosecretory system in *Rhabditis oxycerca*. This system takes the form of two large bipolar cells whose bodies lie close to the median bulb. They each give off, posteriorly, a process which runs ventrally under the bulb and, anteriorly, a larger process which may either be a cell or a secretory reservoir. The processes running anteriorly from these structures run on either side of the excretory pore and disappear. In some cases, these processes run through a small, strongly stained swelling close to the excretory pore.

We must bear in mind the limitations of these techniques on their own but, as work progresses, these areas which stain with the paraldehyde–fuchsin techniques will be examined both under the electron microscope and physiologically. In fact, an area close to the excretory pore, which may be analogous to that described above in *Rhabditis oxycerca* (Messner and Günther, 1966), has been examined in the infective larva of *Haemonchus contortus* under the electron microscope (Rogers, 1968) and found to contain neurosecretory granules, these being electron-dense granules 700–1900 Å in diameter.

The hypothesis of Rogers and Sommerville (1963) mentioned earlier in Chapter 4 on molting, has stimulated research on neurosecretory activity in relation to molting. The group most notably involved in this type of research so far has been Davey and his co-workers (Davey, 1964, 1966; Davey and Kan, 1967, 1968). Davey (1964, 1966) describes twenty structures in *Ascaris* which stain with paraldehyde–fuchsin and are thus thought to have a neurosecretory function. These are the six outer labial papillae, the four cephalic papillae (Figs. 25B and 38A), the two amphidial ganglia, and eight cells associated with the lateral ganglia, four in each. Davey (1964) points out that, although *Ascaris* is large and more is known about its nervous system than any other nematode, these advantages are offset by the difficulties encountered in maintaining this nematode in a physiological state *in vitro*. He noticed that staining was more pronounced in specimens fixed 4 to 6 hr after removal from the host than in material fixed immediately after removal from the host's intestine and that there was practically no staining in material fixed 24 hr after removal from the host. Davey (1964) suggests that stress caused by removing the worm from its natural environment may be the cause of this release of neurosecretory material.

Because of the physiological decline which appears to take place in *Ascaris in vitro*, Davey turned to studying another ascaroid, *Phocanema decipiens*, whose last larval stage appears in the muscles of cod and whose molt into the adult stage in the intestines of seals can be duplicated *in vitro* (Townsley *et al.*, 1963). As a result of their experiments with this nematode, Davey and Kan (1967, 1968) have provided both physiological evidence for neurosecretion in nematodes and support for the hypothesis of Rogers and Sommerville (1963).

It has been found that there are two groups of neurosecretory cells in *Phocanema*, one group of one or two cells in the dorsal ganglion and the other of six cells in the ventral ganglion. These cells undergo a cycle of secretion which is correlated with molting. It can be shown (Davey and Kan, 1967, 1968) that extracts from the areas in the nematode containing these cells stimulate the production of leucine aminopeptidase by the excretory gland of 4th-stage larvae and that the amount of the enzyme produced is greatest when the neurosecretory cells stain most heavily. Thus, evidence is accumulating to support results obtained by staining techniques and goes a long way toward satisfying the criteria mentioned above which were laid down for establishing neurosecretory activity (Bern, 1966).

V. Neuromuscular Connections

Information on the fine structure of neuromuscular connections in the large ascarids has been provided by a number of workers, notably Hinz (1963), Auber-Thomay (1964), and Rosenbluth (1965).

Close to the nerve cord, the muscle arms branch and these branches become entwined and form a cap of interlocking processes over the nerve cord (Figs. 16 and 39). Ultrathin sections have been cut through these neuromuscular junctions in the large ascarids. It has been found (Hinz, 1963) that, contrary to the conclusions of several of the light microscopists, including Goldschmidt, the muscle arm and the nerve cord do not merge but are separated by their cell membranes. The distance between the muscle arm and the nerve cord, in the areas where they appear to touch, has been determined by all three workers mentioned above and has been found to be about 40–50 mμ in *Parascaris* and *Ascaris*.

Both Auber-Thomay (1964) and Rosenbluth (1965) found that the nerve cord is surrounded by hypodermal cytoplasm which comes between the nerve fibers and the tips of the muscle fingers (Fig. 39). However, "bare areas" of variable size occur in which the nerve fibers are covered by the muscle fingers to form the so-called "tight junctions" in which, as mentioned above, the muscle and nerve are only separated by a distance of about 50 mμ. In the region of these myoneural junctions, the nerve fibers have a specialized cytoplasm containing numerous small vesicles and large mitochondria. Since these are restricted to the region of contact of muscle and nerve, it was thought (Hinz, 1963) that they must have a special function in the transfer of the stimulus-generated impulse but it is now known, as a result of research on the electrophysiology of *Ascaris* (Debell, 1965), that the two types of neurohumors mentioned in the previous chapter are released from the nerves into the 50-mμ synaptic space described above. One of these accelerates membrane activity and the other inhibits it.

VI. Function

I do not propose to say much about the function of the nervous system, partly because this book is primarily devoted to a study of structure and partly because little is known about the relation of structure to function in the nervous system of nematodes. In any case, much of what I have to say will be speculative. Furthermore, I shall not concern myself with the results obtained from studies on the physiology and pharmacology of nerve-muscle preparations, which have already been discussed in the preceding chapter and comprehensively reviewed by Del Castillo (1969) and which, of necessity, have been done mostly on the large ascarids.

I propose to discuss the responses of whole, intact nematodes to various stimuli. The sense organs of nematodes, as we have seen, are limited in number and these structures appear to have multiple functions. The problem, of course, has been to relate structure to function. As I have already mentioned in this chapter, this problem will only be overcome when microphysiological techniques that are much more sensitive than those currently employed have been evolved.

Despite these technological shortcomings, the literature on orientation of nematodes to various stimuli continues to grow, together with speculation on the functions of the receptor organs. These behavioral responses, or taxes and kineses, have been reviewed by various authors including Wallace (1961) and Lee (1965). They consist of responses to gravity (geotaxes), responses to an electric field (galvanotaxes), responses to temperature (thermotaxes), responses to touch (thigmokineses), responses to chemicals (chemotaxes) and responses to light (phototaxes).

Taxes differ from kineses (Fraenkel and Gunn, 1940) in that they consist of directed movement toward a source of stimulation, whereas kineses are movements which are not dependent on the direction of the stimulation but depend on its intensity, which changes the rate of locomotion.

Most evidence accumulated so far supports orientation towards an object by chemotaxes and thermotaxes and both have been shown to be involved. Thus, the plant parasitic nematode *Ditylenchus dipsaci* has been shown to be attracted to a carbon dioxide gradient (Klingler, 1965) and to a thermal gradient (El-Sherif and Mai, 1969). In some plant parasitic nematodes, the role of carbon dioxide in orientating the nematode toward the root may be more important than heat, whereas in others, such as *Pratylenchus penetrans* (El-Sherif and Mai, 1969), heat appears to be more important. In any event, it seems that attraction of nematodes to roots probably involves "a combination of factors" (Bird, 1962).

Croll (1967) has demonstrated that *Ditylenchus dipsaci* is capable of acclimatizing itself to temperature over a period of 30 days and that it so adapts itself to the chosen temperature that it will orient itself toward this particular temperature if given the chance. This result suggests, to me, some evidence of a highly integrated nervous system.

Certainly the receptor organs are extremely sensitive. For instance, El-Sherif and Mai (1969) report that the three genera of plant parasitic nematodes that they studied were able to detect, and migrate along, a temperature gradient as small as a $0.033°C$ increase for each 4 cm. Another, and even more dramatic, example of receptor organ sensitivity has been found in the study of nematode sex attractants. These substances have already been found in a number of genera, namely, *Panagrolaimus* (Greet, 1964), *Pelodera* (Jones, 1966), and *Heterodera* (Green, 1966); in *Heterodera* they have recently been extracted and assayed (Greet *et al.*, 1968). It was found that males of *Heterodera* were attracted to a water-soluble sex attractant obtained by washing about 1000 females of this genus for 2 days with a distilled water drip. This substance could not be detected by any physical or chemical methods (Greet *et al.*, 1968). This attractant had volatile components which were able to diffuse through air and accumulate on agar blocks. Thus, it may be classed as a "pheromone," a substance secreted to the outside by an individual and received by a second individual of the same species in which it releases a specific reaction (Karlson and Lüscher, 1959).

This is the first report of such a substance in nematodes and it is a further indication of the sensitivity and versatility of their receptor organs.

VII. Summary

The cephalic sense organs of nematodes consist basically of sixteen papillae arranged in three circles and a pair of laterally placed amphids. This arrangement is modified in many forms. However, electron microscope observations of a number of small nematodes have shown that their fine structure and arrangement is generally similar in all specimens that have been examined.

The amphids, which occur in all nematodes, vary in size and shape. Cross sections cut through the tip of the head in many different species of microscopic nematodes and observed under the electron microscope, reveal that these structures occupy a relatively large area of the head and it is thought that they must have very important sensory functions. It has now been established that nematodes do have cilia, although, in many cases, they are highly modified and show much diversity in the number and arrangement of the microtubules. Cilia are found in the sense organs and the numbers in each organ vary. Thus, only two or three are found in the papillae compared with as many as twenty-three in the amphids. These cilia appear to be derived from the nerve endings of the amphidial nerve. They become packed together and lose their cilialike configuration as they approach the opening of the amphid.

Using a variety of techniques, it has been shown that nematodes are abundantly supplied with free nerve endings, have a peripheral nervous system, and are sensitive to changes in light and heat in parts of their anatomy which are lacking in complicated sensory structures. Variously named structures such as the hemizonids, hemizonions, cephalids, and caudilids are thought to be sensory structures whose cuticular differentiation is visible under the light microscope.

More obvious sensory structures found in some nematodes are paired pigment spots and ocelli. The former have been shown to have a photoreceptor function and the latter, with their lenslike structure and associated pigment material, probably have a similar function.

The caudal sensory organs are similar in structure but not as complex as those found in the head region. They are associated with reproduction and exhibit sexual dimorphism.

7. THE NERVOUS SYSTEM

The peripheral nervous system consists of a latticework of nerves connecting the papillae and setae with each other and with the central nervous
system. There are about 250 nerve cells in *Ascaris* and this number is close
to that found in other species in which counts have been made. The main
nerve centers are around the esophagus and rectum as groups of ganglia.
The esophageal nerve ring itself is composed of packed fibers and contains
few, if any, cells. These two heavily ganglionated areas are connected by
longitudinal nerves, the largest being the ventral which really consists of a
chain of ganglia; the other principal longitudinal nerves, the dorsal and
two laterals, are much smaller.

The nerve cells themselves vary considerably in shape and size, although
cytologically they appear to be very similar. Some of these cells appear to
have a neurosecretory function and physiological, ultrastructural, and
histochemical evidence has now been provided, although not all on the same
nematode, which goes a long way towards establishing neurosecretory
activity in nematodes.

Electron microscope studies of sections through neuromuscular connections show that, in certain areas, the muscle and nerve are separated by
a distance of only about 50 mμ. These areas have a specialized cytoplasm
which is thought to function in impulse transfer.

The responses of nematodes to various stimuli indicate very sensitive
receptor systems which must be coupled with a high degree of nervous coordination.

Anderson R. C. (1968). *Can. J. Zool.* **46**, 181.
Anderson, R. V. (1966). *Can. J. Zool.* **44**, 815.
Anderson, R. V., and Das, V. M. (1967). *Can. J. Zool.* **45**, 243.
Andreassen, J. (1966). *Science* **152**, 231.
Auber-Thomay, M. (1964). *J. Microsc. (Paris)* **3**, 105.
Bastian, H. C. (1865). *Trans. Linn. Soc. London* **25**, 73.
Bastian, H. C. (1866). *Phil. Trans. Roy. Soc. London* **156**, 545.
Beckett, E. B., and Boothroyd, B. (1961). *Proc. Eur. Reg. Conf. Electron Microsc., Delft, 1960* **2**, 938.
Bern, H. A. (1966). *Symp. Soc. Exp. Biol.* **20**, 325.
Bird, A. F. (1962). *Nematologica* **8**, 275.
Bird, A. F. (1966). *Nematologica* **12**, 359.
Bird, A. F. (1968). *J. Parasitol.* **54**, 475.
Bird, A. F., and Saurer, W. (1967). *J. Parasitol.* **53**, 1262.
Browne, H. G., and Chowdhury, A. B. (1959). *J. Parasitol.* **45**, 241.
Browne, H. G., Chowdhury, A. B., and Lipscomb, L. (1965). *J. Parasitol.* **51**, 389.
Bruce, R. G. (1966). *Parasitology* **56**, 359.
Bueding, E., Schiller, E. L., and Bourgeois, J. G. (1967). *Amer. J. Trop. Med. Hyg.* **16**, 500.

Bullock, T. H., and Cowles, R. B. (1952). *Science* **115**, 541.
Bullock, T. H. and Fox, W. (1957). *Quart. J. Microsc. Sci.* **98**, 219.
Bullock, T. H., and Horridge, G. A. (1965). "Structure and Function in the Nervous Systems of Invertebrates," Vols. I and II, 1719 pp. Freeman, San Francisco, California.
Burr, A. (1970). *J. Parasitol. Abst.* **56**, 43.
Caveness, F. E. (1961). *Proc. Helminthol. Soc. Wash.* **28**, 169.
Chabaud, A. G. (1955). *Bull. Soc. Zool. Fr.* **80**, 314.
Chitwood, B. G., and Chitwood, M. B. (1933). *Z. Zellforsch. Mikrosk. Anat.* **19**, 309.
Chitwood, B. G., and Chitwood, M. B., eds. (1950). "An Introduction to Nematology," 213 pp. Monumental Printing Co., Baltimore, Maryland.
Chitwood, B. G., and Wehr, E. E., (1934). *Z. Parasitenk.* **7**, 273.
Cobb, N. A. (1913). *J. Wash. Acad. Sci.* **3**, 145.
Cobb, N. A. (1923). *J. Parasitol.* **9**, 242.
Cobb, N. A. (1929). *J. Wash. Acad. Sci.* **19**, 159.
Crofton, H. D. (1966). "Nematodes," 160 pp. Hutchinson, London.
Croll, N. A. (1965). *Parasitology* **55**, 579.
Croll, N. A. (1966a). *J. Helminthol.* **40**, 33.
Croll, N. A. (1966b). *Parasitology* **56**, 307.
Croll, N. A. (1966c). *Nematologica* **12**, 610.
Croll, N. A. (1967). *Nematologica* **13**, 385.
Croll, N. A., and Maggenti, A. R. (1968). *Proc. Helminthol. Soc. Wash.* **35**, 108.
Davey, K. G. (1964). *Can. J. Zool.* **42**, 731.
Davey, K. G. (1966). *Amer. Zool.* **6**, 243.
Davey, K. G., and Kan, S. P. (1967). *Nature (London)* **214**, 737.
Davey, K. G., and Kan, S. P. (1968). *Can. J. Zool.* **46**, 893.
Debell, J. T. (1965). *Quart. Rev. Biol.* **40**, 233.
de Coninck, L. (1942). *Natuurwetensch. Tijdschr. (Ghent)* **24**, 29.
de Coninck, L. (1965). *In* "Traité de Zoologie. IV (2) Nemathelminthes" (P. P. Grassé, ed.), pp. 1–217 Mason, Paris.
Del Castillo, J. (1969). *In* "Chemical Zoology" (M. Florkin and B. T. Scheer, eds.), Vol. III, pp. 521–554. Academic Press, New York.
Ellenby, C. (1964). *Nature (London)* **202**, 615.
El-Sherif, M., and Mai, W. F. (1969). *J. Nematol.* **1**, 43.
Fraenkel, G. S., and Gunn, D. L. (1940). "The Orientation of Animals," 352 pp. Oxford Univ. Press (Clarendon), London and New York.
Gersch, M. (1957). *Naturwissenschaften* **44**, 525.
Gersch, M., and Scheffel, H. (1958). *Naturwissenschaften* **45**, 345.
Goldschmidt, R. (1903). *Zool. Jahrb. (Anat).* **18**, 1.
Goldschmidt, R. (1908). *Z. Wiss. Zool.* **90**, 73.
Goldschmidt, R. (1909). *Z. Wiss. Zool.* **92**, 306.
Goldschmidt, R. (1910). "Das Nervensystem von *Ascaris lumbricoides* und *Megalocephala*," Festschr Hertwig, Vol. II. Fischer, Jena.
Goodey, J. B. (1951). *J. Helminthol.* **25**, 33.
Goodey, J. B. (1959). *Nematologica* **4**, 157.
Goodey, J. B. (1963). "Soil and Freshwater Nematodes," 544 pp. Methuen, London.
Goodey, J. B., and Hooper, D. J. (1963). *Nematologica* **9**, 303.
Green, C. D. (1966). *Ann. Appl. Biol.* **58**, 327.
Greet, D. N. (1964). *Nature (London)* **204**, 96.
Greet, D. N., Green, C. D., and Poulton, M. E. (1968). *Ann. Appl. Biol.* **61**, 511.
Hinz, E. (1963). *Protoplasma* **56**, 202.

Hirschmann, H. (1959). *Proc. Helminthol. Soc. Wash.* **26**, 73.
Hirumi, H., and Chen. T. A. (1968). *Phytopathology* **58**, 1053.
Hirumi, H., Chen, T. A., Lee, K. J., and Maramorosch, K. (1968). *J. Ultrastruct. Res.* **24**, 434.
Hope, W. D. (1965). *Diss. Abstr.* **26**, 2389.
Hope, W. D., and Murphy, D. G. (1969). *Proc. Biol. Soc. Wash.* **82**, 81.
Hyman, L. H. (1951). "The Invertebrates," 572 pp. McGraw-Hill, New York.
Ishikawa, M. (1961). *Kiseichugaku Zasshi* **10**, 1.
Jamuar, M. P. (1966). *J. Parasitol.* **52**, 1116.
Jenkins, T. (1967). Histochemical and Electron Microscope Studies on Pig Nematodes. Ph.D. Thesis, Univ. of Wales,
Jenkins, T., and Erasmus, D. A. (1969). *Parasitology* **59**, 335.
Jones, T. P. (1966). *Nematologica* **12**, 518.
Joyon, L., and Collin, J. P. (1962). *C. R. Soc. Biol.* **156**, 651.
Karlson, P., and Lüscher, M. (1959). *Nature (London)* **183**, 55.
Kessel, R. G., Prestage, J. J., Sekhon, S. S., Smalley, R. L., and Beams, H. W. (1961). *Trans. Amer. Microsc. Soc.* **80**, 103.
Klingler, J. (1965). *Nematologica* **11**, 4.
Kozek, W. J. (1968). *J. Parasitol.* **54**, 838.
Lee, D. L. (1959). *Parasitology* **49**, 473.
Lee, D. L. (1962). *Parasitology* **52**, 241.
Lee, D. L. (1965). "The Physiology of Nematodes," 154 pp. Oliver & Boyd, Edinburgh and London.
Lee, D. L. (1968). *J. Zool.* **154**, 9.
Lee, D. L., and Anya, A. O. (1968). *J. Zool.* **156**, 9.
Looss, A. (1905). *Rec. Egypt. Govt. Sch. Med.* **3**, 1.
López-Abella, D., Jiménez-Millán, F., and Garcia-Hidalgo, F. (1967). *Nematologica* **13**, 283.
Lyons, K. M. (1969a). *Parasitology* **59**, 611.
Lyons, K. M. (1969b). *Parasitology* **59**, 625.
Madden, P. A., Tromba, F. G., and Vetterling, J. M. (1970). *J. Parasitol.* **56**, 202.
Maggenti, A. R. (1964). *Proc. Helminthol. Soc. Wash.* **31**, 159.
Martini, E. (1916). *Z. Wiss. Zool.* **116**, 137.
Messner, B., and Günther, B. (1966). *Mikroskopie* **21**, 197.
Miller, J. H. (1967). *J. Parasitol.* **53**, 94.
Murphy, D. G. (1963). *Proc. Helminthol. Soc. Wash.* **30**, 25.
Poinar, G. O., and Leutenegger, R. (1968). *J. Parasitol.* **54**, 340.
Ramisz, A. (1965). *Acta Parasitol. Pol.* **13**, 205.
Ramisz, A. (1966). *Acta Parasitol. Pol.* **14**, 91.
Ramisz, A. (1967). *Acta Parasitol. Pol.* **14**, 365.
Raski, D. J., Jones, N. O., and Roggen, D. R. (1969). *Proc. Helminthol. Soc. Wash.* **36**, 106.
Retzius, G. (1906). *Biol. Untersuch.* **13**, 101.
Rogers, W. P. (1968). *Parasitology* **58**, 657.
Rogers, W. P., and Sommerville, R. I. (1963). *Advan. Parasitol.* **1**, 109.
Roggen, D. R., Raski, D. J., and Jones, N. O. (1966). *Science* **152**, 515.
Roggen, D. R., Raski, D. J., and Jones, N. O. (1967). *Nematologica* **13**, 1.
Rosenbluth, J. (1965). *J. Cell Biol.* **26**, 579.
Ross, M. M. R. (1967). *Science* **156**, 1494.
Sanwal, K. C. (1957). *Can. J. Zool.* **35**, 75.
Schulz, E. (1931a). *Zool. Anz.* **95**, 159.

Schulz, E. (1931b). *Zool. Anz.* **95**, 241.

Schuurmans Stekhoven, J. H. (1959). *In* "Bronns Klassen und Ordnungen des Tierreichs: Nematodes," pp. 661–879. Geest & Portig, Leipzig.

Sheffield, H. G. (1964). *J. Parasitol.* **50**, 365.

Siddiqui, I. A., and Viglierchio, D. R. (1970). *J. Nematol.* **2**, 274.

Steiner, G. (1925). *Phytopathology* **25**, 499.

Terashima, S., Goris, R. C., and Katsuki, Y. (1970), *J. Ultrastruct. Res.* **31**, 494.

Timm, R. W. (1960). *Nematologica* **5**, 150.

Townsley, P. M., Wight, H. G., Scott, M. A., and Hughes, M. L. (1963). *J. Fish. Res. Bd. Can.* **20**, 743.

Veglia, F. (1915). *Rep. Vet. Res. S. Afr.* **3/4**, 349.

von Linstow, O. F. B. (1909). *In* "Parasitische Nematoden. Vol. 15: Die Süsswasserfauna Deutschlands," pp. 47–83. Fischer, Jena.

Wallace, H. R. (1961). *Helminthol. Abstr.* **30**, 1.

Wilson, P. A. G. (1966). *Science* **151**, 337.

Wright, K. A. (1963). *J. Ultrastruct. Res.* **9**, 143.

Wright, K. A. (1965). *Can. J. Zool.* **43**, 689.

Wright, K. A. (1970). *J. Nematol.* **2**, 152.

Yuen, P. H. (1967). *Can. J. Zool.* **45**, 1019.

Yuen, P. H. (1968). *Nematologica* **14**, 554.

8
THE PSEUDOCOELOM

The body cavity or pseudocoelom of nematodes differs from that of animals with a true coelomic cavity in that it is not completely lined with tissue of mesodermal origin—it is lined externally by somatic muscle cells, which are mesodermal in origin, and internally by the cells of the alimentary canal, which are ectodermal in origin. The relationship between forms that are either acoelomate, pseudocoelomate, or coelomate is, perhaps, best illustrated diagrammatically (Fig. 40).

The pseudocoelom is filled with fluid which bathes all the internal organs and functions as part of the turgor-pressure system mentioned in Chapter 3 on the exoskeleton.

The hydrostatic pressure in the pseudocoelom has been measured in living specimens of *Ascaris lumbricoides* (Harris and Crofton, 1957; Harpur, 1964). It is high and shows rhythmical fluctuations associated with muscle contraction and expansion which range from 16 to 225 mm Hg, with a mean value of about 70 mm Hg in specimens freshly dissected from the host. Harpur (1964) found that this average pressure dropped during transportation from the abattoirs but was restored *in vitro* after 6 hr. In nematodes obtained within 20 min of the death of the host and maintained in as physiological a state as possible, the mean hydrostatic pressure in the pseudocoelom was as high as 120 mm Hg.

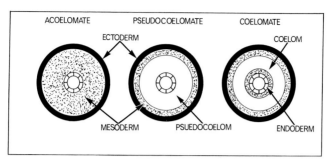

FIG. 40.   Diagrams illustrating the difference between acoelomate, pseudocoelomate, and coelomate body cavities. (After Crofton, 1966.)

The maximum pressure of 225 mm Hg was obtained from a worm in which both the head and tail regions were tightly coiled and contracted (Harris and Crofton, 1957). The internal pressures of nematodes are much higher than those found in the majority of invertebrates that have been measured and it appears that this high pressure system is unique. Because of the limitations that it must impose on variation in structure and function, it is thought by Harris and Crofton (1957) to be largely responsible for the structural uniformity of the Nematoda.

Measurements of internal pressures can, of course, only be done on the large ascarids but it is quite clear to those who handle the microscopic nematodes that they also have a high internal pressure as, when they are cut or pricked, their body contents are forcibly extruded or, in the case of the turgid females of some plant parasitic forms, the nematodes literally burst.

The pseudocoelomic fluid has a complex chemical composition which has been analyzed in some of the larger parasitic nematodes, notably in *Ascaris lumbricoides* by Savel (1955), who also reviewed the earlier work. The first detailed description of the chemical composition of a nematode's pseudocoelomic fluid was that of Flury (1912), who observed that in *Ascaris* it was a clear, slightly pink-colored fluid with a neutral pH and that it contained protein. Rogers (1945) has subsequently shown that it contains glucose, protein, sodium, phosphorus, chloride, potassium, and magnesium as well as small amounts of copper, zinc, iron, hematin, and ascorbic acid. Rogers observed that the constituents of the pseudocoelomic fluid of *Ascaris* differed from those of most tissues which had been examined in that the anion concentration, as chloride, was much lower than the cation concentration and that this was probably partly due to the presence of fatty acids. Fairbairn (1957) also draws attention to this anionic deficit, which he considers is met in part by volatile fermentation acids and by succinate. In fact, about two thirds of the anions present in *Ascaris* pseudocoelomic fluid are highly volatile fatty acids whose ratio varies according to the physiological state of the nematode (Del Castillo and Morales, 1969).

The ionic composition of *Ascaris* pseudocoelomic fluid is similar to that of its host's intestinal fluid (Table VII) although the osmotic pressure of intestinal fluids is greater than that of the pseudocoelomic fluid of *Ascaris* (Hobson *et al.*, 1952). This is true of nematodes freshly dissected from their hosts but it has been shown (Harpur and Popkin, 1965) that the osmotic pressure of the pseudocoelomic fluid of *Ascaris* kept in saline for several hours rises, so that the osmotic gradient across the body wall of the nematode is reversed. This process is assisted by the ejection of feces that are hypotonic to the pseudocoelomic fluid.

Ascaris pseudocoelomic fluid contains approximately 5% proteins of which 2.8% are albumins and the rest α-, β-, and γ- globulins (Savel, 1955). The γ-globulin fraction amounts to about 32% of the total proteins (Fairbairn, 1957).

The pseudocoelom is thought to be lined with a network of fenestrated membranes which help support the visceral organs and yet permit continuity of the pseudocoelomic fluid. The structure of these membranes has been described for the larger nematodes parasitic in animals, in which it has been possible to dissect the nematode but, so far, has not been examined in microscopic forms with the aid of the electron microscope.

Associated with the pseudocoelomic membranes are large, fixed cells known as coelomocytes. These structures are usually two, four, or six in number and are ovoid or many branched. In free-living forms they are smaller and more numerous. In *Ascaris* they are relatively enormous, branched structures 5 mm long, 3 mm wide, and 0.25 mm thick (de Coninck, 1965) whose surface touches the somatic muscles, gut, and the excretory system. Their function is not known; they do not move and are not phagocytic. Although their physiological role remains speculative, there is some

TABLE VII

COMPARISON OF IONIC COMPOSITION OF ASCARIS
PSEUDOCOELOMIC FLUID (APF) AND PIG INTESTINAL FLUID (PIF).[a]

Specimen	Ionic composition (mM)									
	Na	K	Ca	Mg	Cl	P	Zn	Cu	Fe	Dry wt (gm/ml)
APF	129	25	5.9	4.9	53	17	0.14	<0.02	0.13	6.8
PIF	124	27	4.5	5.5	61	24	—	—	—	6.5

[a] After Fairbairn, 1957.

evidence accumulating which suggests that they may have an excretory function. For instance, they can change color from ivory to brown or orange-brown, and they are often close to the excretory system, as has been illustrated in the genus *Plectus* (Maggenti, 1961).

The physiological significance of these interesting structures is as yet unknown. For instance, Weinstein (1961) found that larvae of *Nippostrongylus muris* and *Ancylostoma caninum* accumulated a reddish pigment in the vacuoles of their coelomocytes, the intensity of which was proportional to the concentration of vitamin B_{12} added to the culture media on which they were grown. The nature of this pigment in the coelomocytes was not established; it may have been due to an accumulation of vitamin B_{12} or some other pigment may have been formed. What is clear is that further research into the fine structure and physiology of coelomocytes is required before further speculation should be made.

A number of free-floating bodies have been found in the pseudocoelom of nematodes. In *Hydromermis* sp. (Poinar *et al*, 1970) they are disc-like, have an average diameter of 23.2μ, are proteinaceous and have a distinct crystalline structure. Their function is unknown.

REFERENCES

Crofton, H. D. (1966). "Nematodes," 160 pp. Hutchinson, London.
de Coninck, L. (1965). *In* "Traité de Zoologie" (P. P. Grassé, ed.), Vol. IV, pp. 1–217. Masson, Paris.
Del Castillo, J., and Morales, T. A. (1969). *In* "Experiments in Physiology and Biochemistry" (G. A. Kerkut, ed.), Vol. 2, pp. 209–273. Academic Press, New York.
Fairbairn, D. (1957). *Exp. Parasitol.* 6, 491.
Flury, F. (1912). *Arch. Exp. Pathol. Pharmakol.* 67, 275.
Harpur, R. P. (1964). *Comp. Biochem. Physiol.* 13, 71.
Harpur, R. P., and Popkin, J. S. (1965). *Can. J. Biochem.* 43, 1157.
Harris, J. E., and Crofton H. D. (1957). *J. Exp. Biol.* 34, 116.
Hobson, A. D., Stephenson, W., and Beadle, L. C. (1952). *J. Exp. Biol.* 29, 1.
Maggenti, A. R. (1961). *Proc. Helminthol. Soc. Wash.* 28, 118.
Poinar, G. O., Leutenegger, R., and Thomas, G. M. (1970). *Nematologica* 16, 348.
Rogers, W. P. (1945). *Parasitology* 36, 211.
Savel, J. (1955). *Rev. Pathol. Gen. Comp.* 55, 52.
Weinstein, P. P. (1961). *J. Parasitol.* 47, Abstr. No. 29, 23.

9

THE EXCRETORY SYSTEM

I. Introduction

Various aspects of the so-called excretory system of nematodes have been reviewed in recent years. Among the most comprehensive have been those of Chitwood and Chitwood (1950), Weinstein (1960), de Coninck (1965), Lee (1965), Crofton (1966), and Waddell (1968).

The nematodes excretory system has been assigned an excretory function on morphological grounds. It is unusual in that not only does it appear to be totally absent in a few forms, such as the Trichuroidea and Dioctophymatoidea, and much reduced in forms such as the Dorylaimoidea, Tripylidae, and Mononchidae, but it also appears to lack structures such as flame cells and cilia.

The absence of an excretory system is generally regarded as being a secondary adaptation since an excretory pore has been described in some genera belonging to families in which the excretory system appears to be absent. Most free-living marine and freshwater forms have an excretory system whose structure appears to be the basic type from which the various modifications of the nematode excretory system are thought to have evolved.

An excretory function has not yet been clearly established for these systems. The reasons for this are largely technological, as it is difficult to

178

obtain fluid from the excretory pores of even the large ascarids and, even then, it can only be obtained under unnatural conditions *in vitro*.

It is clear, however, that the so-called excretory system is found in the vast majority of nematodes and exhibits a high degree of structural and functional diversity which I shall now consider in greater detail under the headings of structure and of function.

II. Structure of the Excretory System

The nematode excretory system opens to the exterior through the excretory pore. This is normally situated in the anterior midventral line and is usually found close to the nerve ring. However, its position may vary considerably, even in different stages of the same species. Thus, in *Meloidogyne javanica* (Bird, 1959) the excretory pore is located near the basal region of the median bulb in the infective larva and is found about 25 μ in front of the anterior part of the median bulb in adult females.

In *Tylenchulus semipenetrans*, the excretory pore is located in the posterior region (Maggenti, 1962) but this is atypical and, indeed, its function in this particular instance is unusual, being secretory rather than excretory. I shall discuss the function of this particular excretory system later in this chapter.

There are two types of excretory systems in nematodes, glandular and tubular.

A. GLANDULAR TYPE OF EXCRETORY SYSTEM

A glandular type of excretory system is found in many of the free-living marine and freshwater nematodes and is generally considered to be the primitive, basic type. It usually consists of a single large gland cell situated in the pseudocoelomic cavity, known as the ventral gland or renette, which opens to the exterior by means of a duct which is lined by cuticle at its terminus only and which swells into a small vesicle or ampulla just before the opening (Fig. 41A). The typical glandular type of excretory system shown in this figure in *Chromadora quadrilinea* (Chitwood and Chitwood, 1950) has, in addition to the Chromadoridae, been observed in species belonging to various other families, such as the Cyatholaimidae, Monohysteridae, Enoplidae, Oncholaimidae, Ironidae, and Plectidae.

The genus *Plectus* derives its name from the odd loopings of its excretory duct. Maggenti (1961) has traced this structure in *P. parietinus* (Fig. 41B) and has shown that it loops twice after entering the excretory gland, once on each side of the esophagus. Thus, most of the loops are within the tissues of the

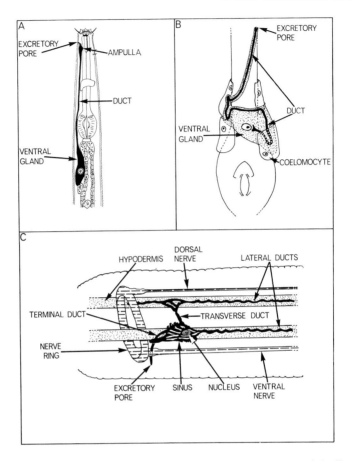

Fig. 41. Diagrams showing different types of excretory systems. (A) *Chromadora quadrilinea* (After Chitwood and Chitwood, 1950). (B) *Plectus parietinus* (After Maggenti, 1961). (C) *Ascaris lumbricoides.*

ventral excretory gland. This gland is dorsoventrally flattened, extends laterally almost to the hypodermal cords, and has a large central nucleus. Unlike the majority of forms which have a glandular excretory system, the terminal duct is cuticularized throughout its length. In this particular respect, it is atypical of the Aphasmidia or Adenophorea described above but resembles those nematodes belonging to the Secernentea or Phasmidia which are partly characterized by having an excretory duct whose lining is similar to that of the cuticle.

The ultrastructure of the excretory system in adult specimens of *Enoplus brevis* has been examined by Narang (H. K. Narang, 1970). This structure consists of a uninucleate gland about 450μ long, whose cytoplasm is full of Golgi bodies, endoplasmic reticulum, and secretory granules. Thus, its fine structure appears to resemble that of the subventral glands in some of the tubular types of excretory systems which I shall now consider.

B. TUBULAR TYPE OF EXCRETORY SYSTEM

The tubular type of excretory system characteristically has long canals which lie in the lateral cords. They are linked to each other by means of a transverse canal which, in turn, is connected to the excretory pore by a median duct. This system, which is described as an H-system, is characteristic of the tubular type of excretory system in many nematodes. It is modified in genera such as *Ascaris* (Fig. 41C), in which it has been described in some detail (Mueller, 1929; Ferguson and Chen, 1951). Mueller's (1929) photomicrographs of the anterior parts of the excretory system of *Ascaris lumbricoides* and *Ascaris megalocephala* (*Parascaris equorum*) are perhaps the clearest low-power photographs available of excretory systems in nematodes and they demonstrate the differences that can occur in these structures in closely related species and the variability that occurs within the same species.

Mueller (1929) obtained his results by injecting a solution of a dye, aniline blue-black in egg albumin, into the excretory canal with the aid of a micromanipulator and then coagulating the dye solution in the excretory system by adding ethanol.

The excretory system in mature, adult *Ascaris lumbricoides* has, perhaps because of its size, been examined more thoroughly than most, and yet, even here, there is disagreement. It is agreed that this system consists of two longitudinal tubes, one in each lateral cord, extending the full length of the body and apparently narrowing and ending blindly at both anterior and posterior extremities. The left tube or lateral excretory canal, is wider than the right one. They are joined to each other by a transverse connecting tube or duct about 2 mm from the anterior end of the nematode. At the junction of the connecting tube and the left lateral tube (Fig. 41C) there is a terminal duct which connects the system to the excretory pore which is located in the midventral position just behind the nerve ring and approximately 1 mm from the tip of the head. The right canal extends forward a little further than the left.

It is when the nuclei of this system are examined that disagreement occurs. There is no doubt that a large structure is found in the left lateral tube in the region of the connecting tube and apparently lying in the outer wall of the excretory tube. This structure, which varies in size but is about 100 μ by 150 μ, is called the excretory nucleus by Mueller (1929) and the sinus nucleus by Chitwood and Chitwood (1950). However, Ferguson and Chen (1951) state: "It is quite possible that this unusually large structure is not a nucleus but a secretory sinus," this statement being based on the response to staining of this structure to Heidenhain's iron hematoxylin. However, giant-sized nuclei often react differently to some histochemical stains than do normal sized nuclei.

Ferguson and Chen (1951) reported an extensive linear series of nuclei lying between the lateral tube and the hypodermis. These nuclei were not part of the structure of the tubes but were closely associated with them.

It is worth noting at this stage that numerous nuclei have been observed within the walls of the posterior lateral canals in the genus *Cucullanus* (Jaegerskioeld, 1894; Toernquist, 1931; Chitwood and Chitwood, 1950). However, although numerous nuclei were observed in the canal region of the 3rd-stage larva of *Stephanurus dentatus*, Waddell (1968) states that "none seemed to be associated with these tubular structures." Furthermore, this worker had no difficulty in identifying and photographing the large excretory nucleus close to the points of entry of the lateral canals (Fig. 43B). Recently, a large structure about 1 cm in length, which was formerly thought to be a sinus in the excretory cell of the fourth stage larva of *Phocanema decipiens*, has been positively identified as a nucleus. (Davey and Sommerville, personal communication). Thus, it seems that the structure called an excretory nucleus in *Ascaris* is more likely to be a large nucleus than a secretory sinus.

In addition to the large excretory nucleus in *Ascaris* and *Stephanurus*, there are several smaller ones associated with the tubular excretory system and lying in the excretory duct (Fig. 43A) or in this and the sinus adjacent to it.

In the forms in which the lateral canals do not extend far beyond the transverse connecting canal the system is known as an inverted U-system. In other forms the system is asymmetric and there is only one lateral canal. This asymmetry is found in some of the ascaridoid parasites of poikilothermic vertebrates including such genera as *Anisakis* and *Contracaecum*, as well as in the plant parasitic tylenchids such as *Radopholus gracilis* (Sanwal, 1957) and *Paraphelenchus myceliophthorus* (Goodey, 1959) and in rhabditids such as *Panagrellus redivivus* (Smith, 1965). In *P. redivivus* a large part of the anterior end of this system has been observed to lie in the pseudocoelom close to the gut wall. In addition, in some nematodes, the H-system is connected to a pair of large subventral glands, a condition known as the rhabditoid system.

These variations in the configuration of the nematode excretory system have been illustrated diagrammatically in various texts. They have, perhaps, best been illustrated by Behrenz (1956), who worked with a wide range of living nematodes using fluorescent dyes and was able to trace their uptake and concentration from the pseudocoelomic cavity into the tubular excretory system and out through the excretory pore in nematodes with both H- and inverted U-systems. Using these techniques he was able to equate structure with function and to show that in those forms in which ventral glands were connected with an H-shaped tubular system, excretion of dye along the lateral line and out through the excretory pore did not occur.

There is considerable speculation on the origin of the excretory system. Cobb (1890, 1925) thought that the H-type system was derived from a single cell from which ultimately the lateral canals arose. He considered that the ventral gland was the original type of nematode excretory system and pointed out that a simple glandular system was found in what are thought to be the most primitive nematodes and that the larval stages of many parasitic nematodes appeared to have a single ventral gland system, whereas the adults had the tubular system. Furthermore, he observed this process of development in *Oxyuris obvelata* and *Rhabditis icosiensis* (Cobb, 1890, 1925) and described its origin as an outgrowth from a single, invaginated hypodermal cell. This gave considerable support to the primary single cell concept. However, as the Chitwoods (1950) have pointed out, "Study of the excretory system in young specimens is technically very difficult and open to considerable error due to the delicacy of the structures." These workers (Chitwood and Chitwood, 1950) were not able to confirm Cobb's observations. They found the H-type system in the youngest stages that they examined and came to the conclusion that Cobb had not seen all of the system in the young larvae that he examined. It may be that the H type of excretory system is the primitive type and that the simple ventral gland of the marine species is a pedomorphic structure, i.e., arrested in its development and remaining in an embryonic state. If this were the case these nematodes would then be regarded as specialized rather than primitive. However, Sprent (1962) considers that the developmental anatomy of the excretory system of ascaridoids indicates that they are derived basically from a single cell, as in the Enoploidea. Along with this view he considers that the marine ascaridoids with a one-sided excretory system, as outlined by Hartwich (1954), are more primitive than the terrestrial forms, which have a two-sided system.

The terminal duct opening through a ventral pore is the one structure common to all nematode excretory systems. It has been suggested (Golovin, 1902) that it arises as an invagination of the hypodermis which meets and fuses with the excretory sinus and lateral canals.

It has been stated (Chitwood and Chitwood, 1950; Waddell, 1968) that the lateral canals arose as extensions or outgrowths of the sinus cell and that the tubular system is developmentally and structurally distinct from the subventral glands. In *Stephanurus dentatus* (Waddell, 1968) the lateral canals and sinus cell were found to be histologically similar and not separated from each other by a membrane. Furthermore, the former do not appear to have any nuclei of their own.

Chitwood and Chitwood (1950) state that *Oesophagostomum* and *Strongylus* appear to be exceptions to this idea, since, in these genera, the canals do not empty into the sinus directly but by way of the subventral glands. However, it now appears (Waddell, 1968) that this is not the case in both *Oesophagostomum dentatum* and *Strongylus edentatus* and that the canals diverging from the sinuses of these two nematodes are not interrupted by the subventral glands, although they are intimately associated with them.

By means of the electron microscope, Waddell (1968) has shown that the fine structure of the subventral glands in *Stephanurus dentatus* bears little resemblance to that of the tubular portion of this nematode's excretory system.

The two subventral glands in *S. dentatus* develop from two large elongate cells which lie in the body cavity of 3rd-stage larvae between the genital primordium and the pharyngointestinal junction. Not only are they not connected to the tubular system at this stage of their development but their nuclear contents appear histochemically different from those of the nuclei adjacent to the tubular portion of the excretory system.

After the third molt, which marks the transition from a free-living habit to a parasitic one, great changes were observed to take place in the excretory system of *S. dentatus*. The fine duct and ampulla of the 3rd-stage larva (Fig. 42A) were replaced by a thick-walled structure which was not clearly divided into two parts in the 4th-stage larva. It had a narrow convoluted lumen and contained two nuclei although it consisted of only one cell. There is little difference between the excretory systems of 4th-stage larvae and adults of *S. dentatus*. This type of excretory system is perhaps best illustrated diagrammatically as a series of cross sections (Fig. 43). The terminal portion of the duct, which passes through the hypodermis, is deeply folded and lined with cuticle.

Light microscope observations on the excretory system of the genus *Ditylenchus* have revealed that the terminal duct consists of an anterior

---

FIG. 42. Photographs showing parts of the excretory system. (A) Photomicrograph of part of the 3rd-stage larva of *Stephanurus dentatus* viewed from the ventral surface and stained with ammoniacal silver nitrate. × 2,000. (Courtesy of Dr. A. H. Waddell; Waddell, 1968.) (B) Electron micrograph of a cross section through the terminal excretory duct of the second stage larva of *Meloidogyne javanica*. × 60,000 (C) Electron micrograph of a cross section through a portion of the terminal excretory duct of an adult female *Meloidogyne javanica*. × 30,000. (D) Electron micrograph of a longitudinal section through a portion of the excretory duct of an adult female *Meloidogyne javanica* showing vesicles surrounding it. × 15,000.

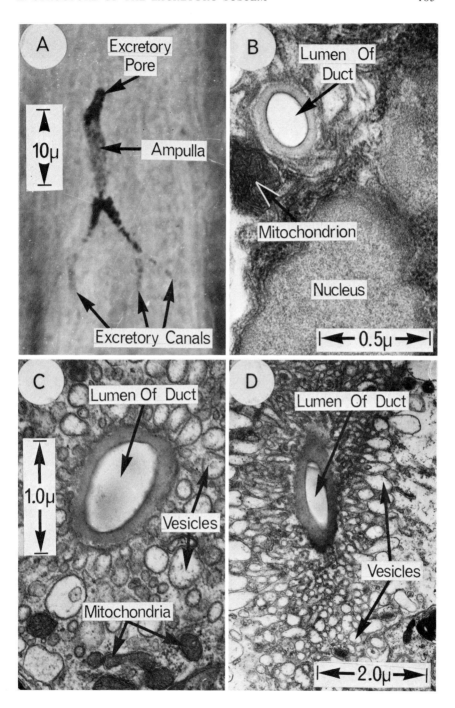

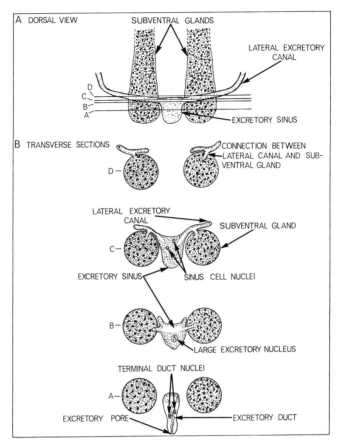

FIG. 43. Diagrams of the excretory system of an adult specimen of *Stephanurus dentatus*. (After Waddell, 1968.) (A) Dorsal view showing areas through which transverse sections depicted in Fig. 43B were cut; (B) transverse sections as cut through lines A, B, C, and D in Fig. 43A.

thin-walled portion separated from a posterior thick-walled portion by a constriction which is thought to be caused by a muscle which operates a valve-like structure, so controlling release of excretory material (Evans and Fisher, 1970).

The terminal portion of the duct of the excretory system of adult female *Meloidogyne javanica* is shown in electron micrographs of transverse (Fig. 42C) and longitudinal (Fig. 44) sections. These electron micrographs show the thickness of the cuticle lining the duct and its relationship to the external cuticle.

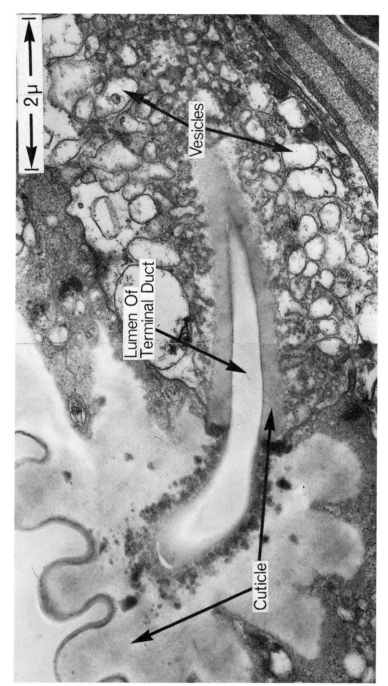

FIG. 44. Electron micrograph of a longitudinal section through the terminal excretory duct of a female specimen of *Meloidogyne javanica*. × 20,000.

In adult *Stephanurus dentatus* (Fig. 43) the excretory duct connects with the subventral glands on either side and the excretory sinus into which it expands, divides, and extends on each side as the lateral canals. Thus, in *S. dentatus* the union of the glandular and tubular portions of the so-called excretory system does not take place until after the third molt and is thus associated with a marked change in the nematode's environment.

Waddell (1968) points out that the ampulla (Fig. 42A) ceases to pulsate prior to the union of the glandular and tubular portions and assumes that this is associated with the change from a variable to a relatively stable osmotic environment.

This idea that structural differences observed in the excretory systems of the same species of nematode at different stages of its life cycle are associated with changes in the nematode's environment, is supported by observations made on other genera at high magnification using the electron microscope. For instance, the 3rd-stage larva of *Neoaplectana carpocapsae* (Poinar and Leutenegger, 1968) may exist either as a normal larva which grows and molts within its host or, if there is a shortage of food, it may develop into an infective 3rd-stage larva which is enclosed within the 2nd-stage cuticle. This stage appears to lack lateral excretory canals whereas the normal larva has an H-type excretory system with lateral canals in the hypodermal cords. In *Meloidogyne javanica* the excretory duct of the preparasitic larva is not only much thinner than that of the adult female (Fig. 42B,C, and D) but the ultrastructure of the tissue surrounding these ducts appears to be completely different. Here again we are considering stages in different environments. The preparasitic infective larva is exposed to the fluctuating environment of the soil whereas the adult female lies in the relatively stable environment of its host's roots.

The diameter of the terminal excretory duct in larval forms of *Meloidogyne javanica* (Fig. 42B) and *Neoaplectana carpocapsae* (Poinar and Leutenegger, 1968) is similar in both genera and is slightly less than 0.3 μ with a lumen whose diameter is slightly less than 0.2 μ. These dimensions may be typical for larvae and free-living forms because, as we have seen in Chapter 3 on the exoskeleton, cuticular structures tend to be of similar dimensions in these forms. However, this is purely speculative, as the appropriate measurements of these structures in marine and freshwater nematodes have yet to be made.

In adult, parasitic nematodes the diameter of the terminal excretory duct is greater and is probably at least partly associated with the increase in thickness of the cuticle. In *Meloidogyne javanica* its diameter in the adult female is about 1 μ with a lumen of about 0.6 μ in diameter.

The dimensions of the lateral excretory canals in some of the adults of nematodes parasitic in animals are relatively enormous. In *Stephanurus dentatus* (Fig. 45) the lumen is approximately 6 μ wide by 32 μ long and in

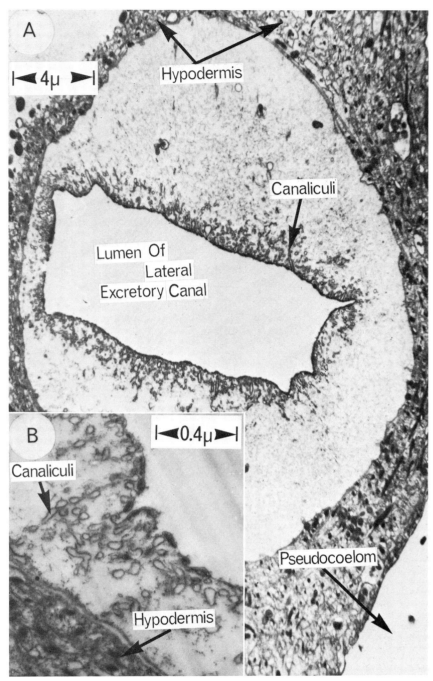

FIG. 45. Electron micrograph of a cross section through one of the lateral excretory canals of an adult specimen of *Stephanurus dentatus*. (Courtesy of Dr. A. H. Waddell; Waddell, 1968.) (A) Whole canal and its lumen, × 5500; (B) Part of the canal wall at higher mag.: × 55,000.

189

Ascaris lumbricoides it is about 30 μ wide by 70 μ long or, when circular in outline, the lumen in this nematode is about 55 μ in diameter. These measurements for *Ascaris* were taken from transverse sections of wax-embedded material and so may be slightly greater in living specimens. The measurements obtained by Ferguson and Chen (1951) for *Ascaris* are a little less. Thus, they found that the lumen of the left excretory canal, just behind the connecting canal, was 49 μ in diameter, whereas that on the right was 32 μ in diameter. The diameter of the lumen of the connecting canal was about 36 μ and that of the excretory pore was 10 μ.

The excretory system of both larval and adult *Strongylus vulgaris* has been examined by Enigk and Grittner (1952). In 4th-stage larvae and adults these structures differ from those described for other nematodes in that transverse sections normally reveal a pair of excretory canals in each lateral cord, a straight one and a winding one. The winding canal starts blindly mid-way between the nerve ring and the anterior tip of the nematode and winds backward in the lateral cord toward the tail where it joins the straight canal just before the anal opening. The straight canal begins blindly near the tip of the tail and runs forward to unite with the other straight canal running forward in the opposite lateral hypodermal cord to form an excretory vesicle just prior to the excretory pore. It is thought that substances move posteriorly in the winding canal and anteriorly in the straight canal and that they enter these canals through fine cytoplasmic processes which occur at irregular intervals and connect the canals to hypodermal cells. This type of connection has now been demonstrated in *Stephanurus dentatus* by Waddell (1968) (Fig. 45). Two ventral glands communicate with the straight lateral canals just in front of their entry into the excretory vesicle. These glands, which run from the excretory pore to the tail, have a dense cytoplasm, which is associated with the synthesis of numerous granules that are contained within the ventral glands and which Enigk and Grittner (1952) have observed to move to and fro in response to the nematode's movements.

The subventral glands vary in size and are largest in the young 4th-stage larva of *Strongylus vulgaris* during its active migratory stage when it moves from the lumen of the intestine into the mucous membrane of the crypts.

Thus, the differences in size of the subventral glands in this nematode are a reflection of its physiological state. An analogous situation is, perhaps, found in the subventral esophageal glands of the 2nd-stage larva of *Melo-idogyne javanica* (Bird, 1967, 1968; Bird and Saurer, 1967) which undergo both chemical and morphological changes before hatching from the egg and again once they are within the host root. This will be discussed in greater detail in Chapter 10. It is interesting to note, however, that, in both cases, the contents of the glands are granular and that similar functions in nematodes may be performed by tissues whose structure is similar but which are completely nonhomologous. A classic example of this is the excretory system of *Tylenchulus semipenetrans* (Maggenti, 1962), which is responsible for the production of the gelatinous matrix that in the genus *Meloidogyne* is produced by the rectal glands (Maggenti and Allen, 1960) and in the genus *Heterodera* by the cells of the uterine wall (Mackintosh, 1960).

The glandular parts of the excretory systems in *Nippostrongylus* (Lee, 1969, 1970) and *Stephanurus* (Waddell, 1968) also contain granules. When sections of these structures are examined with the aid of the electron microscope, it is seen that their fine structure is similar. Thus, both contain Golgi bodies, a granular endoplasmic reticulum, and electron-dense granules and resemble secretory structures to such an extent that Lee (1969, 1970) prefers to call them "exo-digestive glands" in *Nippostrongylus* where they are thought to secrete histolytic enzymes which are passed to the exterior through the excretory pore.

The excretory system in *Phocanema decipiens* (Davey and Kan, 1968) consists of a long, ribbonlike gland running in the anterior right lateral half of the nematode and about 1 cm in length, which leads into a short, tubular duct that opens as a ventral excretory pore at the base of the subventral lips. There are two nuclei in this system, a duct nucleus that occurs at the level of the nerve ring and a gland nucleus in the anterior part of the gland.

The excretory systems of members of the Dorylaimoidea are usually reduced or rudimentary. Recently, however, it has been shown (Aboul-Eid, 1969) that *Longidorus macrosoma*, which belongs to this group, has a well-developed excretory system consisting of a ventral pore at the level of the nerve ring that is connected by a canal to two nucleated gland cells embedded in the ventral ganglion.

The excretory system of nematodes thus varies considerably in structure. In many parasitic forms its function in the larval stages appears to be different from that of the adult stage and its morphology appears to be governed by the physiological state of its environment. In the adult stage it often appears to have at least a dual function. Maggenti's (1970) analysis of the excretory system in nematodes further emphasizes the gaps in our knowledge of their phylogenetic relationships.

Apart from the work of Waddell (1968), Wu (1968), Lee (1969, 1970) and Narang (1970), very little high-resolution work has been done on the excretory system of nematodes; even here, apart from Narang's work, the examinations tend to be restricted to the areas around the ducts rather than to areas in the vicinity of the excretory nuclei although, as mentioned above, Lee (1969, 1970) and Waddell (1968) have examined sections cut through the subventral glands.

In the Tylenchida, the area around the ducts consists of numerous characteristic vesicles (Figs. 42C, and D, and 44) which appear to be larger than the canaliculi in *Stephanurus* (Fig. 45) and which do not appear to connect with the lumen of the canal as the canaliculi do.

It is quite clear that detailed electron microscope studies of the excretory systems in a wide range of nematodes are needed in order to clarify the work of the light microscopists.

III. Functions of the Excretory System

The problems associated with obtaining information on the physiological functioning of the excretory system in nematodes are extremely hard to overcome and doubtless account for the paucity of information on this subject.

First, it is often difficult to identify the excretory system in small nematodes. It is usually best seen in the living state, often in a specimen which has been deliberately starved in order to reduce the number of intestinal storage granules which often conceal parts of the system. This technique was used by Goodey (1959) in his study of the excretory system of *Paraphelenchus myceliophthorus*.

Other techniques that have been used as aids in determining the structure and function of the excretory system include the use of vital stains, chemical indicators, fluorescent dyes, and serological and fluorescent antibody techniques (Mueller, 1929; Enigk, 1938; Sarles, 1938; Behrenz, 1956; Jackson, 1961; Taffs, 1961; Taffs and Voller, 1962; Bird, 1964; Smith, 1965). But despite the wide range of techniques now available to the experimental physiologist, we know incredibly little about the functions of the nematode excretory system.

The tubular parts of the system appear to be capable of movement in some forms and pulsation of these vessels has been reported by various workers in different species of nematodes. The results of their observations have been reviewed by Weinstein (1952) in a concise and informative paper on the function of this system. He did experiments using the 3rd-stage larvae of *Nippostrongylus muris* and *Ancylostoma caninum*, which showed that their excretory systems were concerned with the regulation of water balance.

The excretory system of these larvae is H-shaped and consists of two excretory cells that open into an ampulla, which runs forward as a canal and bends downward at right angles to terminate in the excretory pore. The ampulla pulsates rhythmically and Weinstein (1952) has been able to show that there is an inverse relationship between this pulsation rate and the solute concentration of the nematode's environment. Of course, this inverse relationship only occurs within a certain range of concentrations; at high concentrations of sodium chloride or sucrose the pulsations virtually ceased but a rapid pulsation was attained when these larvae were transferred to distilled water. Furthermore, Weinstein was able to calculate that, in distilled water, the 3rd-stage larva of *N. muris* will excrete its equivalent body volume through the excretory pore in approximately 11 hr, whereas the 3rd-stage larva of *A. caninum* does the same thing in approximately 75 hr.

The role of the excretory system as a water-balance regulating system is, perhaps, just restricted to these types of larvae. Where measurements have been made in adult forms such as *Ascaris lumbricoides* (Savel, 1955), it is clear that the excretion of nitrogenous waste products and fluid appears to take place through the anus rather than the excretory pore, although the *in vitro* nature of these experiments may have stressed the nematode and led to an unnatural functioning of this system. Savel (1955) placed his ascarids in inverted U-tubes with their heads and tails in saline, the heads and tails being separated by a gap of moist air. He found that the nematodes transferred about 10 ml of saline from the front tube to the rear tube within 24 hr and that there were little or no nitrogenous waste products in the front tube containing the mouth and excretory pore, although these products were easily detected in the saline in which the anus was immersed.

It has been mentioned above that the lateral canals in some forms are connected with the cytoplasm of the hypodermis. Further observations may show that this is common to many nematodes. Certainly some observations indicate that there is extreme metabolic activity along the entire length of the lateral canal. For instance, Sanwal (1957), working with adult *Radopholus gracilis*, observed the excretory system in living specimens using methylene blue as an intravital stain. He noted that all along the length of the lateral canals "structures resembling ampullae and vacuoles appear and disappear continuously in the living worm."

There is no doubt that material, sometimes of considerable molecular dimension, is extruded through the excretory pore. As long ago as 1876, Leuckart reported that he once saw the contents of the excretory tube ejected from the body of a living specimen of *Uncinaria criniformis* (Leuckart, 1876); more recently, Goodey (1959) reported a somewhat similar occurrence in *Paraphelenchus myceliophthorus*, stating: "I once observed the rapid expulsion from the excretory pore of a short length of some excretory product. This remained in the water near the animal retaining its stringlike form but swelling slightly." Furthermore, I have observed material in electron micrographs of longitudinal sections of the terminal duct of *Meloidogyne javanica*. These all appear to be examples of natural elimination of a relatively insoluble excretory product, unlike that described by Weinstein and Haskins (1955) where an excretory pore precipitate develops in the 3rd-stage larva of *Nippostrongylus muris* as a result of an interaction between amines and quinones to form an insoluble polymeric substance.

The most obvious example of solid material being exuded through the excretory pore is in the female of the citrus nematode, *Tylenchulus semipenetrans* (Maggenti, 1962) which, as I have said above, has a highly modified excretory system that occupies approximately 30% of the body cavity volume. There is no anus in this nematode and it is thought that the excretory system is of sufficient capacity to eliminate metabolic wastes and other soluble products. It also exudes the proteinaceous gelatinous matrix. This is a classic example of the modifications that can take place in the excretory system of nematodes in response to environmental pressures such as those induced by a sedentary, parasitic mode of life.

Despite the experiments of Enigk and Grittner (1952), who were unable to detect proteolytic enzyme activity in a medium containing 200 dissected *Strongylus* subventral glands triturated in Tyrode's solution at pH's of 4.5 and 7.5, evidence is accumulating which shows that both enzymes and antigenic substances are liberated via the excretory system in many nematodes. Thus, it appears that the enzyme, leucine aminopeptidase, may be associated with the excretory system in various strongyle larvae (Rogers, 1965, 1970). It is also found in the excretory gland of *Phocanema decipiens* (Davey and Kan, 1967, 1968) where it is synthesized and released together with non-specific esterases at the time of ecdysis.

It is now well established in many different species of nematodes that antigenic substances are liberated through the excretory pore and photographs of these types of excretory pore exudates are now quite common and include such widely phylogenetically separated genera as *Neoaplectana* (Jackson, 1961), *Ascaris* (Taffs, 1961), *Nippostrongylus* (Sarles, 1938), *Meloidogyne* (Bird, 1964), and *Ditylenchus* (Webster and Hooper, 1968).

In addition to these substances with a relatively high molecular weight, various salts are probably excreted, whose solubility would make them extremely difficult to detect. In some of the largest nematodes, the fluid exuded from the excretory pore may be collected and Chitwood (1938) has estimated that excretory pore fluid contains about 0.02% urea. Experiments in which excretory products of nematodes are collected in culture media *in vitro* are open to the criticisms that they may be contaminated with bacteria and that there is no information as to which opening to the exterior the material passed through. It must only be a matter of time before material that has been shed through the excretory pore can be collected and analyzed using the sophisticated micromethods now available. I expect that when this is done, we shall find a wide and variable range of excretory or secretory products such as inorganic and organic substances of relatively low molecular weight associated with osmoregulation or excretion and substances of higher molecular weight including various proteins.

Certainly there appears to be a high degree of nervous coordination within the excretory system, as nerve elements are often observed in close contact with parts of the excretory system in sections viewed under the electron microscope. At lower magnification, the proximity of the excretory duct and its terminal pore to either the nerve ring, ventral ganglion, retrovesicular ganglion or hemizonid has been commented on in Chapter 7 on the nervous system. Futhermore, the observations of Behrenz (1956), who, with the aid of fluorescent dyes, has demonstrated the ejection of material taken orally as a fine jet through the excretory pore in various ascarids and Weinstein (1952) on the excretory ampulla of 3rd-stage strongyle larvae described above, suggest a high degree of nervous coordination within the excretory system.

At the moment, nothing is known about nervous coordination and control of the excretory system in nematodes. What is clear is that the functions of their excretory systems are extremely variable, but they may be considered first, in a general way, under excretion, which is associated with a tubular system functioning to maintain an osmotic balance or to eliminate waste products or both, and second, under secretion, which is associated with a glandular system functioning to produce enzymes, hormones, or protective mucoproteins. Apparently either of these systems may predominate or, in some cases, both may function together and these functions may change at different stages of the nematode's life cycle.

IV. Summary

The excretory duct, which opens to the exterior through an excretory pore that is commonly situated in the anterior midventral line close to the nerve ring, is the only part of the nematode excretory system common to nematodes which possess such a system.

There are two basic types: a glandular type of excretory system and a tubular type of excretory system. The former consists of a large cell in the pseudocoelomic cavity known as the ventral gland, which is connected to the excretory pore by a duct that terminates in an ampulla. This system is found in many free-living marine and freshwater forms.

There are several different types of tubular excretory systems. Characteristically, it consists of two long canals in the lateral hypodermal cords connected anteriorly to each other by means of a transverse canal that is connected to the excretory pore by a median duct. This system is known as an H-system for obvious reasons. In other forms there is a reduction of the anterior lateral canals and the system is then known as an inverted U-system. In forms with only one lateral canal the system is asymmetric. In other forms, paired subventral glands open into the transverse canal or sinus. These glands are embryologically and morphologically different from the tubular part of the system. They have a granular cytoplasm and are thought to be secretory in function, whereas the tubular part of the system, particularly in forms in which this is the only type, appears to have an excretory function.

The excretory system shows considerable variability in both structure and function throughout the Nematoda. Of all the structures described so far, it appears to be the most plastic and most influenced by environmental changes. It is clear that a wide range of chemical compounds passes out of the excretory pore, including some of relatively high molecular weight such as polypeptides and proteins. Under certain conditions, such as during molting, these substances may be of very great physiological importance.

Despite some excellent experiments accomplished under extreme technical difficulties, many questions, particularly on embryological and functional aspects of the nematode excretory system, remain unanswered.

REFERENCES

Aboul-Eid, H. Z. (1969). *Nematologica* **15**, 437.
Behrenz, K. W. (1956). *Z. Wiss. Zool., Abt. A* **159**, 129.
Bird, A. F. (1959). *Nematologica* **4**, 31.
Bird, A. F. (1964). *Exp. Parasitol.* **15**, 350.
Bird, A. F. (1967). *J. Parasitol.* **53**, 768.
Bird, A. F. (1968). *J. Parasitol.* **54**, 475.
Bird, A. F., and Saurer, W. (1967). *J. Parasitol.* **53**, 1262.
Chitwood, B. G. (1938). *Proc. Helminthol Soc. Wash.* **5**, 18.
Chitwood, B. G., and Chitwood, M. B., eds. (1950). "An Introduction to Nematology," 213 pp. Monumental Printing Co., Baltimore, Maryland.
Cobb, N. A. (1890). *Proc. Linn. Soc. N.S.W.* **5**, 168.
Cobb, N. A. (1925). *J. Parasitol.* **11**, 219.
Crofton, H. D. (1966). "Nematodes," 160 pp. Hutchinson, London.
Davey, K. G., and Kan, S. P. (1967). *Nature (London)* **214**, 737.
Davey, K. G., and Kan, S. P. (1968). *Can. J. Zool.* **46**, 893.
de Coninck, L. (1965). *In* 'Traité de Zoologie" (P. P. Grassé, ed.), Vol. IV, pp. 1–217. Masson, Paris.
Enigk, K. (1938). *Z. Parasitenk.* **10**, 386.
Enigk, K., and Grittner, L. (1952). *Z. Parasitenk.* **15**, 267.
Evans, A. A. F., and Fisher, J. M. (1970). *J. Nematol.* **2**, 260.
Ferguson, F. F., and Chen, Y. C. (1951). *Trans. Amer. Microsc. Soc.* **70**, 257.
Golovin, E. P. (1902). *Uch. Zap. Imp. Kazan. Univ.* **64**, 71.
Goodey, J. B. (1959). *Nematologica* **4**, 157.
Hartwich, C. (1954). *Wiss. Z. Martin-Luther Univ., Halle-Wittenberg, Math-Naturwiss Reihe* **3**, 1171.
Jackson, G. J. (1961). *Exp. Parasitol.* **11**, 241.
Jaegerskioeld, L. A. (1894). *Zool. Jahrb (Anat.)* **7**, 449.

Lee, D. L. (1965). "The Physiology of Nematodes," 154 pp. Oliver & Boyd, Edinburgh and London.
Lee, D. L. (1969). *Symp. Brit. Soc. Parasitol.* **7**, 3.
Lee, D. L. (1970). *Tissue Cell* **2**, 225.
Leuckart, R. (1876). "Die Menschlichen Parasiten und die von ihnen Herrührenden Krankheiten," 410 pp. Winter'sche, Leipzig & Heidelberg.
Mackintosh, G. McD. (1960). *Nematologica* **5**, 158.
Maggenti, A. R. (1961). *Proc. Helminthol. Soc. Wash.* **28**, 118.
Maggenti, A. R. (1962). *Proc. Helminthol. Soc. Wash.* **29**, 139.
Maggenti, A. R. (1970). *J. Nematol.* **2**, 7.
Maggenti, A. R., and Allen, M. W. (1960). *Proc. Helminthol. Soc. Wash.* **27**, 4.
Mueller, J. F. (1929). *Z. Zellforsch. Mikrosk. Anat.* **8**, 361.
Narang, H. K. (1970). *Nematologica* **16**, 517.
Poinar, G. O., and Leutenegger, R. (1968). *J. Parasitol* **54**, 340.
Rogers, W. P. (1965). *Comp. Biochem. Physiol.* **14**, 311.
Rogers, W. P. (1970). *J. Parasitol.* **56**, 138.
Sanwal, K. C. (1957). *Can. J. Zool.* **35**, 75.
Sarles, M. P. (1938). *J. Infec. Dis.* **62**, 337.
Savel, J. (1955). *Rev. Pathol. Comp. Hyg. Gen.* **55**, 213.
Smith, L. (1965). *Comp. Biochem. Physiol.* **15**, 89.
Sprent, J. F. A. (1962). *J. Parasitol.* **48**, 818.
Taffs, L. F. (1961). *Parasitology* **51**, 327.
Taffs, L. F., and Voller, A. (1962). *J. Helminthol.* **36**, 339.
Toernquist, N. (1931). *Handlingar, Ser. B.* **2**, 1.
Waddell, A. H. (1968). *Parasitology* **58**, 907.
Webster, J. M., and Hooper, D. J. (1968). *Parasitology* **58**, 879.
Weinstein, P. P. (1952). *Exp. Parasitol.* **1**, 363.
Weinstein, P. P. (1960). *In* "Host Influence on Parasite Physiology" (L. A. Stauber, ed.), pp. 65–92. Rutgers Univ. Press, New Brunswick, New Jersey.
Weinstein, P. P., and Haskins, W. T. (1955). *Exp. Parasitol* **4**, 226.
Wu, L.-Y. (1968). *Can. J. Zool.* **46**, 467.

10
THE DIGESTIVE SYSTEM

I. Introduction

In this chapter I propose to consider not only the digestive or alimentary tract but also the various glands which are associated with this structure and to mention their different functions.

Information on the structure of the nematode digestive system, at the level of magnification of the light microscope, has been reviewed in a number of comparatively recent texts (Chitwood and Chitwood, 1950; Hyman, 1951; de Coninck, 1965; Lee, 1965; Crofton, 1966).

The nematode digestive system is essentially a tube into which some glands open. It starts at the mouth as a cuticular inpushing known as the stomodeum, which incorporates the buccal cavity and esophagus, and ends at the anus as another cuticular invagination that is known as the proctodeum, which includes the rectum in females and the cloaca in males. As has been mentioned in Chapter 4 on molting, the linings of the stomodeum and proctodeum are shed with the cuticle when the nematode molts. The middle part of the digestive system is the intestine or midgut; this is the only part that is endodermal in origin. The ducts of the esophageal glands enter the stomodeum and the ducts of the rectal glands enter the procotodeum.

The ultrastructure of the digestive tract and its associated glands has been examined in a wide range of nematodes. As I have already mentioned in Chapter 7 on the nervous system, some of the early investigators thought that they had detected cilia lining the intestinal lumen. We now know, as a result of numerous studies on the ultrastructure of various species of nematodes, that these structures are really microvilli.

In this chapter I shall consider the stomodeum with its great structural diversity, the structures of the intestine, the proctodeum, the glands, and, finally, the respective functions of these various parts of the nematode's digestive system.

II. The Stomodeum

The stomodeum includes the mouth and lips, the buccal cavity, and the pharynx or esophagus. I shall consider these structures individually.

A. THE MOUTH AND LIPS

These structures have already been mentioned in the section on sense organs in Chapter 7 on the nervous system (Figs. 25 and 27). The general pattern is a head with six lips. This may, however, be reduced by partial fusion to three or by complete fusion to form a united ring around the mouth. In some nematodes the lips may be elaborate and have spines or hooks on them, or the outline of the head may be changed by the size and direction of the amphidial apertures (Geraert, 1965). The considerable variability that is found in the structure of the mouth and lips of nematodes has been illustrated and discussed in great detail by Chitwood and Chitwood (1950) and de Coninck (1965) and the reader in search of further information on this topic is referred to these comprehensive accounts. There is not only great variability between different species but great differences can also exist within the same species and care must be taken in descriptions of these structures if they are to be used for taxonomic purposes. These variabilities in structure are shown particularly well when specimens are observed with the scanning electron microscope.

B. THE BUCCAL CAVITY

The buccal cavity or stoma, which lies between the mouth and the pharynx, varies considerably in shape and reflects the method of feeding of the nematode (Fig. 46). Thus, the bacterial feeders such as the genus *Rhabditis* have

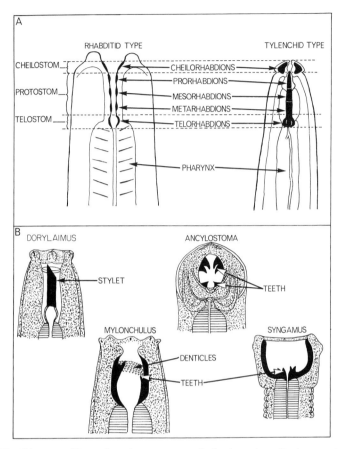

FIG. 46. Diagrams illustrating the structure of the buccal cavity in nematodes. (A) Nomenclature of two types of mouth parts, a bacterial feeder and a plant parasitic nematode. (After Jones, 1965.) (B) Structure of the mouth parts of four different genera of nematodes.

a relatively narrow and smoothly lined buccal cavity, whereas plant parasitic nematodes (Fig. 46) have a hollow buccal spear or stylet whose lumen is usually less than $1\,\mu$ in diameter. The stylet can, therefore, act as a bacterial filter as well as a type of microhypodermic needle through which material may be injected into the plant cell and through which nutrients from the plant are ingested by the nematode. A buccal spear is also found in other parasitic nematodes as well as in predatory forms (Fig. 46). The latter may either pierce their prey and suck out their contents using a buccal stylet, as in *Dorylaimus* and *Seinura* (Linford and Oliveira, 1937; Jenkins and Taylor, 1967), or they may puncture their prey by means of teeth, as in *Mylonchulus* (Fig. 46).

A toothed buccal cavity is found in numerous animal parasitic nematodes, such as *Ancylostoma* and *Syngamus* (Fig. 46). In these forms the arrangement and shape of the teeth are of considerable taxonomic importance. Nematode teeth may be considered under two categories, depending on their origin (Cobb, 1919), namely, odontia which arise from the labial region and onchia which arise more posteriorly and are associated with the esophagus. In some forms, such as *Ancylostoma*, for example, there are both odontia and onchia in the buccal cavity. The two ventrolateral cutting plates at the entrance to the buccal cavity are odontia and the sharp teeth found at the base of the buccal cavity are onchia. In some species of marine Enoplida the components of the buccal cavity are also derived from different sources (Inglis, 1964). Thus, in addition to three large onchia, there are three massive mandibles which are formed from a thickening of the cuticle lining the buccal cavity.

The buccal stylet of nematodes may also be either odontial or onchial in origin. Thus, in forms such as the Tylenchida, the stylet (Figs. 46A, 47B, and 58), which is a hollow, tripartite, cuticular structure, usually with basal knobs or swellings for the attachment of muscles, is developed, at least in part, from a fusion of the walls of the buccal cavity or stoma (Allen, 1960) and is known as a stomatostyl. In forms such as the Dorylaimida, the anterior part of the buccal stylet originates from the same region as do onchia and the spears in these nematodes are referred to as onchiostyls. There is some disagreement on the use of this term and some workers (Coomans and de Coninck, 1963) prefer to use the term odontostyl for the anterior part of the stylet and basal portion for the posterior part. I prefer the term onchiostylet because I think it fits in better with Cobb's (1919) definition of odontia and onchia, as outlined above.

The process of stylet formation in *Xiphinema* has been studied by Coomans and de Coninck (1963), who examined larvae, that had been fixed during molting, at different stages of development. They found that, between molts, these larvae possessed two onchiostyls (odontostyls), a functioning one in the stoma and a reserve one in the esophageal wall. However, during molting it is common to find three onchiostyls (odontostyls) in a larva, the first being the functional one of the previous larval stage in the process of expulsion, the second the former reserve onchiostyl now moving up the buccal cavity to become the functional stylet of the following larval stage, and the third one the new developing onchiostyl, of varying size depending on the stage which the molt has reached.

The cell in the esophageal wall, from which the onchiostylet develops, undergoes characteristic changes at the onset of molting (Coomans and de Coninck, 1963). Its nucleus becomes larger and its cytoplasm becomes granular, so that, in some respects, it resembles an esophageal gland. When

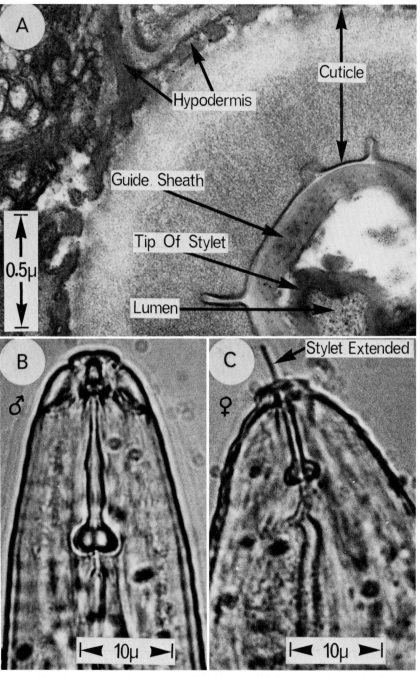

FIG. 47. Buccal stylets in the genus *Meloidogyne*. (A) Electron micrograph of a cross section through the stylet of a male specimen. × 60,000. (B) Photomicrograph showing the whole stylet of a male specimen. × 2500. (Bird, 1968b.) (C) Photomicrograph showing the whole stylet of a female specimen. × 2500. (Bird, 1968b.)

202

no stylet is being formed, the nucleus is smaller and the cytoplasm is difficult to detect under the light microscope. So far as I know, this sequence of changes has not been observed under the electron microscope. It would be interesting to compare the ultrastructure of this cell during active protein synthesis with that of other gland cells which actively synthesize protein in nematodes and which I shall describe later in this chapter.

Cuticular structures in the wall of the relatively unspecialized buccal cavity of the Rhabditida have been named (Steiner, 1934) and the phylogenetic relationship of the buccal stylet of the Tylenchida to these structures has been discussed and speculated upon (Andrássy, 1962; Goodey, 1963). This relationship is illustrated in Fig. 46. Thus, the basal knobs of the tylenchid stylet correspond to the telorhabdians, the shaft to the metarhabdians, whereas that part of the spear which is cast during molting corresponds to the mesorhabdians and prorhabdians and the head skeleton is thought to correspond with the cheilorhabdians. There is, as may be expected, some disagreement on these relationships. I have followed (Fig. 46) the system outlined by Jones (1965) which is essentially that of Steiner (1934).

Sections of the lips and buccal cavities of several different types of nematodes have been examined at high magnification with the aid of the electron microscope. The relatively simple mouthparts of *Panagrellus silusiae* have been examined by Yuen (1968b), who found that the six lips were divided internally by structureless tissue which connected the cuticle to the wall of the buccal cavity. The lip tissues, which consisted of mitochondria and membranes together with the cephalic nerves and amphids, were gradually replaced by hypodermis and somatic muscle posteriorly.

The cuticle lining the buccal cavity of *Panagrellus silusiae* consists of three layers: a thin, electron-dense layer lining the cavity, which is presumably equivalent to the external cortical layer of the outer cuticle; a thicker, less-dense middle layer; and a more electron-dense outer layer. The shape of the buccal cavity changes throughout its length. Immediately behind the lips it is subcircular but it becomes triangular and then triradiate more posteriorly. Two pairs of teeth are found on the subventral walls of the posterior part of the buccal cavity and a duct, which is thought to be the dorsal gland duct (Yuen, 1968b), opens into this region through the mid-dorsal wall.

A nematode which exists in a completely different environment from that of *Panagrellus silusiae* is the animal parasitic *Nippostrongylus brasiliensis*, whose 3rd-stage larva enters its host, the rat, by penetrating its skin. The lips of this larva are modified to form a circumoral ring of cuticle which acts as a sucker when applied to surfaces and so aids in concentrating any histolytic secretions from the mouth, thus facilitating penetration of the host. The buccal cavity in this nematode (Lee, 1968, 1969a) is triangular in cross section and is lined with a cuticle which differs from the external cuticle in that, apart from an outer membrane, it is not subdivided into layers.

Sections of the buccal cavity of normal 3rd-stage larvae of the insect parasitic nematode *Neoaplectana carpocapsae* (Poinar and Leutenegger, 1968) have also been examined at high magnification; electron micrographs of the nematode show that it is almost circular in cross section, whereas in infective larvae of this species, the mouth is closed and the digestive tract does not function.

The buccal cavities of several different genera of plant parasitic nematodes have been examined, notably *Xiphinema* (Wright, 1965; Roggen *et al.*, 1967; López-Abella *et al.*, 1967), *Ditylenchus* (Yuen, 1967), *Trichodorus* (Hirumi *et al.*, 1968; Raski *et al.*, 1969), *Longidorus* (Aboul-Eid, 1969), and *Meloidogyne* (Bird, 1968b; Bird, unpublished) (Figs. 27 and 47).

The stomatostyl of forms such as *Ditylenchus* and *Meloidogyne* consists of a cylinder with a central lumen. At its base there are three knobs or swellings upon which the stylet protractor muscles are inserted (Fig. 58). It acts rather like a hypodermic needle through which substances, probably from the dorsal esophageal glands, are injected into its host's cells.

As a result of observations made with both conventional and scanning electron microscopes (Bird, 1969; Ellenby and Wilson, 1969), we now know that the stomatostyl in some of the endoparasitic tylenchids is about 1 μ in width with a lumen which is less than 0.5 μ. This whole structure tapers at its tip to a width of just over 0.25 μ (Fig. 47A) so that it acts as an efficient bacterial filter. Thus, only relatively small particles and juices are ingested by these nematodes. A guide sheath (Fig. 47A) extends from the anterior part of the stoma to the stylet knobs. This structure has been described and illustrated diagrammatically in *Ditylenchus dipsaci* (Yuen, 1967) and *Xiphinema index* (Roggen *et al.*, 1967).

The buccal cavity in *X. index* is surrounded by a thick cuticle which is continuous with the external cuticle (Fig. 48A). The relationship between this stomatal cuticle, the guide sheath and the stylet in this nematode is depicted diagrammatically (Fig. 48B). The stomatal wall and spear of *Longidorus macrosoma* (Aboul-Eid, 1969) are similar in structure to those of *X. index*.

C. THE PHARYNX OR ESOPHAGUS

The terms pharynx and esophagus are synonymous. The former is more correct but the latter is generally accepted through common usage.

The pharynx or esophagus of nematodes is extremely diverse, in both structure and function. The structural diversity, as seen with the aid of the light microscope, has been reviewed extensively by Chitwood and

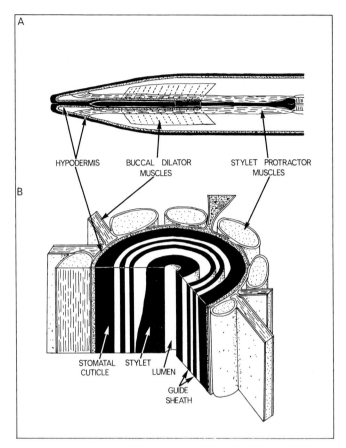

FIG. 48.   Diagrams of stylet of *Xiphinema*. (After Roggen *et al.*, 1967.) (A) Whole stylet;
(B) three-dimensional diagram of a cross section of portion of the stylet.

Chitwood (1950) and de Coninck (1965) and the reader is referred to these
works which include diagrams of whole mounts of esophagi in numerous
genera and diagrams of transverse sections through these structures
together with tables depicting the distribution of the various types of
esophageal nuclei. Despite the differences, there are some structural
characteristics which are shared by most nematodes. Thus, the pharynx
is a muscular pumping organ with a triradiate, cuticle-lined lumen of which
one ray normally projects ventrally (a fact originally discovered by
Schneider, 1866) and two project laterodorsally (Fig. 18A). The pharynx
contains radial muscles, esophageal glands (to be described later in this
chapter), and valves which prevent the regurgitation of food.

In some nematodes, both the median and posterior parts of the pharynx are swollen to form muscular bulbs; in others there may be only one bulb whereas some forms do not have a muscular bulb.

The variability in shape of the nematode pharynx is well documented and nearly all texts carry a diagram illustrating this in different groups. The nomenclature of these types varies a little. Thus, Allen (1960) considers that there are three general kinds: a one-part cylindrical in which the entire pharynx is cylindrical; a two-part cylindrical in which there is a slender, anterior, nonmuscular part and a swollen posterior part which is glandular and muscular; and a three-part cylindrical. The three-part cylindrical pharynx contains three, well-defined regions, namely, the corpus, the isthmus and the bulb. The corpus may be further modified (Fig. 49A) to form a procorpus and a swollen posterior part, the metacorpus.

Filipjev's and Schuurmans Stekhoven's (1941) classification contains eight headings, largely named after the groups of nematodes in which they were first described. Hence, they use terms such as rhabditoid, diplogasteroid, tylenchoid, aphelenchoid, and mermithoid. Generally, this classification can be fitted into that of Allen described above, for the purpose of simplification. It is quite conceivable that further high-resolution studies on these structures may result in their reclassification.

The pharynx or esophagus was originally thought to be syncytial in all nematodes because cell walls had not been detected by earlier workers such as Goldschmidt (1905) and Hsü (1929). However, as a result of observations with the electron microscope on various species of nematodes, such as *Ditylenchus dipsaci* (Yuen, 1968a), *Panagrellus silusiae* (Yuen, 1968b), and the infective larva of *Nippostrongylus brasiliensis* (Lee, 1968), it is now known that in these forms the pharynx is a cellular structure with distinct muscle cells, supporting cells, nerve cells, and gland cells. It seems likely that this may be true of numerous other species of nematodes, although apparently a syncytial condition does exist in some nematodes, since Reger (1966), as a result of his electron microscope studies on the pharynx of *Ascaris lumbricoides*, describes this structure as being "composed of syncytially arranged myoepithelium surrounding a triradiate lumen." In his discussion of his work, however, Reger (1966) mentions that he could not be certain that the myoepithelium was a complete syncytium because he had not cut serial sections through the entire pharynx. Thus, it is possible that further work along these lines may show that the assumptions of Goldschmidt (1905) and Hsü (1929) that the pharynx of this nematode is syncytial may be incorrect and that the pharynx may prove to be cellular in all nematodes when sections of these structures are examined carefully at high resolution.

Because many of the structures associated with the pharynx in nematodes

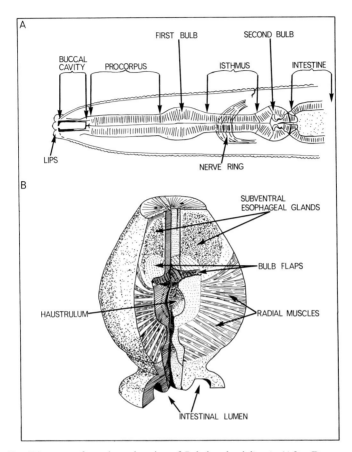

FIG. 49.   Diagrams of esophageal region of *Pelodera lambdiensis*. (After Doncaster, 1962.) (A) Whole esophageal region; (B) three-dimensional diagram of the second esophageal bulb.

can be readily seen and measured with the aid of the light microscope and because there is remarkable nuclear constancy of the pharynx within certain groups which have similar nuclei arranged in a definite manner, these structures have received considerable attention from the taxonomists.

Thus, the shape of the lumen, the position of the gland openings, and the configuration of the esophagointestinal valve, if present, are all points of taxonomic significance.

As mentioned above, the pharynx is a pumping organ and I shall discuss its methods of functioning in several different species later in this chapter.

Detailed observations on the structure of the pharynx have been made over a wide range of nematodes. One of the earliest descriptions which fit

208   10. THE DIGESTIVE SYSTEM

into this category is that of Looss (1905) on *Ancylostoma duodenale*. His
drawings of transverse sections through the pharynx show that the lumen
of this structure is circular in cross section anteriorly and rapidly becomes
triradiate, thus resembling, in some respects, the lumen of the metacorpus
in *Ditylenchus dipsaci* (Yuen, 1968a) which changes from round to triradiate
at the valve. In the anterior third, it can be seen (Fig. 50) that the lumen is
round in cross section, in the middle of the valve it is triradiate with heavily
sclerotized tips, and in the posterior third it remains triradiate but with
a uniformly sclerotized surface.

Studies on the ultrastructure of the esophagus of several species of nematodes have been made recently, notably by Reger (1966) on *Ascaris*, Yuen
(1968a,b) on *Ditylenchus* and *Panagrellus*, and Lee (1968, 1969a) on *Nip-*

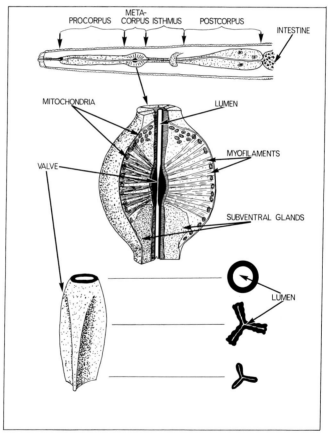

FIG. 50.   Diagrams of the esophagus and esophageal region of *Ditylenchus dipsaci* with
enlargements of the metacorpus and its valve. (After Yuen, 1968a.)

postrongylus. It is interesting to note how some of these observations carried out at high resolution complement some of the observations made by Looss in 1905. For instance, Looss observed that the muscles in the esophagus of *Ancylostoma* consist of two types, namely, marginal fibres which run from the tips of the triradiate lumen to the periphery and stain more readily than the ordinary fibers which run from the sides of the triradiate lumen to the periphery and are thus more numerous. Reger (1966), working with *Ascaris*, cut thick Epon sections which he stained with Mallory Azure II–Methylene Blue and thin sections which he viewed under the electron microscope. He found that the fibers found at the apices of the triradiate lumen (marginal fibers) were intensely stained in the thick (1–2 μ) Epon sections and were found to be composed of tightly packed bundles of filaments 75–100 Å thick when observed under the electron microscope. The radially directed fibers (ordinary fibers) were only very lightly stained and consisted of interdigitating thin and thick myofilaments 35–75 A and 140–175 A in diameter, respectively, and were orientated transversely to the long axis of the esophagus.

Lee (1968) has also observed these radial muscles in the esophagus of *Nippostrongylus* (Fig. 51) and has noted that they occurred as a series along its length and that there were three, one to each sector, in any transverse section. Each cell was divided into two parts by the gland cell of that sector and the two parts joined at the apex of the sector. These muscles contain both thick and thin myofilaments which Lee (1968) presumed corresponded to myosin and actin. He also noticed that fibrils, which are difficult to resolve, run from cells at the apices of the triradiate lumen to the outer surface of the esophagus where they are attached, as are the radial muscles, by half-desmosomes to the plasma membrane (Fig. 51). The nuclei of these apical cells contain much more electron-dense heterochromatin than the nuclei of the muscles and gland cells. These fibrils are clearly similar to the marginal fibers observed by Looss (1905) in *Ancylostoma* and recently described by Yuen (1968b) in *Panagrellus*.

In *Ditylenchus dipsaci* the esophagus consists of a procorpus, metacorpus, or median bulb, isthmus, and postcorpus or basal bulb (Fig. 50). The anterior part of the procorpus is two-celled in cross section but becomes four-celled posteriorly. The metacorpus (Fig. 50) consists of twelve cells which, according to Yuen (1968a), "fit together much as the segments of an orange." Six of these cells are muscle cells. The muscle cells of the metacorpus are well supplied with mitochondria, as can be seen in the electron micrograph of a longitudinal section through the median bulb of a female *Meloidogyne* (Fig. 52). This probably reflects the intense activity of these muscles in this particular stage of this nematode, when the activity associated with feeding predominates that of movement. In this section the

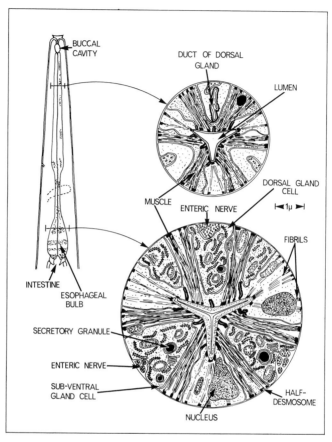

FIG. 51.   Diagrams of the esophagus of *Nippostrongylus brasiliensis* showing cross sections through the anterior and posterior regions. (After Lee, 1968.)

muscle fibers are cut in various planes—tangential, longitudinal, and in cross section. In the latter case both thin and thick myofilaments can be seen (Fig. 52).

The wall of the isthmus is reduced to a thin basement membrane, whereas that of the postcorpus is of uneven thickness and may be regarded as an elastic sac containing the dorsal and subventral glands through which the esophageal lumen passes. In *Ditylenchus* the lumen is surrounded throughout its length by eight or nine pairs of membranes which Yuen (1968a) calls the lumen complex. The esophageal lumen in *Ditylenchus* is circular from the base of the stylet to the valve of the metacorpus and from here to the junction of the esophagus and intestine it is triradiate.

Yuen (1968a) noticed that the two subventral glands in *Ditylenchus* become fused in the anterior half of the postcorpus although the dorsal gland remains a separate entity. This fusion of esophageal glands was first observed by Looss (1905) in *Ancylostoma* and he stated that "the subventral glands in the *Ankylostoma* show a very interesting and, so far as we know at present, unique peculiarity. At the posterior end of the esophagus, they have become fused one with another and with the dorsal gland."

It has been noted (Bird, 1968b) that in adult females of *Meloidogyne* the esophageal glands become compact and it is difficult to resolve their boundaries. It seems to me that this may be another example of fusion of these structures.

Connecting the esophagus to the intestine is the esophagointestinal valve or cardia which is triradiate and lined with cuticle and which, it is thought, functions to prevent regurgitation from the intestine. This is also a structure which Looss (1905) described and illustrated in *Ancylostoma*. He considered that in this nematode it was formed from four intestinal cells and showed that it consisted of a three-lobed prominence which projected into the intestine and which was thought to have been formed by bending

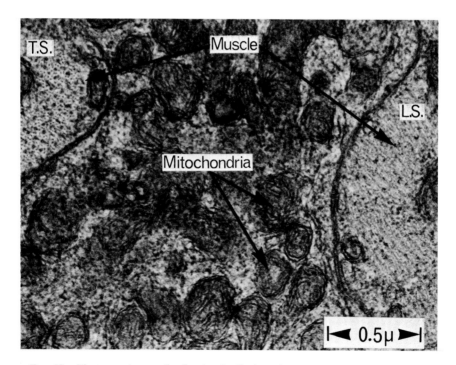

FIG. 52. Electron micrograph of a longitudinal section through the median bulb of a specimen of *Meloidogyne javanica.* × 50,000.

and telescoping of the intestinal wall. In *Nippostrongylus* (Lee, 1968) the cells which form the esophagointestinal valve are continuous with the cells of the intestine although the cuticular lining of this valve also lines the esophagus, which Lee (1968) demonstrates by an electron micrograph of a longitudinal section cut through this region. The shape of the valve varies in different species of nematodes. In *Plectus* (Maggenti, 1961) it is dorsoventrally flattened and is composed of approximately twelve cells. In the Mononchidae there are two types of valves, a tuberculate type and a nontuberculate type (Clark, 1960). In the former case the ends of the arms of the triradiate lumen become inflated and thickened to form conspicuous hollow tubercules. These structures are not found in nontuberculate types. Both forms have a funnel-shaped valve induced by expansion of the lumen, together with a supporting annulus.

Clark's observations on these structures were made either on living specimens under anesthetic or immediately after relaxing the nematodes with heat. He noticed that in fixed material some of the valve structures were either obscure or invisible and that within 15–20 min of death the valve funnel may become obscure. This is an important observation and should be taken into account in future studies on these types of structures in nematodes.

It has been suggested by Mapes (1965a) that the pharyngointestinal valves of forms such as *Ascaris*, *Oxyuris*, *Aplectana* and *Panagrellus* may have evolved from the type of valve found in the Enoplina, a group which is considered to be primitive (Filipjev, 1934; Sprent, 1962). In the Enoplina, the esophageal element is completely separated from the rest of the esophagus and the intestine. It is suggested (Mapes, 1965a) that, during the course of evolution, a state is eventually reached which is similar to that in the genera mentioned above where the esophageal and intestinal elements are intimately related.

Changes in the cellular structure of this valve during nematode growth and development have been observed in *Oesophagostomum* and *Rhabdias* (Goodey, 1924a, b) and in *Amplicaecum* (Sprent, 1963). It is clear that further studies along these lines on the developmental morphology of these structures are needed, particularly at high resolution, if we are to know more about their relationships in different nematodes.

The pharynx or esophagus of nematodes contains nervous elements, namely, the esophageal enteric or sympathetic nervous system which has already been mentioned in Chapter 7 on the nervous system. The three principal longitudinal nerves of this system have been detected in transverse sections through the esophagus of various nematodes as well as *Ascaris*, including *Ancylostoma* (Looss, 1905), *Plectus* (Maggenti, 1961), and in ultrathin sections of the larva of *Nippostrongylus* (Lee, 1968) where they can be readily recognized (Fig. 51) in the dorsal and lateral or subventral regions. These structures are not always easy to detect in some nematodes and both Mapes (1965a) and Yuen (1968a) have failed to observe them in the esophageal regions of the nematodes that they studied.

III. The Intestine

The nematode intestine is a simple tube consisting of a single layer of epithelial cells. These vary in number from about a million in large forms such as the adults of *Ascaris* down to about thirty in some adult rhabditids. Even fewer are found in the larval stages. In the strongyloid nematodes, which have few intestinal cells, there may be only two visible in a cross section, the epithelium being composed of two longitudinal rows of very large cells which are polynuclear in adults (Looss, 1905; Andreassen, 1968). As a result of his electron microscope studies on *Ancylostoma caninum*, Andreassen has shown that these cells in the mid intestine region of adults form a syncytium. In larvae the intestine is composed of about thirty uninuclear cells (Nichols, 1956). In *Strongylus equinus* (Chitwood and Chitwood, 1950) the intestinal cells may be up to 4 mm long and 0.5 mm wide, compared with those of *Capillaria* (Wright, 1963) which are about 3 μ wide and 7 μ long, not including their brush border of microvilli. There is considerable variation in the size of these intestinal epithelial cells in different species, as is shown in Table VIII.

The intestine is generally divided into three regions which merge into each other without any perceptible boundaries. These are the anterior or ventricular region, the midintestinal region, and the posterior or prerectal region. In most forms the intestine is a straight tube although in a few cases an outpushing or cecum, known as a diverticulum, occurs in the anterior region. This structure, which is common in the Ascaridoidea in genera such as *Amplicaecum*, is similar cytologically to the rest of the intestine and, apart from increasing its size, appears to have no specific function.

These intestinal caeca usually project anteriorly, as has been demonstrated in the genera *Porrocaecum*, *Contracaecum*, *Dujardinia*, and *Angusticaecum* (Hyman, 1951). However, occasionally, as in *Raphidascaris* and *Leidynema*, they project posteriorly. There may even be more than one diverticulum, as in the genus *Multicaecum*, a parasite in crocodiles. However, as stated these evaginations are exceptions to the normal simple tubular intestine of nematodes. In other exceptional cases, the intestine may function as a food storage organ and its lumen is lost. This happens in the adult female of *Meloidogyne* where there is no connection between the

TABLE VIII

INTESTINAL CELLS OF NEMATODES

Nematode	Height of intestinal cell (μ) (excluding microvilli)	Width of intestinal cell (μ)	Microvilli (μ)	Reference
Ancylostoma caninum	16	—	8 × 0.1	Andreassen (1968)
Ancylostoma caninum	—	—	3 × 0.09	Miller (1967)
Ascaris suum	100	10	5 × 0.09	Bretschneider (1954)
Ascaris suum	—	—	6 × 0.1	Kessel et al. (1961)
Ascaris suum	50	10	6 × 0.08	Sheffield (1964)
Ascaris suum	115	15	—	Del Castillo and Morales (1969)
Aspiculuris tetraptera	15	6	1.2 × ?	Lee and Anya (1968)
Capillaria hepatica	7	3	—	Wright (1963)
Dirofilaria immitis	70	—	—	Lee and Miller (1969)
Metastrongylus sp.	40	—	—	Jenkins and Erasmus (1969)
Neoaplectana carpocapsae (larva)	—	—	0.25 × 0.08	Poinar and Leutenegger (1968)
Nippostrongylus brasiliensis	—	—	1 × 0.2	Jamuar (1966)
Nippostrongylus brasiliensis	—	—	1 × ?	Lee (1969a)
Parascaris equorum	150	14	7 × 0.1	Joyon and Collin (1962)
Phocanema decipiens	—	—	4 × 0.1	Andreassen (1968)
Strongylus equinus	4000	500	—	Chitwood and Chitwood (1950)
Trichinella spiralis (larva)	—	—	0.7 × 0.1	Bruce (1966)

anus and the intestine and, to an even greater extent, in the Mermithidae where connection with both the pharynx and anus is lost.

Chitwood and Chitwood (1950) have attempted to classify nematode intestinal cells according to their number and have divided them into three groups, namely, oligocytous, polycytous, and myriocytous. The division into the first two groups is based on work done by Martini (1903) on embryonic development. Martini found that when ten cleavages had occurred and an organism with a theoretical number of 1024 cells had been formed, the expected number of cells in the endoderm should be 128. He noticed that this number was, in fact, much less, although the mesodermal cells of the somatic musculature of the meromyarian nematode that he examined had their correct theoretical number. Thus, nematodes such as *Rhabditis*, *Ditylenchus*, and *Strongylus*, which have less than 128 intestinal cells, are oligocytous; forms such as *Plectus*, *Enoplus*, and *Dorylaimus*, which have between 128 and a little over 8000 cells, are polycytous, whereas nematodes with well over 8000 odd intestinal cells, such as *Ascaris*, *Spironoura*, and *Dioctophyme* are myriocytous. Clearly, this type of classification only serves as a rough guide but it does draw attention to potential areas of research into the forces which control cell division and multiplication in the endoderm of nematodes.

The intestine has proved to be one of the anatomical regions of the nematode that is most suited for electron microscope studies. This is probably because it can normally be easily dissected out from within the nematodes, thus permitting rapid and uniform fixation and, for the same reason, embedding, cutting, and staining are facilitated.

As can be seen (Table VIII) most of the work done so far on the ultrastructure of intestinal cells has been on nematodes which are parasitic in animals. Thus, *Setaria cervi* (Kagei, 1961), *Litomosoides carinii* (Kagei, 1963), *Ancylostoma caninum* (Browne *et al.*, 1965; Miller, 1967; Andreassen, 1968), *Ascaris suum* (Bretschneider, 1954; Kessel *et al.*, 1961; Sheffield, 1964), *Parascaris equorum* (Joyon and Collin, 1962), *Capillaria hepatica* (Wright, 1963), *Nippostrongylus brasiliensis* (Jamuar, 1966; Lee 1969a,b), *Trichinella spiralis* (Bruce, 1966), *Aspiculuris tetraptera* (Lee and Anya, 1968), *Neoaplectana carpocapsae* (Poinar and Leutenegger, 1968), *Dirofilaria immitis* (Lee and Miller, 1969), and *Metastrongylus* sp. (Jenkins and Erasmus, 1969) all come under this category. However, work on *Rhabditis strongyloides* (Peebles, 1957) and the plant parasitic nematodes *Anguina calamagrostis* (Wu, 1968) and *Heterodera rostochiensis* (Wisse and Daems, 1968) suggests that the intestinal cell ultrastructure is basically similar throughout the group. This is not surprising in view of the similarities that exist, in some respects, with the intestinal cells of forms as far removed as the mammals. The classic examples are, of course the microvilli which project into the lumen of the intestine and make up the bacillary layer or brush border. These structures, although variable in length (Table VIII) and number [for instance, in the larva of *Heterodera rostochiensis* (Wisse and Daems, 1968) there are only a few and in the larva of *Nippostrongylus brasiliensis* they are short and widely spaced], are, nevertheless, all about 0.1 μ in diameter.

The microvilli are fingerlike projections of the plasma membrane into the intestinal region. In cross section it can be seen (Fig. 53) that each microvillus has an electron-dense central cytoplasmic core which is clearly visible

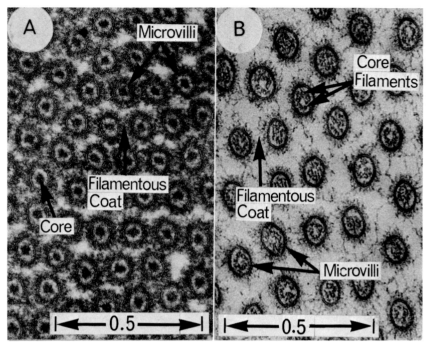

Fig. 53.   Electron micrographs of cross sections through intestinal microvilli. × 80,000.
(A) Microvilli of *Ancylostoma caninum*. (Courtesy of Dr. J. H. Miller; Miller, 1967.) (B)
Microvilli of *Ascaris suum*. (Courtesy of Dr. H. G. Sheffield; Sheffield, 1964.)

in the electron micrograph of a section cut through the intestinal epithelium
of *Ancylostoma caninum* (Fig. 53A). This core is made up of longitudinal
filaments which appear to be tubular, although this has not been established.
These filaments can be seen in the electron micrograph of a transverse
section cut through the microvilli of *Ascaris suum* (Fig. 53B). The microvilli
are covered with a fine filamentous coat or surface fuzz and occasionally
strands of this material extend out into the space between them (Fig. 53).
This material is PAS-positive and is thought to be mucopolysaccharide or
mucoprotein in nature (Wright, 1963; Bruce, 1966).

     The cores of the microvilli are joined at their bases by an electron-dense
network of fibrils which form a cytoplasmic region known as the terminal
web (Fig. 54). It has already been mentioned that microvilli and the nematode intestinal epithelium may vary in length and number; they may also
vary in shape. Thus, it has been shown that in *Metastrongylus* sp the microvilli are variable in form and possess dilated, balloonlike tips (Jenkins and
Erasmus, 1969) which give the appearance of being budded off into the

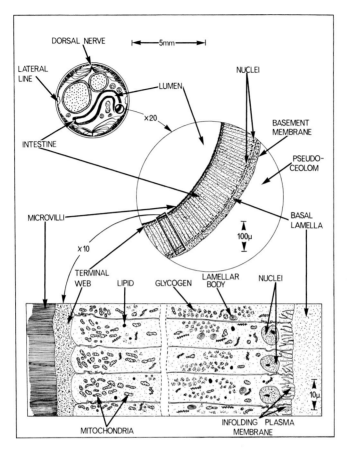

FIG. 54.   Diagram of a cross section through *Ascaris suum* showing enlargements of the intestinal cells.

lumen. These structures are thought to function as secretory cells in contrast to the usual microvilli whose presumed basic function is that of absorption. The cytoplasm at the base of the microvilli in forms such as *Dirofilaria immitis* (Lee and Miller, 1969) and the larva of *Trichinella spiralis* (Bruce, 1966) is not differentiated to form a distinct terminal web.

Usually, the cytoplasm of a nematode intestinal epithelial cell is rich in mitochondria, Golgi complexes, endoplasmic reticulum, ribosomes, glycogen granules, and lipid droplets, and contains a nucleus which is usually either in the middle of the cell or, more commonly in myriocytous nematodes, in its basal portion. In addition, lamellar bodies or electron-dense granules with myelin figures of varying sizes and configurations have been observed in the middle of the intestinal cells in a number of nematodes including *Ascaris suum* (Sheffield, 1964), *Ancylostoma caninum* (Andreassen, 1968), *Trichinella spiralis* (Bruce, 1966), *Metastrongylus* sp (Jenkins and Erasmus, 1969), and *Dirofilaria immitis* (Lee and Miller, 1969). The function of these lamellar bodies is unknown. They are abundant in the anterior region of the intestine in *Dirofilaria immitis* and are rarely found in the posterior region. It has been suggested (Weinstein, 1966) that these cyto-plasmic structures should be classified as lysosomes. In *Ascaris suum* these structures vary in size from approximately 0.5 to 10 μ and are present in nearly all of the intestinal cells. They are thought by Sheffield (1964) and Jenkins and Erasmus (1969) to be involved in the destruction and elimination of waste materials. It seems feasible to me to speculate at this stage on another possible function for these structures, namely, that they may be associated with the synthesis of the mucopolysaccharide or mucoprotein which is found in many nematodes as PAS-positive extracellular material in the lumen close to the microvilli and sometimes referred to as glyocalyx (Miller, 1967). Also, the lamellar bodies in *Ascaris suum* are similar in size and configuration to those in the rectal gland cytoplasm of *Meloidogyne javanica* (Bird and Rogers, 1965), described later in this chapter, which are thought to secrete a mucopolysaccharide material.

Each intestinal cell is surrounded by a plasma membrane and the whole intestine is separated from the pseudocoelom by a basement membrane (Fig. 55). The number of cells seen in a cross section of the intestine varies, as has already been mentioned, from one or two to roughly about eight hundred in an adult female of *Ascaris suum*. These two extremes are depicted diagrammatically for *Ascaris suum* (Fig. 54) and for the larva of *Trichinella spiralis* showing an intestine consisting of four cells in cross section (Fig. 55).

Light photomicrographs and electron micrographs both show that in an intestinal cell of *Ascaris* there is an abundance of variously shaped mito-chondria in the apical end just beneath the terminal web (Fig. 54). In the middle of the cell there are numerous vesicles of rough endoplasmic reticu-lum, lamellar bodies and large deposits of glycogen and the nucleus lies in the basal portion (Fig. 54). In forms in which only a few cells line the intes-tine, the nucleus and various subcellular cytoplasmic components are rather randomly distributed throughout the cell (Fig. 55). Some idea of the varia-bility in intestinal cell number and shape is given by the diagrams shown by Chitwood and Chitwood (1950) of transverse sections through this region of many different species of nematodes examined under the light microscope.

In addition to glycogen and lamellar bodies, the intestinal cells of nema-todes often contain large protein and lipid or fat bodies. These make up the principal storage material in the infective larvae of many parasitic nema-todes. For instance, it has been calculated (Van Gundy *et al.*, 1967) that the lipid globules make up 30% of the total dry weight of larvae of *Meloidogyne*

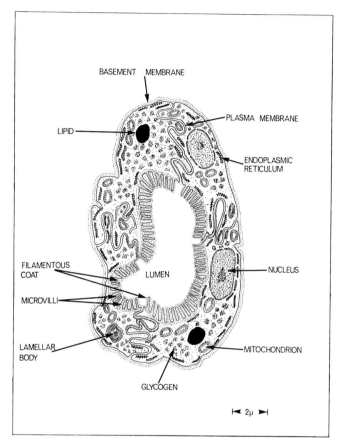

BASEMENT MEMBRANE

PLASMA MEMBRANE

LIPID

ENDOPLASMIC
RETICULUM

FILAMENTOUS
COAT

LUMEN

NUCLEUS

MICROVILLI

LAMELLAR
BODY

MITOCHONDRION

GLYCOGEN

2μ

FIG. 55. Diagram of a cross section through the intestine of *Trichinella spiralis* as seen with the aid of the electron microscope. (After Bruce, 1966.)

javanica. It was calculated by measuring electron micrographs of cross sections through the intestines of larvae of *Meloidogyne javanica* and *Tylenchulus semipenetrans* that lipid made up 43 and 53%, respectively, of the total area and that about 60% of this lipid in *M. javanica* was lost through physiological aging in 10 days.

These fat bodies or lipid droplets in nematodes are large structures, usually several microns in size and clearly visible under the light microscope. Their irregular shape is most pronounced in sections viewed under the electron microscope (Wisse and Daems, 1968).

Another type of intestinal cell inclusion consists of crystalline spheres, about 1–3 μ in diameter, called rhabditin by Cobb (1914), who first described these structures in detail in the intestinal cells of *Rhabditis monohystera*. Cobb found that these rhabditin structures, which appeared to be made up of a carbohydratelike substance, were "arranged in relatively large groups round the centrally located nuclei of the intestinal cells, and sometimes constitute a large fraction of the mass of the cells." Cobb (1914) showed that these structures exhibit birefringence when examined under polarized light and it may be that, as Weinstein (1966) suggests, they are lysosomes.

Weinstein (1966) found that birefringent inclusions in the intestinal cells of *Nippostrongylus brasiliensis* show a fine granular structure enclosed in a single membrane when observed under the electron microscope. One would tend to expect lamellar bodies to have optical activity due to the orderly array of their parallel membranes, as suggested by Sheffield (1964), and it is equally likely that Cobb's rhabditin structures may be lamellar bodies.

Some nematodes possess a network of muscle around at least part of the intestine. These fibers do not form a continuous layer and they are usually confined to the posterior part of the intestine (Chitwood and Chitwood, 1950).

In most nematodes, food is moved along the intestine by the ingestion of more food and by the locomotory activity of the worm. However, Lee and Anya (1968) observed that in oxyurid nematodes there was a definite contraction of the intestine, indicating muscular control. They examined living specimens of *Aspiculuris tetraptera* and noticed that the intestine, which can be readily seen through the transparent body wall of this nematode, frequently underwent peristalticlike movements. When this material was sectioned, it was found that the outer surface of the whole intestine was covered with a network of fibrous material. When viewed under the electron microscope, it was revealed that this network consisted of muscle fibers similar in structure to those in the nematode's body wall and whose myofilaments consist of thick and thin filaments. This muscle is attached to the basal lamella and its surface adjacent to the pseudocoelom is covered by a thin amorphous layer of material. Lee and Anya (1968) also noticed that fibers ran from the surface of this intestinal muscle network to the body wall and also to the nematode's reproductive system. This intestinal muscle is considered to be specialized somatic muscle rather than a type of *muscularis mucosae* and connections between the somatic muscle and the intestine have already been described in Chapter 6 on musculature.

A number of microorganisms have been detected in the lumen of the nematode intestine. These include a species of flagellate protozoan thought to belong to the genus *Chilomastix* which has been observed in the gut of *Nippostrongylus brasiliensis* (Jamuar, 1966) both by phase contrast microscopy, which shows them in constant motion, and by electron microscopy, which resolves the fine structure of their flagella in both transverse and longitudinal sections.

In their observations on the ultrastructure of the intestine of *Aspiculuris tetraptera*, Lee and Anya (1968) noticed that yeastlike microorganisms in the lumen were attached to the apical surface of the intestinal cell and were apparently responsible for reducing the number of microvilli. In addition, these workers detected a number of rodlike bacteria which mostly lay free in the lumen.

It is certain that, as further studies on the fine structure of the intestine of various species of nematodes are made, more of these different sorts of microorganisms will be discovered and our knowledge of their influence on the physiology of nematodes will increase.

IV. The Proctodeum

The proctodeum or rectum is a cuticle-lined invagination into which rectal glands open in many nematodes. In the female, the proctodeum normally consists of a simple tube leading to the anus, whereas in the male, the reproductive system opens into it to form a cloaca which contains the spicules and other copulatory structures which will be discussed in more detail in Chapter 11.

The intestine is modified to form an intestinorectal valve at its junction with the rectum. This is a very simple structure (Chitwood and Chitwood, 1950) and in oligocytous forms such as *Rhabditis*, it consists of the posterior parts of intestinal cells surrounded by a sphincter muscle. In polycytous and myriocytous nematodes, the intestinal cells, which are smaller and more numerous, may form a valve projecting into the rectal lumen. The intestinorectal valve is closed by means of a unicellular sphincter muscle which is thought to be universally present in the Nematoda (Chitwood and Chitwood, 1950).

In *Nippostrongylus brasiliensis* (Lee, 1968) a ring of cells without microvilli separates the intestine from the rectum. Lee noted that the cuticle of the rectum is much thinner than the external cuticle in this nematode and that the cells of the rectum contain a nucleus, mitochondria, and a small amount of rough endoplasmic reticulum. The rectal cuticle in *Plectus* (Maggenti, 1961) is thicker on its ventral surface along which a median groove runs throughout its length. In nematodes such as the dorylaims, a distinct region known as the prerectum occurs between the intestine and the rectum.

The anus consists of a slitlike structure on the ventral surface, whose opening is controlled by the unicellular, H-shaped depressor ani muscle previously mentioned in Chapter 6 on musculature, which acts by raising the dorsal wall of the rectum and pulling on the posterior lip of the anus to open it.

V. Glands

Information on the structure and function of glands associated with the digestive system in nematodes has in the past been limited to a few paragraphs in most texts.

Thanks to the use of a combination of techniques, including anesthetics, different types of light microscopy, histochemistry, and electron microscopy, it has been possible to observe these structures at high magnification in living specimens as well as the ultrastructure of their internal components.

It is clear that the reason why these glands have not been described before in some specimens, is that they are extremely difficult to resolve clearly in fixed material; even in the living state, they can be detected much more readily with the aid of phase or interference contrast microscopy than with normal transmitted light microscopy. Again, even with these aids, the movements of these nematodes often prevent the observer from using high-powered objectives unless an anesthetic is employed.

These glands fall into two main classes, namely, the esophageal or pharyngeal glands which enter the stomodeum, and the rectal glands which enter the proctodeum.

A. The Esophageal Glands

Typically there are three, uninucleate esophageal glands, one dorsal and two ventrolateral or subventral, although, in some forms such as the Enoplida, Spirurida, and Dorylaimida, they may be multinucleate or uninucleate and three, five [as in *Longidorus* (Aboul-Eid, 1969)], or seven in number, but this is unusual.

These glands connect with the lumen of the esophagus by means of cuticularized ducts, often by way of a terminal swelling or ampulla. The dorsal gland usually opens much further forward than do the subventrals and may open into or close to structures such as teeth or stylets. However, in some instances, all three glands may open into the buccal cavity or all may open further back in the esophagus, but this is atypical.

Christie (1960) suggests that these glands are of two kinds. Evidence for this conclusion is based partly on morphological grounds, namely, the different positions of their orifices, and partly on developmental grounds, namely, the marked difference in the genus *Agamermis* between the multinucleate dorsal esophageal (salivary) gland and the two subventral glands which atrophy after the larva of this genus enters its host. The evidence that is accumulating supports the contention that the esophageal glands are of two kinds, each type possibly having several functions. Sometimes these glands may be enlarged for a particular purpose, as in the case of the infective stage of the nematode *Tripius sciarae* where the two salivary glands are involved in penetration of the host (Poinar and Doncaster, 1965). These glands are probably homologous with the two subventral esophageal glands of other nematodes. In *Howardula aoronymphium*, a nematode parasitic in the larvae of drosophilid flies (Welch, 1959), it is difficult to separate the dorsal gland from the subventrals. These glands reach their largest size in fertilized females when the esophageal lumen is displaced ventrally by the enlarged dorsal gland which in turn becomes deflated after the nematode has penetrated into its final host. It is thought (Welch, 1959) that this gland is associated with "the production of a material for penetration into the final host," presumably in much the same way as the genus *Agamermis* is thought to produce a chitinase (Christie, 1960).

Sometimes the dorsal esophageal gland may be more highly developed than the subventrals. In adult *Nippostrongylus* (Lee, 1969a), for instance, the two subventrals open into the esophageal lumen in its posterior half, while the dorsal gland, which is very well developed, dilates into an ampulla which opens through a duct to the exterior at the tip of the nematode's mouth. This enables secretions from the dorsal gland to pass out of the nematode and on to the tissues of its host in a manner similar, in some respects, to that of the plant parasitic tylenchids which can, of course, inject their dorsal gland secretions directly into their hosts' cells.

In the free-living nematode *Pelodera lambdiensis* (Doncaster, 1962) the dorsal esophageal gland lies embedded in the radial muscles of the posterior half of the second bulb and opens into the anterior end of the procorpus, while the two subventral glands lie embedded in the anterior half of the second bulb (Fig. 49) and open into the posterior half of the first bulb.

The structure of the esophageal glands in both larvae and adults of *Meloidogyne javanica* has been observed using both the light and electron microscopes (Bird, 1967, 1968a,b, 1969; Bird and Saurer, 1967). It was noted that, shortly before the 2nd-stage larva of this species hatched from the egg, granules accumulated in the ducts of the subventral esophageal glands. These granules are seen most easily in living specimens observed under the phase or interference contrast microscopes. As these larvae are small, being approximately 475 μ long by 17 μ wide, and quite active, they have to be restrained under anesthetic during observation. When viewed under the electron microscope (Fig. 56A), these granules in the infective larva can be seen to be about 0.6–0.8 μ in diameter and to have an irregular shape and a distinct outer membrane. These granules are synthesized in the subventral glands from ribosomes associated with characteristic rough endoplasmic reticulum (Fig. 56B). They are thought to contain enzymes which assist both with penetration of the egg shell and the host root because,

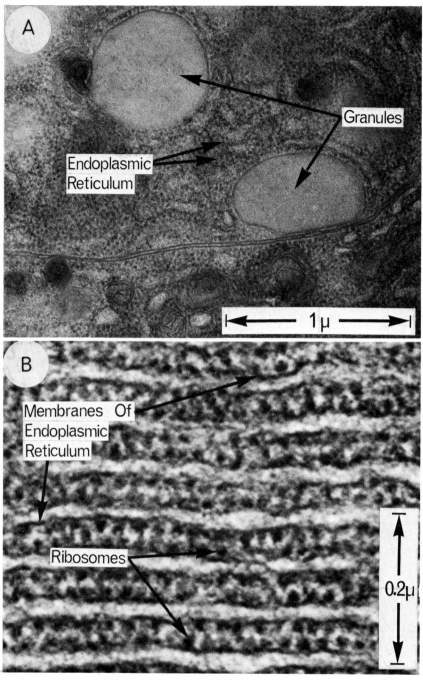

Fig. 56. Electron micrographs of cross sections through a subventral esophageal gland of an infective larva of *Meloidogyne javanica* (Bird 1968a). (A) Granules, × 50,000; (B) high-power electron micrograph showing structure of endoplasmic reticulum. × 200,000.

shortly after the larva penetrates its host's root, both chemical and morphological changes take place in the subventral glands. These changes can be
observed most readily by comparing the subventral glands of an infective
larva with those from a larva which had entered its host plant 2 days previously (Fig. 57). It can be seen under phase contrast that the subventral
glands of the infective larva are granular, whereas those of the parasitic larva
are not and so are much more difficult to detect. However, when these larvae

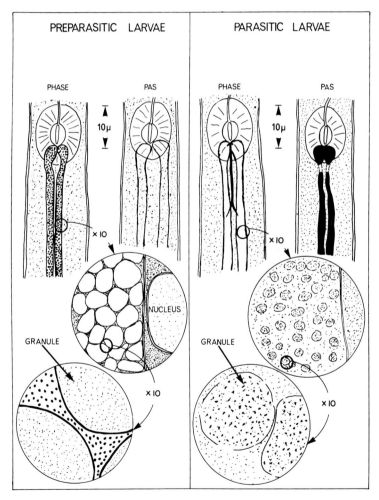

Fɪɢ. 57. Diagrams depicting both histochemical and morphological changes that take
place in the subventral esophageal glands of *Meloidogyne javanica* with the onset of parasitism.
(Bird, 1971.)

are stained by means of the PAS technique, the subventral glands of the parasitic larva stain much more strongly than do those of the infective larva (Fig. 57). Clearly, these glands undergo considerable change as the environment of the nematode changes. The changes become even more apparent when observed under the electron microscope (Fig. 57). Thus, the granules in the subventral glands of the parasitic larva differ from those in the infective larva in that they are smaller, lack a distinct surrounding membrane, and have a speckled appearance.

As these parasites grow in their hosts' roots, the dorsal esophageal gland enlarges and the subventrals become smaller. In adult females of *Meloidogyne javanica*, the dorsal esophageal gland clearly has a most important role in feeding, a role which was first demonstrated in this genus by Linford (1937) and subsequently demonstrated in various other nematodes, as will be discussed later in this chapter. In *Meloidogyne*, the dorsal gland cell nucleus lies behind the median bulb and it is here that much of the synthesis of the granules appears to take place. This gland extends anteriorly to swell into an ampulla just before the terminal duct which connects with the esophageal duct at the base of the buccal stylet.

The granules of the dorsal esophageal gland in *Meloidogyne* (Figs. 58 and 59B) differ from those found in the subventral esophageal glands of the infective larva in that they are a little smaller, having an average diameter of about 0.5 to 0.6 μ, and do not appear to be bounded by a membrane. Furthermore, they have invaginations which give rise to irregularities in their internal structure.

Dorsal esophageal gland granules have also been examined under the electron microscope in *Ditylenchus dipsaci* (Yuen, 1968a) in which they appear similar in structure to those in *Meloidogyne*, although smaller, and in larvae and adults of *Nippostrongylus brasiliensis* (Lee, 1968, 1969a). In the larva of *N. brasiliensis* they are of similar size to those in *Meloidogyne*, but their structure appears to be variable (Fig. 59A). Some of them resemble the dorsal esophageal gland granules of *Meloidogyne* in that they have similar internal irregularities, although they appear to be bounded by a membrane but other adjacent granules are bounded by multilayered membranes which either surround a homogeneous matrix or a vacuolated matrix. Lee (1968) has observed these granules in living larvae under phase contrast moving anteriorly along the gland. In *Nippostrongylus brasiliensis* the components of all three glands appear to be similar in the larval stage. In adults (Lee, 1969a) the secretory granules of the dorsal esophageal gland appear to resemble those described in *Meloidogyne* (Bird, 1969) although they seem to be smaller. It is possible that some of the morphological differences described in these granules viewed under the electron microscope may be partly due to differences in methods of fixation, staining, and embedding.

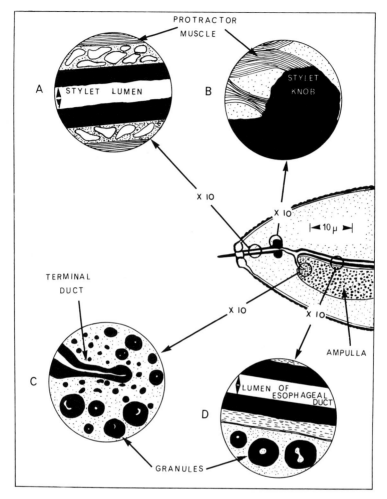

Fig. 58. Diagrams showing the dorsal esophageal gland ampulla and duct and their relationship to the buccal stylet in a female specimen of *Meloidogyne javanica*. (Bird, 1971.)

By means of the UV microspectrograph and by various histochemical tests, it has been shown (Bird and Saurer, 1967; Bird, 1968b) that these granules in *Meloidogyne javanica* consist predominantly of protein and carbohydrate and do not appear to contain either lipid, nucleic acids, or the following enzymes—acid phosphatase, alkaline phosphatase, succinic dehydrogenase, cytochrome oxidase, leucine aminopeptidase, and esterase—although Lee (1969a) detected nonspecific esterase in the region of the esophagus of the 3rd stage larvae of *Nippostrongylus brasiliensis* where the

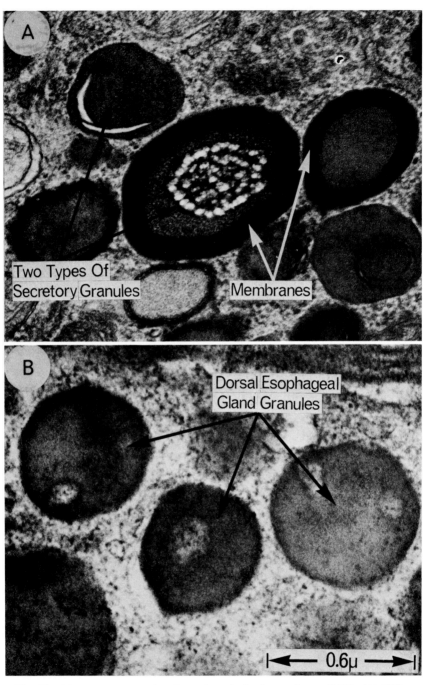

Fig. 59.   Electron micrographs of esophageal gland granules. × 67,000. (A) Different types of granules in *Nippostrongylus brasiliensis*. (Courtesy of Dr. D. L. Lee; Lee, 1968.) (B) Dorsal esophageal gland granules in a female specimen of *Meloidogyne javanica*.

secretory granules were most abundant. Certainly it seems likely that these granules in nematodes may be associated with enzymes such as chitinase or various proteinases which cannot, at the moment, be easily detected by histochemical techniques, or they may contain enzyme precursors which lead to the production of enzymes when in contact with the cytoplasm of the host.

It is known that the material exuded from the dorsal esophageal gland through the stylet of adult female *Meloidogyne javanica* contains basic protein with some of the properties of histones (Bird, 1968b) as well as glycoproteins and/or mucopolysaccharides. It is these substances which are responsible for the development, control and maintenance of the tumorlike giant cells in the numerous species of plants on which these nematodes feed (Bird, 1961, 1962).

Although enzymes have not yet been detected in the buccal exudates from plant parasitic nematodes, they have been reported from nematodes such as *Strongyloides*, *Ancylostoma*, and *Nippostrongylus* (Lewert, 1958), causing host tissue alterations as they penetrate.

B. The Rectal Glands

The number of rectal glands varies in different species and also varies within the same species depending on the sex. Rectal glands are completely absent in some groups of nematodes.

The early literature on these glands has been reviewed by Chitwood and Chitwood (1950), who point out that in forms such as the rhabditoids, there are six of these glands in the male and three in the female. They are rarely, if ever, found in members of the Aphasmidia or Adenophorea although Maggenti (1961) describes three of these structures in females of *Plectus parietinus*. These rectal glands were at least three times the size of the other rectal epithelial cells.

The six rectal gland cells of adult female *Meloidogyne javanica*, perhaps because of their size, recently have been studied more than those of any other nematode (Maggenti and Allen, 1960; Minton, 1965; Bird and Rogers, 1965). They are approximately 100 μ long and 40 μ wide and each contains a large, irregularly shaped nucleus of about 25 μ in diameter which contains a nucleolus about 10 μ in diameter.

In *Meloidogyne*, as has been previously mentioned in Chapter 6, the rectal glands produce a gelatinous matrix which is extruded through the anus as a result of rhythmic contractions of the depressor ani muscle. By means of histochemical and chromatographic techniques, it has been shown (Bird, 1958; Bird and Rogers, 1965) that this gelatinous matrix consists predominantly of protein and mucopolysaccharide with traces of lipid and some enzymes.

When sections of these rectal gland cells are examined under the electron microscope (Bird and Rogers, 1965), some very interesting structures are revealed (Figs. 60 and 61). The nuclear envelop or membrane is indistinct, as are the membranes of the Golgi bodies, and this is possibly a reflection of the intense synthesis of protein which is taking place. The Golgi bodies occur close to structures of variable size known as multivesicular lamellar bodies (Fig. 61) which have also been detected in the intestine of *Ascaris* (Sheffield, 1964) and *Metastrongylus* (Jenkins and Erasmus, 1969). Similar structures, which are thought to be associated with the synthesis of mucopolysaccharide, have been observed in cells of the gill epithelium of the salamander *Amblystoma mexicanum* (Schulz and De Paola, 1958) and in the cytoplasm of HeLa cells (Robbins *et al.*, 1964). These multivesicular lamellar bodies are thought to act as frameworks on which enzymes of many different types may be supported.

The rectal glands in nematode larvae are difficult to resolve. In *Meloidogyne javanica* infective larvae they become visible after staining by means of the PAS technique (Bird and Saurer, 1967) and consist of a single, bulblike

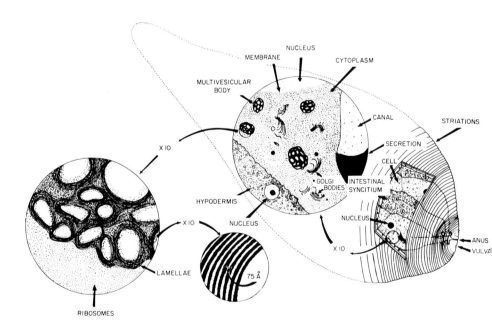

Fig. 60. Diagram showing the position and ultrastructure of the rectal glands in the posterior region of a female of *Meloidogyne javanica*. (Bird and Rogers, 1965.)

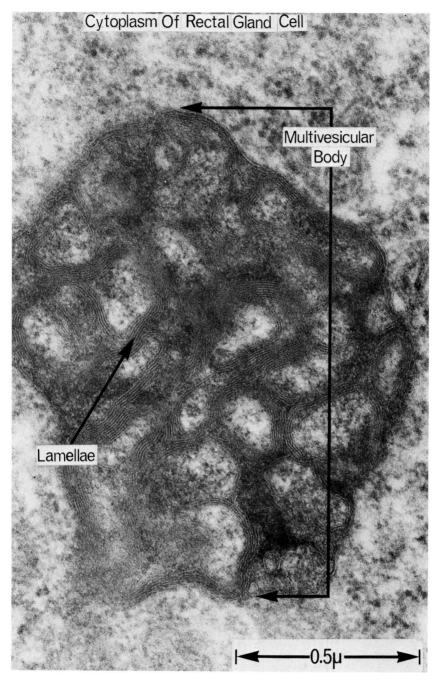

Cytoplasm Of Rectal Gland Cell

Multivesicular Body

Lamellae

|←————0.5μ————→|

FIG. 61. High-power electron micrograph of a section through a multivesicular lamellar body in the rectal gland cell cytoplasm of a female specimen of *Meloidogyne javanica*, × 100,000. (Bird and Rogers, 1965.)

231

structure. This structure is more difficult to see in the parasitic larvae, as it tends to become obscured because of the growth of the nematode.

VI. Function

I propose to consider the functions of the digestive system under the four headings of feeding, secretion, excretion and defecation.

A. FEEDING

The pharynx or esophagus is normally the only obviously motile part of the digestive system in nematodes. An exception to this is, of course, the peristaltic movement described above (Lee and Anya, 1968) in the intestine of *Aspiculuris tetraptera*. In *Ascaris* this pharyngeal pump has been shown to have a very high capacity (Mapes, 1966; Del Castillo and Morales, 1969). It is thought to function as a simple two-stage diaphragm pump. The contraction of the myofibrils transforms the narrow, cuticle-lined lumen into a wide, triangular canal (Fig. 62A, 1 and 2) and this leads to the development of a negative pressure which results in food being sucked in through the mouth. When the myofilaments relax, the lumen narrows again and the increased pressure leads to the food being ejected into the intestine. This posterior flow of food is controlled by a nonreturn valve at each end of the esophagus. It has been estimated by Mapes (1966) that the suction force generated by this pharyngeal pump should be well above 1 atm and thus it can easily bring about the ingestion of food against the internal pressure of the nematode which, as has been mentioned previously, has a mean value of about 70 mmHg.

The rate of pumping of the pharynx during feeding is rapid and occurs at least once every 4 sec in those nematodes in which it has been measured (Table IX) and may occur up to 20 times a second in short bursts (Crofton, 1966).

The feeding habits of free-living and migratory plant parasitic nematodes lend themselves to observation much more readily than do those of the sedentary plant parasitic nematodes or nematodes parasitic in animals. The reasons for this are of course, that observations of this sort invariably necessitate *in vitro* techniques which are not strictly physiological for parasitic forms.

Linford and his co-workers (Linford and Oliveira, 1937; Linford, 1937 1942; Linford *et al.*, 1949; Rhoades and Linford. 1961), using simple techniques, made careful observations which were undoubtedly responsible for

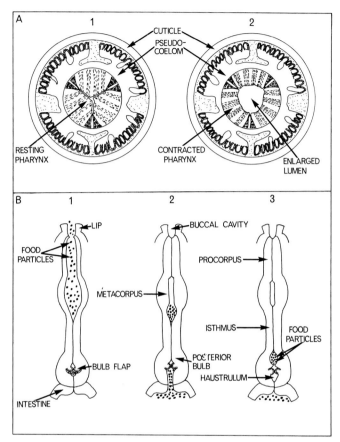

Fig. 62. Diagrams illustrating some of the changes which take place in the nematode pharynx during feeding. (A) Pharynx of *Ascaris* in' the resting and contracted states. (After Mapes, 1966.) (B) Path taken by food particles through the pharynx of a rhabditid during feeding. (After Lee, 1965.)

stimulating interest in this field. Linford's observations drew attention to the role of the dorsal esophageal glands in the feeding of both predatory and parasitic forms; his paper (Linford, 1937) on the feeding of *Meloidogyne* in root tissue is, in some respects, still unsurpassed.

The first detailed observations on nematode feeding mechanisms were made by Doncaster (1962) on the genera *Rhabditis* and *Pelodera* using cine-photomicrographic techniques. In *Pelodera lambdiensis* the process of feeding consists of a repeated cycle of actions which can overlap each other. Ingestion in this nematode is accomplished by a sudden contraction of the radial muscles in the procorpus and first bulb (Figs. 49 and 62B) which causes

TABLE IX

RATE OF PUMPING OF THE PHARYNX IN NEMATODES

Nematode	Rate (pumps/min)	Reference
Meloidogyne sp (larva)	180–240	Linford (1942)
Paratylenchus minutus	80–200	Linford *et al.*, (1949)
Paratylenchus projectus	100–180	Rhoades and Linford (1961)
Paratylenchus dianthus	100–180	Rhoades and Linford (1961)
Ancylostoma caninum	120–250	Wells (1931)
Ancylostoma caninum	240	Roche *et al.* (1962)
Ditylenchus destructor	120	Anderson (1964)
Ditylenchus destructor	257	Doncaster (1966)
Ditylenchus myceliophagus	267	Doncaster (1966)
Rhabditis axei	300	Mapes (1965b)
Panagrellus silusiae		
Corpus	120–240	Mapes (1965b)
Isthmus	60–120	Mapes (1965b)
Posterior bulb	60–120	Mapes (1965b)
Ascaris lumbricoides	240	Mapes (1966)
Ascaris lumbricoides	1200	Crofton (1966)
	(short bursts)	
Hemicycliophora	15–120	McElroy and Van Gundy
arenaria		(1968)

the lumen to enlarge so that it is nearly circular in cross section and food is sucked back as far as the anterior part of the isthmus (Fig. 62B, 1). The food is passed back along the isthmus by a wave of contraction which draws it to just in front of the bulb flaps (Fig. 62B, 3). From here it is drawn between the bulb flaps by dilation of the haustrulum which leads to an inversion of these flaps (Fig. 62B, 1). After this the esophagointestinal valve dilates and the food is passed into the intestine (Fig. 62B, 2), this process being accelerated by the closure of the haustrulum. The bulb flaps (Figs. 49B and 62B) are thought (Doncaster, 1962) to serve both to crush food particles and to close the valve in the posterior bulb when they invert. However, Mapes (1965b) was unable to detect breakdown of food in the posterior bulb of *Rhabditis* and concluded that the principal role of the bulb flaps was a valvular rather than a crushing one.

Mapes (1965b) examined pumping of the pharynx in *Panagrellus, Aplectana*, and *Rhabditis* and concluded that the passage of food through to the intestine was a complex process involving three stages in the first two genera and two stages in *Rhabditis*. He also concluded that regurgitation of the intestinal contents was prevented both by valves and by the internal pressure of the nematode forcing the walls of the pharynx together.

Following the work of Linford described above, on the feeding of stylet-bearing plant parasitic nematodes, a number of detailed studies have been made. Both Anderson (1964) and Doncaster (1966) have studied the feeding mechanisms of migratory plant parasitic nematodes belonging to the genus *Ditylenchus* and McElroy and Van Gundy (1968) have observed this process in *Hemicycliophora arenaria*. Generally speaking, these processes are similar and will be described together.

Digestive juices which originate from the dorsal esophageal gland, which is filled with small, refractive, granulelike bodies, as in *Meloidogyne* (Fig. 58), are injected into the host plant cell by means of the buccal stylet. Intact granules were not observed being injected into the cells. During feeding, a distinct zone develops around the stylet tip in the host cell. There are two feeding phases. The first is the injection or salivation phase, during which the flow of juices into the host cell may be enhanced by contractions of the lateral muscles of the median bulb. The second phase is the ingestion phase, during which rhythmical contraction of the posterior part of the esophagus associated with the median bulb and, in some forms, the eso-phago-intestinal valve or cardia, results in the ingestion of material from the host.

Both Anderson (1964) and Doncaster (1966) noticed that the nematode was firmly attached to the cell on which it was feeding and that it had to move its head vigorously from side to side before it could detach its lips and retract its stylet on completion of feeding. McElroy and Van Gundy (1968) also commented on the firmness of this attachment in *Hemicyclio-phora arenaria* and these workers found that in this nematode it was brought about by an adhesive polysaccharide plug whose precise origin was unknown.

McElroy and Van Gundy (1968) have summarized the observations of various workers on feeding in seventeen different species belonging to the Tylenchidae and, as can be seen from a modification of their table (Table X), injection or salivation times range from 20 sec to 2 hr and ingestion times range from 0.5 min to 1 week. From the summary of work outlined in Table X, it has been postulated (McElroy and Van Gundy, 1968) that the more primitive nematodes, such as the fungal feeders belonging to the genus *Ditylenchus*, have a short spear, a relatively small median bulb, and use the cardia as their principal ingestion mechanism, whereas the more advanced parasitic forms have a large and well-developed median bulb and dorsal esophageal gland. The median bulb functions as the ingestion mechanism and there is a tendency for digestion to become extraoral, with an increase in ingestion time, and for the intestine to become a storage organ with a reduced lumen and a vestigial rectum. The chemical composition of the saliva from the dorsal esophageal gland of an adult female *Meloidogyne*

TABLE X

SALIVATION OR INJECTION TIME, INGESTION MECHANISM, AND INGESTION
TIME IN NEMATODES[a]

Nematode	Salivation or injection time	Ingestion mechanism	Ingestion time	Reference
Tylenchus emarginatus	20 sec	Median bulb	102 sec	Sutherland (1967)
Tylenchus agricola	—	Median bulb	6 min	Khera and Zuckerman (1963)
Tylenchus bryophilus	—	Median bulb	30–95 min	Khera and Zuckerman (1963)
Tetylenchus joctus	—	Median bulb	0.5–7 min	Zuckerman (1960)
Tylenchorhynchus claytoni	—	Median bulb	30 min	Krusberg (1959)
Tylenchorhynchus dubius	30 sec	Median bulb	10 min	Klinkenberg (1963)
Ditylenchus destructor	4–5 min	Cardia	10–15 min	Anderson (1964)
Ditylenchus destructor	41 min	Cardia	56 min	Doncaster (1966)
Neotylenchus linfordi	5–15 min	Cardia	35–180 min	Hechler (1962)
Pratylenchus crenatus	—	Median bulb	> 35 min	Klinkenberg (1963)
Meloidogyne sp	15 min	Median bulb	60 min	Linford (1937)
Rotylenchus uniformis	20 min	Median bulb	—	Klinkenberg (1963)
Helicotylenchus nannus	15 min	Median bulb	—	Sledge (1959)
Criconemoides xenoplax	—	Median bulb	18 hr	Thomas (1959)
Paratylenchus projectus	1–2 hr	Median bulb	3–7 days	Rhoades and Linford (1961)
Hemicycliophora similis	—	Median bulb	80 hr	Khera and Zuckerman (1963)
Hemicycliophora arenaria	1–2 hr	Median bulb	2–6 days	McElroy and Van Gundy (1968)

[a]Modified from McElroy and Van Gundy (1968).

javanica, a nematode which must be considered as an extreme in this type of parasitic development, has been considered above. Whether or not histonelike proteins make up part of these salivary secretions in other nematodes remains to be seen.

B. SECRETION

The role of the various glands associated with the digestive tract in secretion has already been considered above. The cells of these glands are associated with active protein and mucopolysaccharide synthesis and their products are shed through cuticle-lined ducts either into the stomodeum or proctodeum or directly to the exterior and function in either intra- or extraoral digestion or as external protective or adhesive structures.

The principal role of the intestine with its microvilli, which resemble those in all the higher forms of animals, appears to be absorption of food, although information on the precise mechanism involved in absorption in nematodes is lacking. However, as in the higher forms, the intestinal cells of nematodes also have a secretory function. The evidence for this is largely morphological and results from electron microscope studies. Secretory activity was first described in the intestinal epithelium of a nematode by Kessel *et al.* (1961), who observed blebs between the microvilli of *Ascaris suum* which they thought indicated a secretory process. Later, Wright (1963) drew attention to a potential secretory role for cells of the intestinal epithelium in nematodes as a result of his work on the ultrastructure of these cells in *Capillaria hepatica*. He stated that "the intestinal epithelium must be considered not only as a barrier across which nutrients must be transported, but also as a tissue of considerable importance in the synthetic processes of the organism as a whole." Sheffield (1964) reported blebs similar to those described by Kessel *et al.* (1961), also in *Ascaris suum*, and containing an amorphous mass of cytoplasm. These structures appear to rise from a swelling of the base of the microvillus which either becomes pinched off or bursts and releases its contents into the intestinal lumen. Whether these blebs contain enzymes for the digestion of food or whether they are associated with excretion has not yet been resolved.

Jamuar (1966) has detected many ribosomes and numerous secretory granules in the cytoplasm of intestinal cells of *Nippostrongylus brasiliensis* which suggests "the synthesis and secretion of digestive enzymes."

Most recently, Jenkins and Erasmus (1969) in their studies with the electron microscope on a species of *Metastrongylus* parasitic in the lungs of pigs, have shown, as mentioned above, that the intestinal cell microvilli of this nematode possess dilated tips containing tiny electron-dense particles. Similar vesicles with granular contents occur freely in the lumen and it appears that the tips may become budded off from the microvilli and may be associated with the passage of secretory material out into the lumen of the intestine.

Jenkins and Erasmus (1969) also observed lamellar bodies lying free in the lumen and suggest that the intestinal cells of *Metastrongylus* are involved in three different processes, namely, absorption, secretion, and excretion.

Physiological and biochemical observations on secretory processes in the nematode intestine, at the cell level, lag behind the morphological observations described above. The literature on nematode physiology and biochemistry, particularly with regard to enzymes, has been comprehensively reviewed quite recently (Lee, 1965; Rogers, 1969) and the reader is referred to these reviews for background information. Briefly, these experiments are somewhat limited because, as mentioned by Rogers (1969), apart from the work done on enzymes associated with extracorporeal digestion, there is no evidence that nematodes produce enzymes for extracellular digestion because extracts of intestinal tissues have been analyzed "rather than the material actually secreted into the lumen of the gut." Furthermore, it is important that studies on extracorporeal digestion be made under strictly aseptic conditions so that there is no chance of bacterial enzymatic contamination. Some idea of the problems which face the physiologist in this field of research will be realized when it is remembered that these conditions are often unphysiological for the nematodes.

Despite these technical difficulties, a wide range of enzymes has been detected in nematodes (Lee, 1965; Fairbairn, 1969; Rogers, 1969) including lipases, esterases, proteinases, and various carbohydrate-splitting enzymes, such as cellulase, pectinase, and chitinase, whose presence in tissue homogenates of plant parasitic nematodes has been well established by various workers.

The larvae of skin-penetrating genera, such as *Strongyloides*, *Ancylostoma*, and *Nippostrongylus*, have been shown (Lewert, 1958) to secrete enzymes which cause alterations to the glycoprotein connective tissues of their hosts and it seems equally probable that plant parasitic nematodes also secrete enzymes as they migrate through tissues. However, so far, there is little experimental evidence to demonstrate this beyond reports on the flow of secretions from the dorsal esophageal gland during feeding, as mentioned above. Enzymes have yet to be detected in these secretions which may only contain enzyme precursors (Bird, 1966, 1968b, 1969). The solution of these particular problems is dependent on the development of more specific and precise histochemical techniques and methods in enzymology.

C. Excretion

It has been estimated (Crofton, 1966) that the contents of the intestine of large nematodes of the genus *Ascaris* are completely emptied by defecation every 3 minutes. This high rate of flushing must severely limit the duration of enzymatic breakdown of food within the nematode. However, it makes it possible for the intestine to act as an excretory organ. This function of the intestine in *Ascaris* has already been mentioned in Chapter 9 in conjunction with Savel's work on the excretory system of *Ascaris lumbricoides* (Savel, 1955) and it has been calculated (Crofton, 1966) that water passes through the alimentary canal of this nematode at a rate which would easily enable excretory products to be dissolved and eliminated.

It seems likely that this excretory function may also be found associated with the alimentary tract in various other nematodes parasitic in animals and sharing a similar environment to that of *Ascaris*.

D. DEFECATION

Defecation in nematodes seems to have been first reported by Bastian (1866), who observed the process in *Dorylaimus stagnalis*. He noted that it involved some force, as sudden jets of clear fluid were expelled through the anal cleft at intervals of 4 or 5 min. It is now known that defecation in nematodes is mechanically controlled and always occurs when ingestion of food material has increased the volume of the body to a critical figure (Mapes, 1965b). For instance, in *Ascaris* (Mapes, 1966) the relationship between the rate of saline uptake and the periodicity of defecation is linear. In this nematode, defecation is followed by ingestion of saline equivalent to 10–13% of the body volume, after which defecation takes place again. Thus, defecation is the result of high turgor pressure in the pseudocoelom, brought about by the pharyngeal pump filling the intestine. It probably occurs in response to some type of stretch-receptor reaction when the pumping pressure is unable to overcome the pressure within the intestine (Crofton, 1966).

Defecation, as Bastian (1866) observed, is a violent process in nematodes; in *Ascaris* removed from saline, the jet of feces may be projected for a distance of almost 2 ft. This process is followed by a temporary shortening of the nematode's body due to the fall in turgor pressure following the loss of the intestinal contents.

VII. Summary

The nematode digestive system consists essentially of a simple tube, the intestine, which opens anteriorly through the mouth by way of an invagination, the stomodeum, and posteriorly through the anus by way of another invagination known as the proctodeum.

The stomodeum is made up of the mouth, essentially a six-lipped structure which is variously modified by reduction and partial fusion to give a wide variety of different structures, the buccal cavity or stoma whose structure reflects the nematode's method of feeding, and the pharynx or esophagus which is also extremely diverse in both structure and function.

The pharynx is a muscular pumping organ with a triradiate, cuticle-lined lumen. It contains radial muscles, esophageal glands, and valves which prevent the regurgitation of food. Electron microscope studies of the pharynx in different nematodes indicate that it is usually cellular rather than syncytial as was previously thought.

Pharyngeal muscles appear to consist of two types of fibers, radially directed or ordinary fibers which run from the side of the pharyngeal lumen to the periphery and consist of both thick and thin filaments and marginal fibers which run from the apices of the lumen to the periphery and consist of tightly packed bundles of filaments of one thickness. When the myofibrils contract, they transform the narrow, cuticle-lined lumen of the pharynx into a wide, triangular canal and food is sucked in through the mouth and ejected into the intestine when the myofibrils relax and the lumen closes. This flow is controlled by valves. The valve which separates the pharynx or esophagus from the intestine is called the esophagointestinal valve or cardia. This is triradiate and lined with cuticle and functions principally to prevent regurgitation of the intestinal contents, although it is also used as a pump in some forms.

There is considerable variability in the morphology of the nematode pharynx or esophagus, but generally it may be considered under three basic types, namely, esophagi that are entirely cylindrical, those in which there is an anterior nonmuscular part and a swollen glandular and muscular posterior part, and third, those which may be divided into three basic parts, a corpus, an isthmus, and a bulb; the corpus may be further modified to form a procorpus and a swollen, muscular metacorpus. The muscles of pumps such as the metacorpus are well supplied with mitochondria. In many plant parasitic nematodes, this structure is particularly well developed in what appear to be the most highly evolved parasitic forms.

The muscular activity of the nematode pharynx appears to be largely coordinated by means of an enteric or sympathetic nervous system whose principal components, detected by means of the electron microscope in transverse sections, are the dorsal and two subventral enteric nerves.

The nematode intestine is a simple tube consisting of a single layer of epithelial cells which, although they may vary in number in adults from about thirty cells to a million in large parasitic forms, nevertheless show remarkable constancy in the fine structure of individual cells, even though these may vary considerably in size.

The intestine is separated from the pseudocoelom by a basement membrane and each cell is surrounded by a plasma membrane. The number of cells seen in a cross section varies from one or two to about eight hundred. Each cell contains mitochondria, rough endoplasmic reticulum, glycogen, fat bodies and protein bodies, lamellar bodies, and a nucleus. The position of these cytoplasmic components varies according to the size and shape of the cell. Projecting into the lumen of the intestine are fingerlike extensions of the plasma membrane, the microvilli, which can vary in length but which are nearly always about 0.1 μ in diameter, as is the case in other animals in which these structures are described. They considerably increase the surface area of the intestine and are thought to be associated with absorption, although, in some cases, it appears that they are concerned with secretion.

In most cases food is moved along the intestine by the ingestion of more food and by the locomotory activity of the nematode, although some nematodes posses intestinal muscles which can bring about peristalticlike movements of this structure. These muscles have both thick and thin myofilaments and resemble those found in the body wall. In some nematodes in which the contents of the intestine are emptied at regular intervals, the intestine acts as an excretory organ.

The intestine is modified to form an intestinorectal valve at its junction with the proctodeum or rectum. The rectum consists of a cuticle-lined tube leading to the anus in females and it incorporates the opening of the reproductive system to form a cloaca in males.

The anus consists of a slitlike structure on the ventral surface whose opening is controlled by the H-shaped depressor ani muscle responding to stretch-receptors.

The principal glands associated with the digestive system in nematodes are the esophageal or pharyngeal glands which open into the stomodeum and the rectal glands which enter the proctodeum. Typically, there are three esophageal glands, one dorsal and two subventral. The number of rectal glands varies in different species and between the sexes in the same species. So far, there is little information on the physiological role that these glands have in many different species of nematodes. They have been studied most thoroughly in the genus *Meloidogyne* in which the esophageal glands appear to have important roles in hatching, host penetration, and the establishment of a complex host–parasite relationship; the rectal glands are responsible for the production of copious amounts of a gelatinous mucopolysaccharide matrix which serves to protect the eggs.

The ultrastructure and histochemical composition of these gland cells and their components are described, as well as the granular material exuded from the dorsal esophageal gland for several different genera of nematodes. In plant parasitic nematodes, feeding can be divided into two distinct phases. First of all there is the injection or salivation phase, during which material from the dorsal esophageal gland is injected into the host cell; second, the ingestion phase, during which food is taken up into the nematode. The precise nature of the ingested material is unknown but the salivary material that is injected into the host cell appears to contain basic proteins with histonelike properties.

REFERENCES

Aboul-Eid, H. Z. (1969). *Nematologica* **15**, 451.
Allen, M. W. (1960). *In* "Nematology" (J. N. Sasser and W. R. Jenkins, eds.), pp. 136–139. Univ. of North Carolina Press, Chapel Hill, North Carolina.
Anderson, R. V. (1964). *Phytopathology* **54**, 1121.
Andrássy, I. (1962). *Acta Zool (Budapest)* **8**, 241.
Andreassen, J. (1968). *Z. Parasitenk.* **30**, 318.
Bastian, H. C. (1866). *Phil. Trans. Roy. Soc. London* **156**, 545.
Bird, A. F. (1958). *Nematologica* **3**, 205.
Bird, A. F. (1961). *J. Biophys. Biochem. Cytol.* **11**, 701.
Bird, A. F. (1962). *Nematologica* **8**, 1.
Bird, A. F. (1966). *Nematologica* **12**, 471.
Bird, A. F. (1967). *J. Parasitol* **53**, 768.
Bird, A. F. (1968a). *J. Parasitol.* **54**, 475.
Bird, A. F. (1968b). *J. Parasitol.* **54**, 879.
Bird, A. F. (1969). *J. Parasitol.* **55**, 337.
Bird, A. F. (1971). *In* "Plant Parasitic Nematodes" (B. M. Zukerman, W. F. Mai, and R. A. Rohde, eds.), pp. 35–49. Academic Press, New York.
Bird, A. F., and Rogers, G. E. (1965). *Nematologica* **11**, 231.
Bird, A. F., and Saurer, W. (1967). *J. Parasitol.* **53**, 1262.
Bretschneider, L. H. (1954). *Proc. Kon. Ned. Akad. Wetensch., Ser. C* **57**, 524.
Browne, H. G., Chowdhury, A. B., and Lipscomb, L. (1965). *J. Parasitol.* **51**, 389.
Bruce, R. G. (1966). *Parasitology* **56**, 359.
Chitwood, B. G., and Chitwood, M. B., eds. (1950). "An Introduction to Nematology," 213 pp. Monumental Printing Co., Baltimore, Maryland.
Christie, J. R. (1960). *In* "Nematology" (J. N. Sasser and W. R. Jenkins, eds.), pp. 432–436. Univ. of North Carolina Press, Chapel Hill, North Carolina.
Clark, W. C. (1960). *Nematologica* **5**, 178.
Cobb, N. A. (1914). *J. Parasitol.* **1**, 40.
Cobb, N. A. (1919). *Contrib. Sci. Nematol.* **8**, 213.
Coomans, A., and de Coninck, L. (1963). *Nematologica* **9**, 85.
Crofton, H. D. (1966). "Nematodes," 160 pp. Hutchinson, London.
de Coninck, L. (1965). *In* "Traité de Zoologie" (P. P. Grassé, ed.), Vol. IV, pp. 1–217. Masson, Paris.
Del Castillo, J., and Morales, T. (1969). *In* "Experiments in Physiology and Biochemistry" (J. K. Kerkut, ed.), Vol II, pp. 209–273. Academic Press, New York.
Doncaster, C. C. (1962). *Nematologica* **8**, 313.
Doncaster, C. C. (1966). *Nematologica* **12**, 417.

Ellenby, C., and Wilson, E. M. (1969). *Nematologica* **15**, 290.

Fairbairn, D. (1969). *In* "Chemical Zoology" (M. Florkin and B. T. Scheer, eds.), Vol. III, pp. 361–378. Academic Press, New York.

Filipjev, I. N. (1934). *Smithson. Misc. Collect.* **89**, 1.

Filipjev, I. N., and Schuurmans Stekhoven, J. H. (1941). "A Manual of Agricultural Helminthology," 878 pp. Brill, Leiden.

Geraert, E. (1965). *Nematologica* **11**, 131.

Goldschmidt, R. (1905). *Zool. Jahrb. (Anat.)* **21**, 41.

Goodey, J. B. (1963). *Nematologica* **9**, 468.

Goodey, T. (1924a). *J. Helminthol.* **2**, 1.

Goodey, T. (1924b). *J. Helminthol.* **2**, 51.

Hechler, H. C. (1962). *Proc. Helminthol Soc. Wash,* **24**, 19.

Hirumi, H., Chen, T. A., Lee, K. J., and Maramorosch, K. (1968). *J. Ultrastruct. Res.* **24**, 434.

Hsü, H. F. (1929). *Z. Zellforsch. Mikrosk. Anat.* **9**, 313.

Hyman, L. H. (1951). "The Invertebrates," 572 pp. McGraw-Hill, New York.

Inglis, W. G. (1964). *Bull. Brit. Mus (Natur. Hist.) Zool.* **11**, 266.

Jamuar, M. P. (1966). *J. Parasitol.* **52**, 1116.

Jenkins, T., and Erasmus, D. A. (1969). *Parasitology* **59**, 335.

Jenkins, W. R., and Taylor, D. P. (1967). "Plant Nematology," 270 pp. Reinhold, New York.

Jones, F. G. W. (1965). *In* "Plant Nematology" (J. F. Southey, ed), Tech. Bull. No. 7, pp. 3–29. H. M. Stationery Office, London.

Joyon, L., and Collin, J. P. (1962). *C. R. Soc. Biol.* **156**, 651.

Kagei, N. (1961). *Acta Med. Univ. Kagoshima.* **3**, 237.

Kagei, N. (1963). *Acta. Med. Univ. Kagoshima.* **5**, 43.

Kessel, R. G., Prestage, J. J., Sekhon, S. S., Smalley, R. L., and Beams, H. W. (1961). *Trans. Amer. Microsc. Soc.* **80**, 103.

Khera, A., and Zuckerman, B. M. (1963). *Nematologica* **9**, 1.

Klinkenberg, C. H. (1963). *Nematologica* **9**, 502.

Krusberg, L. R. (1959). *Nematologica* **4**, 187.

Lee, D. L. (1965). "The Physiology of Nematodes," 154 pp. Oliver & Boyd. Edinburgh and London.

Lee, D. L. (1968). *J. Zool.* **154**, 9.

Lee, D. L. (1969a). *Symp. Brit. Soc. Parasitol.* **7**, 3.

Lee, D. L. (1969b). *Parasitology* **59**, 29.

Lee, D. L., and Anya, A. O. (1968). *J. Zool.* **156**, 9.

Lee, C. C., and Miller, J. H. (1969). *J. Parasitol.* **55**, 1035.

Lewert, R. M. (1958). *Rice. Inst. Pam* **45**, 97.

Linford, M. B. (1937). *Phytopathology* **27**, 824.

Linford, M. B. (1942). *Phytopathology* **32**, 580.

Linford, M. B., and Oliveira, J. M. (1937). *Science* **85**, 295.

Linford, M. B., Oliveira, J. M., and Ishii, M. (1949). *Pac. Sci.* **3**, 111.

Looss, A. (1905). *Rec. Egypt. Govt. Sch. Med.* **3**, 1.

López-Abella, D., Jiménez-Millán, F., and Garcia-Hidalgo, F. (1967). *Nematologica* **13**, 283.

McElroy, F. D., and Van Gundy, S. D. (1968) . *Phytopathology* **58**, 1558.

Maggenti, A. R. (1961). *Proc. Helminthol. Soc. Wash.* **28**, 118.

Maggenti, A. R., and Allen, M. W. (1960). *Proc. Helminthol. Soc. Wash.* **27**, 4.

Mapes, C. J. (1965a). *Parasitology* **55**, 269.

Mapes, C. J. (1965b). *Parasitology* **55**, 583.

Mapes, C. J. (1966). *Parasitology* **56**, 137.

Martini, E. (1903). *Z. Wiss. Zool.* **74**, 501.

Miller, J. H. (1967). *J. Parasitol.* **53**, 94.

Minton, N. A. (1965). *Proc. Helminthol. Soc. Wash.* **32**, 163.

Nichols, R. L. (1956). *J. Parasitol.* **42**, 363.

Peebles, C. R. (1957). *J. Parasitol.* **43**, Suppl., 45.

Poinar, G. O., and Doncaster, C. C. (1965). *Nematologica* **11**, 73.

Poinar, G. O., and Leutenegger, R. (1968). *J. Parasitol.* **54**, 340.

Raski, D. J., Jones, N. O., and Roggen, D. R. (1969). *Proc. Helminthol. Soc. Wash.* **36**, 106.

Reger, J. F. (1966). *J. Ultrastruct. Res.* **14**, 602.

Rhoades, H. L., and Linford, M. B. (1961). *Proc. Helminthol. Soc. Wash.* **28**, 185.

Robbins, E., Marcus, P. I., and Gonatas, N. K. (1964). *J. Cell Biol.* **21**, 49.

Roche, M., Martinez-Torres, C., and Macpherson, L. (1962). *Science* **136**, 148.

Rogers, W. P. (1969). *In* "Chemical Zoology" (M. Florkin and B. T. Scheer, eds.), Vol. III, pp. 379–428. Academic Press, New York.

Roggen, D. R., Raski, D. J., and Jones, N. O. (1967). *Nematologica* **13**, 1.

Savel, J. (1955). *Rev. Pathol. Comp. Hyg. Gen.* **55**, 213.

Schneider, A. (1866). "Monographie der Nematoden," 357 pp. Reimers, Berlin.

Schulz, H., and De Paola, D. (1958). *Z. Zellforsch. Mikrosk. Anat.* **49**, 125.

Sheffield, H. G. (1964). *J. Parasitol.* **50**, 365.

Sledge, E. B. (1959). *Nematologica* **4**, 356.

Sprent, J. F. A. (1962). *J. Parasitol.* **48**, 818.

Sprent, J. F. A. (1963). *Parasitology* **53**, 7.

Steiner, G. (1934). *J. Parasitol.* **20**, 66.

Sutherland, J. R. (1967). *Nematologica* **13**, 191.

Thomas, H. A. (1959). *Proc. Helminthol. Soc. Wash.* **26**, 55.

Van Gundy, S. D., Bird, A. F., and Wallace, H. R. (1967). *Phytopathology* **57**, 559.

Weinstein, P. P. (1966). *In* "Biology of Parasites" (E.J.L. Soulsby, ed.), pp. 143–154. Academic Press, New York.

Welch, H. E. (1959). *Parasitology* **49**, 83.

Wells, H. S. (1931). *J. Parasitol* **17**, 167.

Wisse, E., and Daems, W. T. (1968). *J. Ultrastruct. Res.* **24**, 210.

Wright, K. A. (1963). *J. Ultrastruct. Res.* **9**, 143.

Wright, K. A. (1965). *Can. J. Zool.* **43**, 689.

Wu, L.-Y. (1968). *Can. J. Zool.* **46**, 467.

Yuen, P. H. (1967). *Can. J. Zool.* **45**, 1019.

Yuen, P. H. (1968a). *Nematologica* **14**, 385.

Yuen, P. H. (1968b). *Nematologica* **14**, 554.

Zuckerman, B. M. (1960). *Nematologica* **5**, 253.

11
THE REPRODUCTIVE SYSTEM

I. Introduction

The majority of nematodes are dioecious organisms in which the males are smaller than the females and are equipped with various copulatory organs such as bursae, papillae, and spicules.

Both hermaphroditism and parthenogenesis have been shown to occur in nematodes. Crofton (1966) considers that hermaphroditism in nematodes is brought about by specialization to an ecological situation in which male and female individuals have only a slight chance of meeting one another. Hermaphroditism is, however, quite common in some groups such as the rhabditoids and occurs in species of free-living, soil-inhabiting nematodes such as *Caenorhabditis briggsae* and *Caenorhabditis elegans* (Nigon, 1949; Dougherty *et al.*, 1959) which are forms well known to physiologists. All laboratory cultures of *C. briggsae*, for instance, are descended from a single nematode which was isolated from the soil at Stanford University in California. In these hermaphroditic forms the gonad usually produces sperms first and these are stored until they fertilize the eggs which are produced from the same gonad after sperm formation is completed. Hermaphroditism presumably gives rise to progeny with a less variable genetic constitution than those produced by normal sexual reproduction. The obvious disadvantage of hermaphroditic forms is that they may not be able to withstand a fluctuating environment as successfully as a more genetically variable form. On the other hand, they may have evolved in a stable environment to which they have become particularly well adapted so that changes in the nematode's genetic constitution are more likely to be detrimental than advantageous.

Parthenogenesis is not uncommon in plant parasitic nematodes and has been reported in various genera including *Meloidogyne*, *Heterodera*, *Tylenchulus*, and *Hemicycliophora* (Tyler, 1933; Mulvey, 1958; Van Gundy, 1958, 1959). It is, perhaps, best known in the genus *Meloidogyne* where, in species such as *Meloidogyne javanica*, it is the normal means of reproduction. Males are usually only found in this species when the nematodes are exposed to some form of environmental stress (Triantaphyllou, 1960; Bird, 1970). Parthenogenesis appears to be a means by which the genus *Meloidogyne* can take full advantage of its highly specialized parasitic environment.

Parthenogenesis has also been demonstrated in the free-living, soil-inhabiting nematodes. Much information about reproduction has been obtained in these forms because of the comparative ease with which they have been cultured under laboratory conditions by workers such as Maupas (1900), Potts (1910), Honda (1925), and Nigon (1949).

Intersexes are found in some genera. These are individuals that have a blending of male and female characters. Usually they are females which show secondary male characteristics. For instance, Hirschmann and Sasser (1955) observed that *Ditylenchus triformis* had well-developed ovaries with uteri, vagina, and vulva. They also had spicules, bursal muscles, and genital papillae. In many cases these female intersexes copulated with males and were fertile. Male intersexuality has been reported in *Meloidogyne javanica* (Chitwood, 1949) where, in addition to its normal male complement, this species often has a range of secondary female characteristics.

The early literature on the anatomy of the reproductive system of nematodes has been reviewed by Chitwood and Chitwood (1950) and de Coninck (1965) and work on the physiology and cytology of reproduction in nematodes has been reviewed by Triantaphyllou and Hirschmann (1964), Nigon (1965), and Triantaphyllou (1971).

The sex organs are simple tubular structures which are continuous with their ducts so that neither sperm nor eggs can be shed into the body cavity. This continuity of sex organs and ducts enables the reproductive system to function efficiently despite the high turgor pressure of the pseudocoelomic cavity.

Usually there is one testis in the male and two ovaries in the female but there may be two testes in the male and some cases are known in which there is only a single ovary in the female.

In the past, work on the reproductive systems of nematodes, notably the large ascarids, has led to fundamental discoveries of great importance in zoology. As Nigon (1965) and Crofton (1966) have pointed out, the two most notable examples of this are the work of van Beneden (1883b), whose observations of individual chromosomes led to the discovery that equal amounts of nuclear material come from the sperm and the egg during fertilization, and that of Boveri (1899), who showed that the fate of the cell during embryogenesis was determined at early cleavage. Both of these discoveries profoundly influenced the sciences of genetics and embryology respectively.

   In this chapter I propose to consider principally the structure of the reproductive systems of normal, dioecious nematodes, dealing first of all with the male reproductive system, spermatogenesis, including the fine structure of sperm, and copulation, second, with the female reproductive system and oogenesis, including the fine structure of the oocyte, and finally with the types of fertilization and chromosome numbers in various nematodes.

II. The Male Reproductive System

   The male reproductive system arises from genital primordia which arise in the larval stages and which are identical for both sexes at this early stage of development. They have been observed and photographed under the electron microscope in the larvae of *Heterodera rostochiensis* (Wisse and Daems, 1968). The development of the reproductive systems from this early stage onward has been observed in various plant parasitic nematodes including *Tylenchulus semipenetrans* (Van Gundy, 1958), *Radopholus similis* (Van Weerdt, 1960), *Meloidogyne incognita* (Triantaphyllou, 1960), *Ditylenchus dipsaci* (Yuksel, 1960), and *Ditylenchus triformis* (Hirschmann, 1962). The stage of development of the genital primordium has proved to be a useful characteristic for differentiating the various larval stages in some instances. The manner in which the male and female genital primordia develop is often the only reliable way to distinguish males from females before the fourth molt. Thus, in *Radopholus similis* the two cells of the genital primordium in the male remain together, whereas in the female they become separated by somatic cells.

   Hirschmann (1962), in her detailed studies on the growth of *Ditylenchus triformis*, observed the genital primordium in this species even before the embryo had assumed the vermiform shape. The genital primordium in this nematode consists of a large, central germinal nucleus bordered by two small somatic nuclei (Fig. 63A), whereas in *Diploscapter coronata* (Hechler, 1968) there are two large germinal nuclei. The genital primordium increases

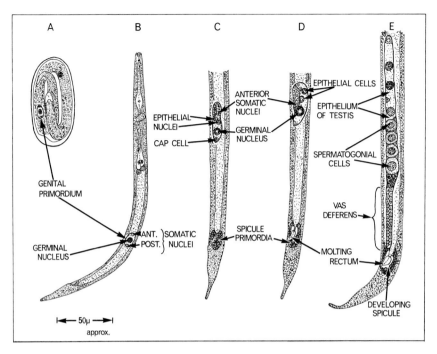

FIG. 63. Diagrams showing the development of the male reproductive system in *Ditylenchus triformis*. (After Hirschmann, 1962.)

slightly in size in the 2nd-stage larva (Fig. 63B) but does not divide until the second molt. The anterior somatic nucleus divides several times to give rise to several nuclei which eventually, in turn, give rise to the male gonoduct and the posterior somatic nucleus divides once to give a cap cell nucleus and a somatic nucleus which migrates anteriorly to the germinal nucleus and ultimately gives rise to the epithelial cells of the testis.

In the 3rd-stage male larva (Fig. 63C) the anterior part of the gonad consists of about twelve small cells which are set off from the posterior part which consists of two large epithelial nuclei, a germinal nucleus and a cap cell nucleus. In the rectal region a large group of small nuclei appears and these nuclei eventually give rise to the spicules and gubernaculum. At the third molt (Fig. 63D) the anterior group of cells has differentiated into two rows of small spherical cells which have turned backward and which grow posteriorly along the ventral side, whereas the germinal nucleus, cap nucleus, and epithelial nuclei have moved anteriorly. By the fourth stage (Fig. 63E) the anterior testicular parts of the testis are clearly distinguishable from the posterior somatic parts. The germinal nucleus has divided and there may be as many as four germinal nuclei. The end of the testicular region is marked by a slight constriction and this is followed by an epithelial part which consists of two rows of small spherical cells.

During the fourth molt, the male gonad is clearly differentiated into testis and vas deferens; the latter increases in length and its posterior end opens into the rectum at the completion of the molt; the spicules and gubernaculum become differentiated and at the completion of the molt there may be up to thirteen spermatogonial cells.

Maggenti (1970) in his phylogenetic analysis of the male reproductive system, uses the presence or absence of ejaculatory muscle and glands associated with the testis as criteria for dividing the major groups and points out that ejaculatory glands are associated with terrestrial nematodes of widely divergent types.

Nematodes are monorchic if they possess a single testis (Fig. 64A,B, and C) and diorchic if they have two testes (Fig. 64D). Normally there is a single testis in which the germ cells or spermatocytes are produced at one end, although in a few forms, such as members of the Dioctophymoidea and Trichuroidea, germ cell formation is not just confined to the end of the testis but occurs throughout its length, a condition known as hologonic in contrast to the more normal type which is known as telogonic. The male reproductive system normally consists of three parts, namely, the testis, the seminal vesicle, and the vas deferens (Fig. 64). It may be long and coiled, as in many of the nematodes parasitic in animals (Fig. 64A and B) (in *Parascaris equorum*, for instance, it consists of a single, coiled thread about 6 feet long), or relatively short and uncoiled, as in many of the free-living forms (Fig. 64C and D).

In telogonic nematodes the testis can be divided into two regions, a germinal zone incorporating the blunt tip of the testis in which spermatogonial divisions take place, followed by a growth zone in which the germ cells increase in size (Fig. 64C and D). In some forms the cells of the growth zone radiate out from a central protoplasmic core or rachis while in others they form a row of cells which finally becomes a single line of larger cells (Fig. 64C and D). The testis is covered by a thin epithelium which is continuous with the epithelium of the gonoduct.

Sperms are formed at the posterior end of the testis which merges with the seminal vesicle. This structure is usually dilated and serves as a sperm-storage organ. In forms such as *Ascaris*, a duct known as the vas efferens connects the growth zone of the testis with the seminal vesicle (Fig. 63A) which, in turn, merges into the vas deferens whose structure varies in different groups. However, it is usually divided into an anterior glandular region and a posterior muscular region which forms the ejaculatory duct (Fig. 64D) and opens into the cloaca from the ventral surface in practically

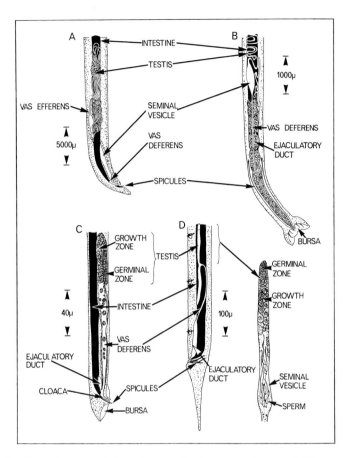

FIG. 64. Scale diagrams of the male reproductive system in several different genera of nematodes. (A) *Ascaris*; (B) *Ancylostoma*; (C) *Rhabditis*; (D) *Tobrilus*, with an enlargement of one of the testes.

all groups. In some nematodes a gland (or a pair of glands) known as the ejaculatory or cement gland surrounds the ejaculatory duct (Fig. 64B). It is thought (Looss, 1905) that this gland secretes an adhesive material which helps hold the male to the female during copulation. However, Sommerville and Weinstein (1964) were not able to obtain any evidence to justify the name "cement gland" in *Nematospiroides dubius* where worms *in copula* were always readily separated.

With few exceptions, male nematodes have copulatory spicules which are lodged in invaginations of the cloaca. Most species have two spicules, although a single spicule is found in many groups. The shape and size of the spicules vary considerably and are often used as diagnostics in nematode taxonomy.

Normally the two spicules of free-living nematodes are of equal size and shape, whereas those of many of the forms parasitic in animals are of different size and shape. This type of asymmetry is found in some of the members of the families Heterakidae, Camallanidae, Cucullanidae, and Atractidae, and in the Spiruroidea and Filarioidea. The reader is referred to Chitwood and Chitwood (1950) for diagrams illustrating the sizes and shapes of copulatory spicules in a wide range of nematodes.

So far as I know, there has not been any detailed work yet on the ultra-structure of sections cut through spicules. However, the spicules of *Heterodera schachtii* have been examined under the stereoscan electron microscope (Green, 1967) and this has revealed that the base of the spicule is ensheathed with cuticle. Sections cut through spicules and examined under the light microscope also show that they are covered with cuticle which is continuous with cuticular lining of the spicular pouch and normally consist of three parts, the head, the shaft, and the blade (Fig. 64). The shaft is tubular and here the cuticle surrounds a central cytoplasmic core.

Spicules appear to have a similar chemical composition to cuticle in that they dissolve when heated in dilute alkali and do not show a chitin X-ray diffraction pattern (Rudall, 1955). They are well supplied with nerves and esterases have been detected in an area close to their base (Lee, 1962; Bird, 1966). Spicules are often accompanied by accessory structures which help to direct them when they are protruded and so prevent damage to the cloacal wall. One of these accessory structures consists of a cuticular thickening which is formed from the walls of the spicular pouch and which is known as the gubernaculum. The gubernaculum is essentially a plate in the groove of which the spicules move. In some species the median part of the guber-naculum projects into the spicular pouch and separates the spicules. Another accessory structure found in some nematodes is the telamon which is an immovable thickening of part of the cloacal wall; it serves to deflect the spicules out of the cloaca in those nematodes in which the opening of the spicular pouch is not immediately opposite the cloacal opening. The spicules are thought to spread open the vulva and vagina during copulation in the majority of nematodes, rather than to transmit sperm. This movement of the spicules is achieved by the spicular muscles. Each spicule is attached at its proximal end to the body wall by a pair of retractor muscles and a pair of protractor muscles.

In some forms the cuticle of the male tail is modified to form a copulatory bursa which functions to hold the nematode in position during copulation. Copulation in nematodes has been described for various species of nema-todes from the earliest workers to those of the present day. Thus, Bastian

(1866) described it in *Cephalobus persegnis* and Sommerville and Weinstein (1964) in *Nematospiroides dubius*. In the majority of nematodes the male, using special copulatory muscles, coils its tail around the vulval region of the female.

The copulatory bursa appears to be a very sensitive structure and Marchant (1970) has described how it extends or "flares" in the presence of a substance emitted from or near the female vulva. This reaction of the bursal muscles is so sensitive that Marchant (1970) suggests that it could be used as an assay for water-soluble stimulatory substances. It is now well established that nematodes emit substances that attract the opposite sex and that the response to this stimulus varies in different species (Greet, 1964; Green, 1966; Jones, 1966; Bonner and Etges, 1967; Greet *et al.*, 1968; Chin and Taylor, 1969b).

The process of copulation has also been observed and described in some detail in *Ditylenchus destructor* (Anderson and Darling, 1964). These workers found that females of this species were only receptive to males for the week after the final molt, whereas males were capable of copulating for a period of 3 weeks after the final molt. A female may copulate several times during her receptive period and with more than one male, several hours usually elapsing between copulations. The male moves directly to the female; its head first touches the vulva and then it twists away and revolves in a spiral parallel to the female. Anderson and Darling (1964) state that "several passes of the male generally occurred before the vulva and spicules became aligned and copulation took place." During this process, the bursa partially encircles the female and holds both worms together, the spicules are inserted deeply into the vagina and 6 to 20 sperm are ejected into the posterior portion of the uterus within a second. The male moves away immediately after copulation and it will also do this if copulation is not achieved within 5 or 10 min of meeting the female.

During copulation in *Nematospiroides dubius* (Sommerville and Weinstein, 1964) the worms lie with their anterior ends in opposite directions and the male (Fig. 65) clasps the female about the vulva with its lateral and ventral bursal rays. The spicules are inserted together through the vulva and vagina into the ovijector. During this process the male releases a colorless substance from a pair of cement or copulatory glands which are associated with the vas deferens. These "copulation pads" tend to thicken and darken with age. At the moment their composition and function remain obscure. Sperm are usually deposited in the vagina and make their way up the female reproductive tract to a sperm-storage organ or spermatheca or, if this is not present, to part of the uterus. The period of time for which a sperm may remain viable in the spermatheca varies, depending on the species under consideration. In *Ancylostoma caninum* it is about 3 weeks (Beaver *et al.*, 1964).

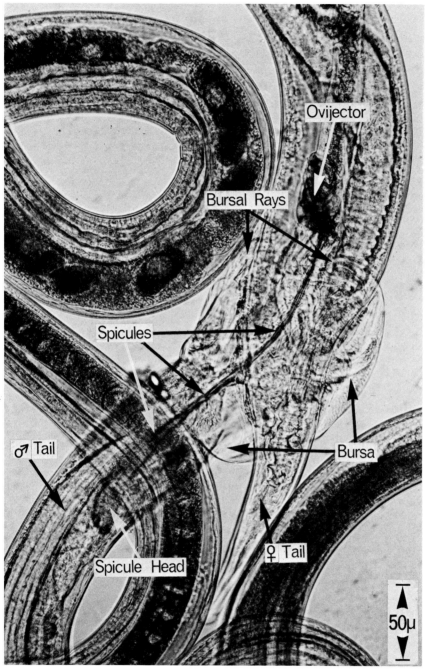

FIG 65. Photomicrograph of *Nematospiroides dubius* copulating. × 400. (Courtesy of Dr. R. I. Sommerville.

During the transition from a male environment to a female environment, a morphological change can take place in the sperm. This has been observed by a number of workers and may prove to be of widespread occurrence in the Nematoda. Thus, the elongate sperms of *Dipetalonema witei* become spherical when they reach the spermatheca (fertilization chamber) of the female (Terry *et al.*, 1961). Fully developed sperm of *Porrocaecum angusticolle* (Nath *et al.*, 1961) are found in the uterus of the female and only spermatids occur in the testis of the male. In *Nematospiroides dubius* (Sommerville and Weinstein, 1964) the sperm changes from being elongate in the male and in the uterus of recently impregnated females to globular in the upper part of the uterus close to its junction with the ovary. It is possible that only the rounded form is capable of fertilizing the egg, but the functional significance of these morphological differences has not yet been established. It has been noted by Foor (1968b) that there is a relationship between the period of time that the sperm of *Ascaris lumbricoides* spends in the uterus of the female and the size of a structure that he refers to as the refringent body. This refringent body is apparently not formed in the sperm of *Ascaris* until it has been deposited in the female reproductive tract.

III. Spermatogenesis

Spermatogenesis starts, of course, in the germinal zone at the tip of the testis. This process consists, briefly, of the production of spermatogonia which consist of closely packed cells with large nuclei and indistinct cell boundaries. Spermatogonial cells of *Anguina tritici* in prophase (Fig. 73D) resemble oogonial cells at this stage (Triantaphyllou and Hirschmann, 1966). The spermatogonia change shape, enlarge, and become more clearly defined in the growth zone (Fig. 64C and D) and become spermatocytes which, in turn, give rise to spermatids which may either develop into spermatozoa in the male, or, as in the free-living marine species *Spirina parasitifera* (Cobb, 1925), the spermatids may be placed in the female during copulation where they may subsequently be seen throughout the length of the two uteri. These spermatids apparently increase quite significantly in size while they are in the uteri and become spermatozoa which are then capable of fertilizing an adjacent ovum.

Spermatogenesis normally involves two maturation divisions resulting in the formation of spermatids which have a haploid chromosome complement. While in recent years the study of sperm formation in nematodes has included widely divergent forms from widely divergent environments, there is no doubt that most of the information that we have is based on studies using the large forms parasitic in animals.

Spermatogenesis has been examined in various species of free-living rhabditids such as *Panagrolaimus rigidus*, *Rhabditis strongyloides*, *Rhabditis dolichura*, and *Rhabditis belari* (Nigon, 1949) and in plant parasitic nematodes such as *Anguina tritici* (Triantaphyllou and Hirschmann, 1966). However, these observations are not nearly as detailed as the work on spermatogenesis in nematodes parasitic in animals.

Work on spermatogenesis started with the studies of van Beneden and Julin (1884) on *Ascaris* and has continued with workers such as Bowen (1925), Sturdivant (1934) and Nath *et al.* (1961). All this work was done with the aid of the light microscope and it is only comparatively recently that spermatogenesis in nematodes has been examined with the aid of the electron microscope. So far, all the ultrastructural work done has been on nematodes parasitic in animals and includes the following species: *Parascaris equorum* (Favard, 1961), *Ascaris suum* (Clark *et al.*, 1967; Kaulenas and Fairbairn, 1968: Foor, 1968b), *Nippostrongylus brasiliensis* (Jamuar, 1966), *Aspiculuris tetraptera* (Lee and Anya, 1967), and *Rhabditis pellio* (Beams and Sekhon, 1967; Beams, personal communication). As Jamuar (1966) states: "The lack of studies on nematode spermatogenesis by modern techniques of electron microscopy has made it difficult to provide a generalized structure of a typical nematode sperm." This is still true although there appear to be certain structures which are peculiar to nematode sperm.

Bowen (1925) described the general structure of *Ascaris* sperm as seen under the light microscope and this has, in essence, been established by various later workers using light microscopy and by the electron microscopists. Briefly, it consists (Figs. 66B and 67A) of a blunt, cone-shaped body containing a nucleus surrounded by mitochondria. At the narrow end lies what Bowen referred to as the refringent body and which various other authors have referred to as the *Glanzkoerper*, *Fettkoerper*, *Kopfkappe*, *Schwanzkappe*, *corps réfringent*, and refringent cone. Electron microscope studies of *in utero* sperm indicate that, in this region, there is a refringent body surrounded by a layer of vesicles made up of characteristic, dense, invaginated membranes (Foor, 1968b). Vesicles are also found in the sperm of *Rhabditis pellio* (Fig. 68C) and homologous structures known as specialized mitochondria (Fig. 66C) have been described in the sperm of *Nippostrongylus brasiliensis* (Jamuar, 1966). Jamuar has given them this name because they are superficially similar to mitochondria and stain with Janus Green and because the number of typical mitochondria in the mature sperm of this nematode is markedly reduced. Jamuar (1966) concludes that either these sperm have little need for mitochondrial enzymes, or that this function is taken over by the specialized mitochondria. Jamuar was not able to determine the origin of these mitochondrian-like vesicles and pointed out that if they did arise from mitochondria, there

256 11. THE REPRODUCTIVE SYSTEM

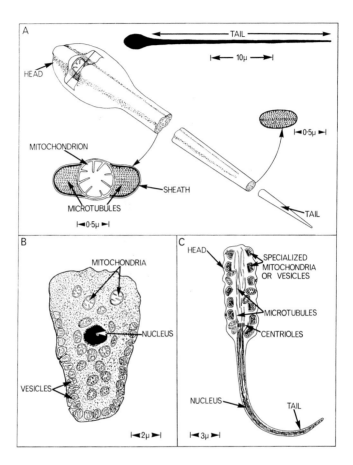

FIG. 66.   Scale diagram of nematode sperm. (A) *Aspiculuris*. (After Lee and Anya, 1967.) (B) *Ascaris*. (C) *Nippostrongylus*. (After Jamuar, 1966.)

would be the unusual situation that some mitochondria in a cell could become modified whereas others in the same cell could not. Bowen (1925) stated that refringent body material first appears in the cytoplasm of the primary spermatocyte in *Ascaris* in the form of granules slightly larger than mitochondria which eventually coalesce to form a structure homologous with the acrosome of flagellate sperm. This homology has subsequently been supported by Sturdivant (1934). However, as a result of improved techniques involving histochemistry and electron microscopy, it seems that in both chemical composition and ultrastructure there is little similarity between the refringent body of nematode sperm and the acrosome of flagellate sperm, although they may be homologous structures. These refringent bodies

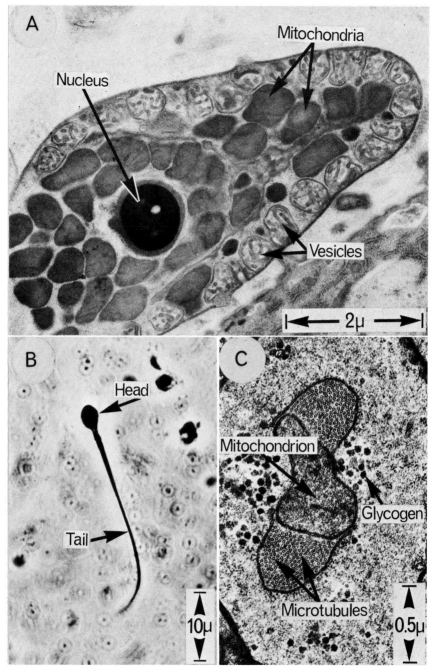

FIG. 67. Photomicrographs of nematode sperm. (A) Electron micrograph of a longitudinal section through an *Ascaris* sperm. × 18,500. (Courtesy of Dr. D. Fairbairn; Kaulenas and Fairbairn, 1968.) (B) Phase contrast photomicrograph of an *Aspiculuris* sperm. × 1,800. (Courtesy of Dr. D. L. Lee; Lee and Anya, 1967.) (C) Electron micrograph of a cross section through the tail of an *Aspiculuris* spermatid. × 40,000. (Courtesy of Dr. D. L. Lee; Lee and Anya, 1967.)

appear to be made up of ribonucleoproteins and do not appear to contain mucopolysaccharide (Nath *et al.*, 1961). The hypothesis that they are derived from Golgi bodies (Bowen, 1925; Sturdivant, 1934) receives support from modern workers (Nath *et al.*, 1961; Favard, 1961; Beams, personal communication).

Beams and Sekhon (1967) have described structures in the pseudocoelom of *Rhabditis pellio* which they were not able to identify with certainty. Subsequently (Beams, personal communication), these structures were identified as sperm and their development has been examined with the aid of the electron microscope (Fig. 68). Beams (personal communication) suggests that Golgi material gives rise to fibrous bodies that are associated with heavy membranes (Fig. 68A) which migrate to the surface of the cell to form the dense invaginated membranes or vesicles (Fig. 68B and C), while the fibrous material probably forms that part of the sperm which is free of organelles. In some respects, these processes resemble what has been described for *Parascaris* (Favard, 1961) and *Nippostrongylus* (Jamuar, 1966). Thus, the fibrous material resembles the crystalloid structure of *Nippostrongylus* and the batonnet of *Parascaris*. Fully developed nematode sperm do not appear to have a nuclear membrane or envelope and this is apparently lost in the early stages of sperm development. Despite these similarities, it is clear from what little has been done so far that there is considerable diversity in sperm structure within the Nematoda. Thus, while diverse forms such as *Ascaris*, *Parascaris*, *Porrocaecum*, *Rhabditis*, and *Syphacia* appear very similar, other forms such as *Nippostrongylus* and *Aspiculuris* are both quite different. These differences are reflected in the measurements for mature sperms in some nematodes, given in Table XI.

Spermatogenesis in *Porrocaecum angusticolle* (Nath *et al.*, 1961) is typical of the ascarid types. The earliest spermatocyte appears as an elongated, conical cell with a central nucleus containing a nucleolus. In the growth phase, this cell becomes polyhedral in shape and mitochondria become universally dispersed throughout the cytoplasm. Groups of phospholipid granules develop which become arranged in small groups within which the refringent bodies arise and develop into spheres about 1 μ in diameter. The phospholipid granules are dispersed and the refringent bodies come to lie free in the cytoplasm. These structures are distributed equally to the spermatids at meiosis and they ultimately fuse into what, under the light microscope, appears to be a single, conical refringent body in the ripe sperm.

The testis of *Nippostrongylus brasiliensis* (Jamuar, 1966) is slender and tubelike. The immature spermatocytes are found as a cluster of cells at the anterior end which is folded back on itself to form a loop. Posteriorly, the developing spermatocytes are arranged in a single row and the mature sperm are found at the posterior end of the testis, stored in a seminal receptacle.

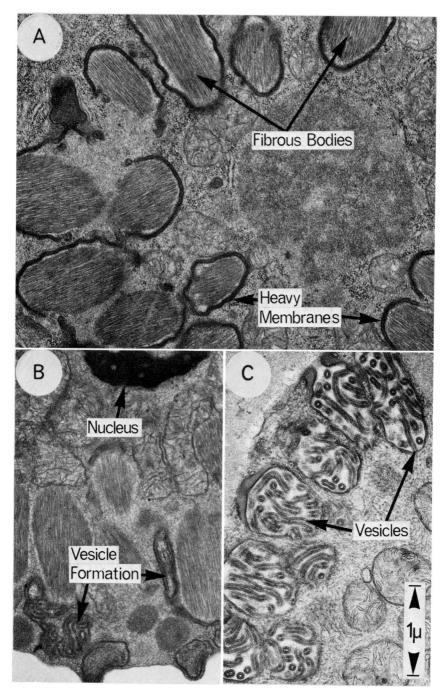

FIG. 68.   Electron micrographs of sections through developing sperm in *Rhabditis pellio*. ×24,000. (Courtesy of Dr. H. W. Beams.) (A) Fibrous bodies and heavy membranes; (B) Part of the nucleus and vesicles in the process of being formed; (C) Several vesicles.

259

TABLE XI

SIZE OF MATURE SPERM IN SEVERAL DIFFERENT SPECIES.

Species	Maximum length (μ)	Maximum width (μ)	Reference
Ancylostoma duodenale	2	0.5	Looss (1905)
Ascaris suum	11	6	Clark et al. (1967)
Aspiculuris tetraptera	35	2.5	Lee and Anya (1967)
Nippostrongylus dubius	20	—	Sommerville and Weinstein (1964)
Nippostrongylus brasiliensis	25	3	Jamuar (1966)
Porrocaecum angusticolle	12	7	Nath et al. (1961)
Rhabditis pellio	10	6	Beams and Sekhon (1967)
Sclerostomum sp.	40	—	Kuhtz (1913)
Tobrilus longus	60	—	Chitwood (1931)
Uncinaria criniformis	10	—	Leuckart (1876)

The structure of one of these sperm cut longitudinally is depicted diagrammatically (Fig. 66C). Histochemically, the head region of the sperm is Feulgen-negative and the tail region is Feulgen-positive. When viewed under the electron microscope, it can be seen that the nuclear material in the tail consists of a bundle of filaments twisted into a spiral (Fig. 66C). The spermatids have very little cytoplasm and each consists largely of a nucleus which has a typical nuclear envelope. As development proceeds, the nuclear material becomes more filamentous and the nuclear envelope disappears. The nucleus in the mature sperm of *Nippostrongylus brasiliensis* is a solid structure at the tip of the tail and becomes tubular more anteriorly (Fig. 66C).

The mature sperm of *Aspiculuris tetraptera* (Fig. 66A) is structurally very different from those already described. This structural difference tends to hide similarities in early development. Thus, the spermatogonia and spermatocytes consist principally of a large round nucleus and the cytoplasm does not contain many organelles. The nucleus is not reconstituted after it divides to give rise to the spermatids but DNA material is located in the tail, as in *Nippostrongylus*, where it is associated with an electron-dense sheath and two bundles of microtubules. Whether or not these structures are homologous with the heavy membranes and microtubules of *Rhabditis pellio* (Fig, 68) remains to be seen. Certainly there are marked differences. For instance, the tail of the sperm is traversed by a long mitochondrion in *Aspiculuris* (Fig. 66A) which is formed from the fusion of several mitochondria in the developing spermatid and which extends almost from the end of the tail to within the head and is flanked by two bundles of microtubules. No other mitochondria are present and there are no vesicles or refringent bodies. Furthermore, this sperm does not alter its shape when it enters the female, as several other types do.

Nematode sperms are usually described as amoeboid and nonflagellate. They do not appear to exhibit much movement, although a detailed report on types of movement is lacking. Bastian (1866) mentions "a slowly oscillating movement" in the short cylindrical sperm of *Rhabditis marina* and "a slowly serpentine movement" in the linear sperm of *Monhysteria disjuncta*. However, no movement of sperm of nematodes parasitic in animals has been reported in recent studies, a point which has been stressed by Sommerville and Weinstein (1964), Jamuar (1966), and Lee and Anya (1967) in their respective papers. Certainly some movement must occur as the sperm must move in the oviduct and must be able to penetrate the ovum. Anya (1966) has suggested that the secretions from the distal end of the vas deferens in *Aspiculuris tetraptera*, which are released with the sperm, are oxytocic and cause the female reproductive tract to contract and so assist sperm ascent to the site of fertilization.

Detailed observations on the ultrastructure of the *in utero* sperm of *Ascaris lumbricoides* have been made by Foor (1968b), whose studies clearly indicate that the broad, clear, anterior region is capable of amoeboid movement. His electron micrographs show that pseudopodia from this region of the sperm interdigitate with the plasma membrane of the uterine cells and thus appear to act as holdfast structures which maintain the sperm's position in the uterus. Foor (1968b) considers that there is little doubt that the pseudopods are motile and they appear to be able to apply considerable force against adjacent cell surfaces. In addition to this clear, amoeboid anterior region, the *in utero* sperm of *Ascaris* (Figs. 66B and 67A) consists of a posterior conical region containing a dense nucleus without a nuclear membrane, dense mitochondria, vesicles (called surface membrane specializations by Foor), and a lipidlike refringent body of variable size which Foor thinks is derived from numerous small, gram-positive granules in the spermatogonia and not from the vesicles. The contents of the refringent body are thought to contribute to the synthesis of ribosomes. It decreases in size after the entry of the sperm into the egg and is usually absent by the time the sperm cytoplasm reaches the center of the egg.

Migration of the sperm of *Ditylenchus destructor* from the uterus to the spermatheca has been described by Anderson and Darling (1962, 1964). In this species the sperm become tightly compressed and discoid as they enter the uterus. They remain in the uterus for about 30 min and undergo changes before migrating anteriorly. They separate from each other and it can be seen that they are connected by a thin membrane. They become ellipsoid in shape and migrate slowly with an amoeboidlike motion into the thin-walled portion of the uterus where they become attached. After a further 30 min they again move forward slowly, this time through the quadricolumella and into the spermatheca. The whole process of migration apparently takes about 2 hr and the sperm appear to have no trouble in moving around eggs coming down the gonoduct. On entering the spermatheca, the sperm chain becomes attached to its walls. An oocyte is impregnated by a single sperm which becomes detached from the end of the chain and loses its identity within 1 or 2 min after penetration. Sperm stored within the spermatheca are bathed in secretions that are exuded from its walls with which the sperm are closely associated. It is thought that these secretions may serve in some way to prolong the longevity of the sperm.

It seems reasonable to speculate that the unfertilized nematode ovum may be able to attract and activate the sperm under natural conditions in the reproductive tract. It also seems likely that, when a sperm is removed from this environment with its presumed stimuli, it rapidly becomes immobile. If the nematodes in question happen to be parasites of warm-blooded animals, the speed with which this occurs may be accelerated. Sperm from the free-living nematode, *Tobrilus longus* (Chitwood, 1931), live, at the most, for only about 3 minutes after being removed from the nematode.

IV. The Female Reproductive System

Work on the morphology of the female reproductive system in nematodes has been comprehensively reviewed by Chitwood and Chitwood (1950), who refer to a series of papers by Seurat from 1913 onward which culminated in a monograph (Seurat, 1920). This work provided the basis for classification of the various types of reproductive systems and its terminology, or modifications of this, has been widely used by subsequent nematode taxonomists. Thus, nematodes are monodelphic if they have one genital tube and didelphic if they have two genital tubes; they are amphidelphic if the uteri are opposed at their origin, prodelphic if the uteri are parallel and anteriorly directed at origin, and opisthodelphic if the uteri are parallel and posteriorly directed at origin. Nematodes that have a single, anteriorly directed genital tube are also considered to be prodelphic.

Hirschmann (1962) gives a detailed description of the development of a typical monodelphic prodelphic type of female reproductive system in *Ditylenchus triformis*. This development (Fig. 69) takes place as follows. Sexual differentiation first occurs in the 2nd-stage larva when male larvae may be separated from female larvae because of the presence of a pair of ventral-cord nuclei in the female which divide once to give rise to a group of four nuclei which lie slightly posterior to the genital primordium and eventually give rise to the vagina. These nuclei are shown (Fig. 69A) at the second molt. Up to this point, development has been similar to that described above for the male larva. Similar ventral-cord nuclei have also been described in the developing reproductive systems of females of *Diploscapter coronata* (Hechler, 1968).

At the second molt in female larvae of *Ditylenchus triformis*, the posterior somatic nucleus of the genital primordium divides several times to form nuclei which eventually give rise to the female gonoduct while the anterior nucleus gives rise to the cap cell nucleus and epithelial nuclei of the ovary. Thus, these nuclei give rise to different cells in the female from those in the male. The female 3rd-stage larva (Fig. 69B), in contrast to the male, has

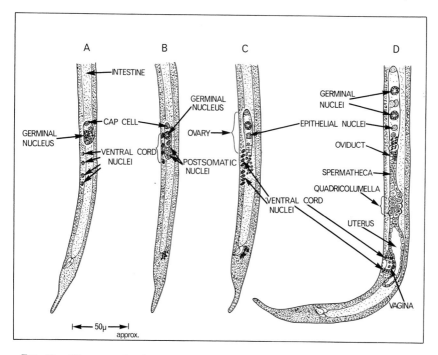

Fig. 69. Diagrams showing the development of the female reproductive system in *Ditylenchus triformis*. (After Hirschmann, 1962.)

the group of small cells at the posterior end of the gonad and there are only a few nuclei in the rectal area. The four ventral-cord nuclei enlarge and lie close to the developing gonad.

By the third molt (Fig. 69C), the posterior cell group has increased in size and the ventral-cord nuclei have increased in number and lie in the posterior region of the gonad. By the fourth molt (Fig. 69D) these nuclei have migrated inward to form the lumen of the vagina and the germinal nuclei have begun to divide. The oviduct is starting to form and consists of two rows of six columnar epithelial cells followed by double rows of six cells which will ultimately form the spermatheca. This is followed by a wider part of sixteen large cells which will form the quadricolumella (Fig. 69D) and this is followed by the uterus and the postvulvar uterine sac which are both formed from a layer of flattened epithelial cells.

In the female reproductive system, as in the male, the gonads may be hologonic or telogonic. The former are restricted to a few aberrant groups such as the Trichuroidea and the Dioctophymoidea, but the vast majority of female nematodes have telogonic ovaries. In this type they are usually didelphic, as is depicted in the diagram of the reproductive system of *Meloidogyne javanica* (Fig. 70), although monodelphic forms, as illustrated in the diagram of the reproductive system of *Anguina tritici* (Fig. 71), are much more common in the Tylenchoidea.

In telogonic forms such as the large ascarids (van Beneden, 1833a, b) the germinal area at the blind end of the ovary is short. This is also true of forms such as *Meloidogyne javanica* (Fig. 70), but is more pronounced in the ascardis such as *Parascaris equorum*, which have ovaries that are about 225 cm in length. Each of these ovaries is filled with oocytes which are attached radially about a central rachis (Fig. 72A). In this nematode, the germinal region contains lipid droplets but no other large cell inclusions (Foor, 1967, 1968a). Both refringent granules and lipid droplets are numerous in young oocytes and their nuclei are situated at the apex of each cell, thus forming a wide circle around the rachis (Fig. 72A).

With the aid of the electron microscope, it can be seen (Fig. 72B) that the oocyte is attached to the rachis by a cytoplasmic bridge which contains many microtubules. The rachis consists of nonnucleated tissue containing lamellar bodies, lipid droplets, dense granules, and what appear to be ribosomes (Foor, 1967, 1968a). Mitochondria and refringent granules are absent.

About 3–5 cm from the oviduct in *Ascaris*, the cytoplasmic bridges between the oocytes and the rachis are weakened and disrupted and the oocytes come to lie freely in the oviduct. The rachis itself ends suddenly about 1–2 cm from the oviduct. Its primary function appears to be to maintain the basic spatial arrangement of the oocytes (Foor, 1968a).

In the majority of free-living nematodes, the growth zone is a single chain

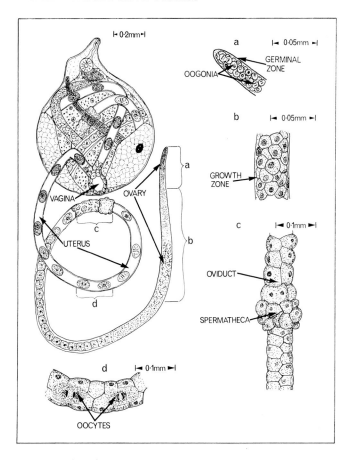

FIG. 70. Diagram of the female reproductive system of *Meloidogyne javanica*, depicting a series of enlargements of different regions throughout its length at a, b, c, and d. (After Triantaphyllou, 1962.)

of cells and there is no distinct rachis. In the large ascarids, the growth zone starts about 30 cm from the germinal end and runs for about 150 cm to within 10 cm of the oviduct. Sections through the germinal and growth zones of the ovary in *Heterakis gallinarum* have been examined under the electron microscope by Lee (1969); they show electron micrographs of the oogonia and oocytes being parasitized by the protozoan *Histomonas meleagridis*. It is interesting to note that the nematode is able to repair damage to the oocyte membrane and ovary wall caused by the penetration of the protozoan, thus demonstrating some degree of ability to repair damage. The oviduct is a narrow tube with walls formed by high columnar cells and is a continuation

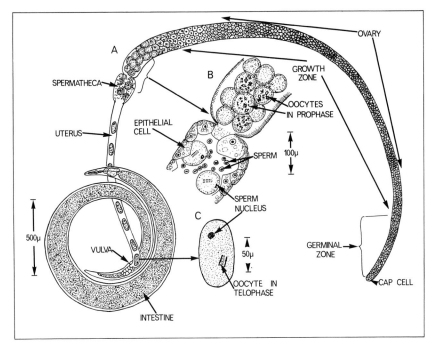

FIG. 71.   Diagram of the female reproductive system of *Anguina tritici*. (After Trianta-phyllou and Hirschmann, 1966.) (A) The entire reproductive system; (B) enlargement of the region between the ovary and the spermatheca; (C) enlargement of an egg at the proximal end of the uterus.

of the epithelial covering of the ovary. At the junction of the oviduct and the uterus is a swelling known as the spermatheca or seminal receptacle which usually contains a large number of sperm and it is here that fertilization takes place.

The spermatheca is an obvious structure, particularly in dioecious forms, which, if males are present, is usually full of sperm. It serves as a storage organ for sperm and they appear to be able to survive in it for quite long periods, for example, for 3 weeks in *Ancylostoma caninum* (Beaver *et al.*, 1964). It seems feasible to suspect that these times may be greater in various free-living and parasitic forms existing in a poikilothermic environment.

In the absence of a morphologically distinct spermatheca, a region of the uterus adjacent to where it meets the oviduct becomes an area where sperms congregate. Structurally distinct spermathecae, such as are seen in nematodes such as *Meloidogyne* and *Anguina* (Figs. 70 and 71) and which have

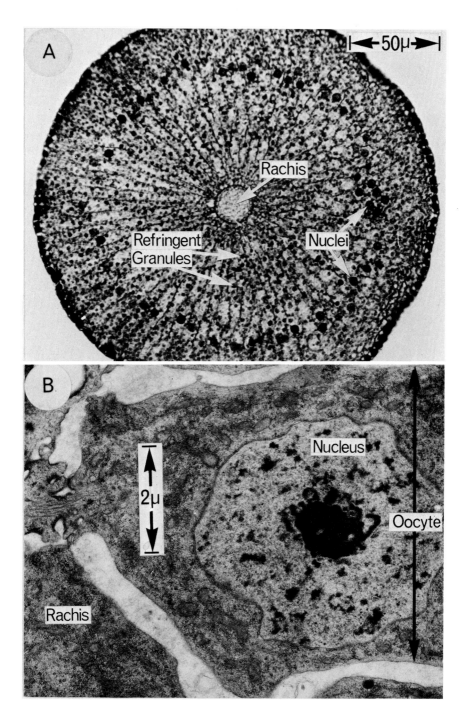

FIG. 72. Photographs of sections through the ovary of *Ascaris suum*. (Courtesy of Dr. W. E. Foor; Foor, 1967.) (A) Photomicrograph of a cross section through the growth zone, × 480, (B) electron micrograph showing a young oocyte connected to the rachis by a cytoplasmic bridge containing microtubules, × 14,000.

been described in a whole range of different nematodes including various have not, so far as I am aware, been sectioned and examined with the aid of the electron microscope. However, sections have been cut through this organ in several of the larger nematodes parasitic in animals and examined with the aid of the light microscope. Thus, Looss (1905) mentions that the epithelial cells of this region in *Ancylostoma duodenale* are "distinguished by their decidedly more finely granular protoplasm from the cells of the rest of the uterus." In *Ascaris* sections have revealed that the cells of the epithelium in this region are elongate and tufted and it has been speculated that they either function as nurse cells to the sperm (Leuckart, 1876) or engulf old and unused sperm (Romieu, 1911; von Kemnitz, 1912; Romeis, 1912). In fact, very little is known about the ecology of the sperm in this environment.

The uterus in some forms is divided into a portion containing secretory cells and known as the quadricolumella (Fig. 69D). This area of the uterus, in some nematodes, functions in the formation of the outermost egg membrane, appropriately known as the uterine layer. The cells of this area in *Ascaris* (Foor, 1967) are rich in mitochondria, Golgi complexes, rough endoplasmic reticulum, and glycogen. In *Helicotylenchus* (Hirschmann and Triantaphyllou, 1967) this structure is known as the tricolumella, as its cellular components are arranged in three rather than four rows. Farther back, the wall of the uterus consists of an epithelium made up of flat or cuboid cells covered by a well-developed muscular layer with circular and oblique fibers. These muscles are not only capable of moving the eggs down the uterus by peristaltic contractions but are responsible for molding the shape of the egg before the shell hardens. A muscular narrowing, of unknown function, in the middle of the uterus in the genus *Xiphinema*, has been described (Luc, 1958; Flegg, 1966) and is known as the Z-organ.

In some forms the posterior part of the uterus may act as a storage organ for the eggs but in the majority of forms it passes directly into the vagina (Fig. 70). Before doing this in some forms, it terminates in a particularly muscular portion, called by Looss (1905) the ovijector (Fig. 65). This structure, whose anatomy has recently been examined at high resolution (Hamada, 1970), appears to function in controlling the movement of eggs in nematodes that are prolific egg layers. The vagina in many cases may have an even thicker muscular wall than the uterus. In all forms it is lined with cuticle that is continuous with the external cuticle and opens to the exterior through a slitlike vulva which is usually in the middle of the body but which in various forms may open either anteriorly or posteriorly. There are exceptions to this general pattern, of course, and de Coninck (1965) describes two cases where the vagina enters the ventral wall of the rectum so that the female opening is not directly to the exterior by the way of the vulva but is indirectly through a cloaca, as in the male. However, this is most uncommon. Normally in free-living soil, freshwater, and marine forms, the ovary, oviduct, uterus, and vagina are comparatively simple, and are uniform in structure and egg output. In the parasitic forms, however, as is the case with most parasitic animals, there is often an enormous increase in the number of eggs laid and a concurrent increase in the size of the reproductive system. One of the classic and best-known examples of this occurs in plant parasitic nematodes of the family Heteroderidae. Thus, nematodes of the genera *Heterodera*, *Meloidodera* and *Meloidogyne* (Fig. 70) show extreme sexual dimorphism in which the females become sedentary and pear-shaped. This pattern of development. in which the female virtually becomes an egg-laying machine, is not restricted to this particular family but is found in various other groups of plant parasitic nematodes such as the family Tylenchulidae, which includes the genera *Sphaeronema*, *Tylenchulus*, *Trophotylenchulus*, and *Trophonema*, and the subfamily Pratylenchinae, which includes the genera *Nacobbus* and *Rotylenchulus*.

In some nematodes parasitic in insects, sexual dimorphism is even more pronounced. de Coninck (1965) describes how the uterus of the gravid female in *Tripius gibbosus* evaginates to form a sacklike hernia which eventually becomes as large as the nematode itself. In the fertilized female of *Sphaerularia bombi* the vagina evaginates and grows to become many times larger than the body of the female which becomes little more than an appendix to this evaginated tube.

While the females of nematodes parasitic in homiothermic animals do not exhibit sexual dimorphism to this degree, their egg output is often much greater than in the parasites of poikilotherms owing to the increase in size of the nematode and its reproductive system. Thus, in *Ancylostoma duodenale* (Looss, 1905) the average length of one of the two female genital tubes is 65 mm; 60 mm of this is ovary and oviduct and the remaining 5 mm is uterus. In *Parascaris equorum* (van Beneden, 1883a; Foor, 1967) the length of one of the female reproductive tubes is about 250 cm and it has been estimated (Kelly and Smith, 1956) that a female *Ascaris suum* may lay as many as 1.6×10^6 eggs per day.

V. Oogenesis

Oogenesis has been studied in many different groups of nematodes including free-living forms as well as parasites in animals and plants.

Oogenesis starts in the germinal zone at the tip of the ovary and includes growth, maturation, and fertilization of the ovum. This latter process takes place in the spermatheca, if this is present. In most forms, fertilization is an important process which, in addition to its obvious genetic role, is responsible for stimulating the egg to initiate shell formation (Foor, 1967); in *Ascaris*, it results in a burst of ribosomal RNA synthesis. Apparently a large fraction of the ribosomes necessary for egg development in this nematode is synthesized after fertilization by the male genome (Kaulenas and Fairbairn, 1968). The influence of fertilization on the morphology of the nematode egg was first observed by Nelson (1852) in *Toxocara (Ascaris) mystax*. He compared the fertilized with the unfertilized ovum and stated "one is immediately struck with the immense difference that exists between them." Nelson's diagrams clearly show this difference, although he appeared to think that several sperm were involved, as he describes the effect of the "spermatic particles" on the ovum.

The process of fertilization in *Parascaris equorum* takes place as follows. The sperm enters the egg cell and, in doing so, initiates the formation of a fertilization membrane, contraction of the egg protoplasm, and the start of shell formation. While the egg membranes are being formed, development within the egg takes place. This involves divisions of the egg nucleus by two maturation divisions, a mitotic and then a meiotic division. The first division gives rise to two lots of 4 chromosomes of which one lot goes into the first polar body and the other lot of 4 chromosomes, which remain in the egg, divides meiotically to form a second polar body and an egg nucleus, each containing the haploid number of chromosomes, in this case 2 chromosomes. The chromosomes of the male and female pronuclei come together at the equatorial plate of the cell which then divides by mitosis giving rise to two cells, each with a normal diploid number.

As mentioned above, the comprehensive work of van Beneden (1883b) on oogenesis and fertilization has led to an understanding of the role of chromosomes in these processes. The large ascarids have proved to be particularly suitable for the study of chromosomes because of their size and number. Thus, in *Parascaris equorum* the diploid number may be 2, 4, or 6, depending on the variety being studied.

More recently, chromosomes from a wide range of nematodes have been studied (Walton, 1959). The chromosomes in many free-living and plant parasitic nematodes are small and numerous and thus are harder to see and count. Work with these species has been reviewed by Triantaphyllou and Hirschmann (1964), Nigon (1965), and Triantaphyllou (1971). Interest in the chromosomes of plant parasitic nematodes was stimulated by the use of the squash technique (Mulvey, 1955). Subsequently, both Hirschmann and Triantaphyllou and their co-workers have published a number of papers on gametogenesis in plant parasitic nematodes which have been of great value in furthering our knowledge of these processes, as they have included

sexual reproduction or amphimixis, whereas *Meloidogyne*, on the other hand, has a basic chromosome number of 18 and usually reproduces parthenogenetically Triantaphyllou (1970) considers the former to represent a progressive line of evolution as opposed to the latter which he considers to represent a regressive or degenerate line of evolution. The relationship of the karyotypes of these two genera still remains obscure (Triantaphyllou, 1969, 1970) despite DNA measurements in 2nd-stage larvae of various members of both genera.

The only species of *Meloidogyne* that has been discovered so far to reproduce by amphimixis is a new species (Triantaphyllou, 1970), *M. carolinensis*, which is thought to have 18 chromosomes. Both *M. naasi* and *M. graminicola* can also reproduce by amphimixis but they normally reproduce by meiotic parthenogenesis. They resemble *M. carolinensis* morphologically and have the same number of chromosomes (Triantaphyllou, 1969). At the other end of the scale are those species which reproduce by mitotic parthenogenesis and are either polyploids or aneuploid derivatives of polyploids, of which *M. javanica* is a good example.

The reproductive systems of *M. naasi* and *M. graminicola* (Triantaphyllou, 1969) resemble that of *M. javanica* (Fig. 70) and the growth of the oocyte is similar to that of *M. hapla* (Triantaphyllou, 1963, 1966). As the oocytes of these species pass from the spermatheca into the uterus, they are in the early stages of the first maturation division, which is the best stage for counting and observing the chromosomes.

In addition to members of the Heteroderidae, the reproduction and cytology of members of various other families of plant parasitic nematodes have been examined in recent years; these include members of the genus *Helicotylenchus* (Hirschmann and Triantaphyllou, 1967; Triantaphyllou and Hirschmann, 1967) in which reproduction can be by mitotic parthenogenesis, as in *Helicotylenchus dihystera*, or amphimictic, as in *H. erythrinae*. In *H. dihystera* the chromosomes are typical in size and shape for those usually found in plant parasitic nematodes (Fig. 73C). Figure 73C shows 35 chromosomes in prometaphase of the first cleavage division from a North Carolina popula-

---

FIG. 73. Photomicrographs of chromosomes in different genera of plant parasitic nematodes. (Courtesy of Dr. A. C. Triantaphyllou.) (A) Oogenesis in an English population of *Meloidogyne javanica* showing 44 paired chromosomes. × 4000. (Triantaphyllou, 1962.) (B) Oogenesis in *Heterodera glycines* showing 9 paired chromosomes, × 4000. (Triantaphyllou and Hirschmann, 1962.) (C) Oogenesis in *Helicotylenchus dihystera* showing 35 paired chromosomes. × 1800. (Triantaphyllou and Hirschmann, 1967). (D) Spermatogenesis in *Anguina tritici* showing several spermatogonial cells in prophase, × 1600. (Triantaphyllou and Hirschmann, 1966.)

tion. This appears to be a polyploid as the dioecious species *H. erythrinae* has a haploid number of 5 chromosomes.

Gametogenesis in free-living nematodes of the genus *Cylindrocorpus* (Chin and Taylor, 1969a) follows a common pattern with mitotic divisions in the germinative zone of the gonads. The oocytes and spermatocytes undergo normal meiosis following maturation. The diploid number is restored by fusion of the sperm and egg nuclei.

Recent work on the cytogenetics of various species of *Pratylenchus* (Roman and Triantaphyllou, 1969) indicates that, as in the Heteroderidae, evolution within this genus has been associated with polyploidy, partheno-genesis, and change in chromosome number. Of the seven species that these two workers studied, there were examples of reproduction by cross-fertiliza-tion, by meiotic parthenogenesis, and by mitotic parthenogenesis. As in *Heterodera, Meloidogyne,* and *Helicotylenchus,* there is considerable variation in chromosome numbers in the different species of *Pratylenchus.*

As a result of studies on gametogenesis in the genus *Xiphinema,* Dalmasso and Younes (1970) conclude that the basic chromosome number is 5 and that *Xiphinema index,* which has 20, is a tetraploid, while *Xiphinema mediter-raneum,* which has 10, is a diploid.

Chromosome numbers within genera appear to be much more uniform in nematodes parasitic in animals, such as members of the Heterakidae ($n = 5$), Oxyuridae ($n = 4$), Strongylata ($n = 6$), and the Strongyloididae ($n = 3$) (Walton, 1959).

Despite the fact that the study of chromosomes in nematodes is still in its infancy, there is already a most impressive amount of information available on chromosome numbers in a wide and rapidly increasing range of nema-todes.

VI. Summary

The development of the male reproductive system, which arises from genital primordia in the larval stages, is described.

Adult nematodes usually have a single testis, although there may be two. The male reproductive system usually consists of three principal parts: the testis, seminal vesicle, and vas deferens.

The testis normally consists of two zones, a germinal zone, in which spermatogonial divisions take place, and a growth zone, in which the sperm-atocytes increase in size. Sperm are formed at the posterior end of the testis and are usually stored in the seminal vesicle. This structure merges into the vas deferens which consists, usually, of an anterior glandular region and a posterior muscular region which opens ventrally into the cloaca.

Most male nematodes have a pair of copulatory spicules which lie in an invagination of the cloaca, have a similar chemical composition to the cuticle, and are thought to function in assisting copulation. They are aided in this function by localized thickenings known as the gubernaculum and telamon which guide and deflect the spicules.

At copulation, sperm are usually deposited in the vagina and make their way up the uterus. During this period, a morphological change may take place in the sperm but little is known of the processes involved.

Spermatogenesis starts in the germinal zone of the testis and the closely packed spermatogonia enlarge in the growth zone to become spermatocytes and then spermatids. This process involves two maturation divisions and ends with the haploid spermatozoa.

There is considerable diversity in sperm structure within the Nematoda. Generally, however, it appears from electron microscope studies that the nucleus of a mature sperm does not appear to have a nuclear envelope as the spermatids do and, in many cases the surface of the sperm is studded with vesicular invaginations of unknown function. Detailed information on movement of nematode sperm is lacking.

The development of the female reproductive system, which also arises from genital primordia in the larvel stages, is described. Sexual differentiation may first occur as early as the 2nd-stage larva.

Usually the ovaries are filled with oocytes attached radially about a central rachis by cytoplasmic bridges. The rachis is anucleate but contains various cytoplasmic inclusions. The oocytes break away from the rachis and come to lie in the oviduct. In most free-living nematodes there is no rachis and the growth zone consists of a single chain of cells.

When present, the spermatheca or sperm-storage organ occurs at the junction of the oviduct and the uterus. It appears to function in keeping the sperm in a viable state.

The uterus is often divided into an anterior glandular portion, whose cells are rich in cytoplasmic components, which is indicative of high metabolic and synthetic activity, and a posterior muscular portion that is associated with movement of the eggs into the vagina, which is also muscular and is lined with cuticle. The eggs are expelled through a vulva that is normally located in the middle of the body.

In parasitic nematodes, there is often extreme sexual dimorphism which results in a considerable increase in egg-laying capacity associated with an enlarged female reproductive system.

Oogenesis, which starts in the germinal zone at the tip of the ovary, involves growth, maturation, and fertilization. This takes place in the spermatheca, if present, and is followed by egg development and shell formation.

The process of fertilization is described. In some forms, this does not take place and reproduction may be by either mitotic or meiotic parthenogenesis. As is to be expected, chromosome numbers vary and aneuploid and polyploid forms are quite common. It appears that evolution within certain plant parasitic genera that have been studied is associated with polyploidy, parthenogenesis, and a change in chromosome number.

REFERENCES

Anderson, R. V., and Darling, H. M. (1962). *Phytopathology* **52**, 722. (Abstr.)
Anderson, R. V., and Darling, H. M. (1964). *Proc. Helminthol. Soc. Wash.* **31**, 240.
Anya, A. O. (1966). *Parasitology* **56**, 347.
Bastian, H. C. (1866). *Phil. Trans. Roy. Soc. London* **156**, 545.
Beams, H. W., and Sekhon, S. S. (1967). *J. Ultrastruct. Res.* **18**, 580.
Beaver, P. C., Yoshida, Y., and Ash, L. R. (1964). *J. Parasitol* **50**, 286.
Bird, A. F. (1966). *Nematologica* **12**, 359.
Bird, A. F. (1970). *Nematologica* **16**, 13.
Bonner, T. P., and Etges, F. J. (1967). *Exp. Parasitol.* **21**, 53.
Boveri, T. (1899). Die Entwicklung von *Ascaris megalocephala* mit besonderer Rücksicht auf die Kernverhältnisse. *Festschrft Kupfer* pp. 383–430.
Bowen, R. H. (1925). *Anat. Rec.* **31**, 201.
Chin, D. A., and Taylor, D. P. (1969a). *Nematologica* **15**, 525.
Chin, D. A., and Taylor, D. P. (1969b). *J. Nematol.* **1**, 313.
Chitwood, B. G. (1931). *J. Wash. Acad. Sci.* **21**, 41.
Chitwood, B. G. (1949). *Proc. Helminthol. Soc. Wash.* **16**, 90.
Chitwood, B. G., and Chitwood, M. B., eds. (1950). "An Introduction to Nematology," 213 pp. Monumental Printing Co., Baltimore, Maryland.
Clark, W. H., Moretti, R. L., and Thomson, W. W. (1967). *Exp. Cell. Res.* **47**, 643.
Cobb, N. A. (1925). *J. Hered.* **16**, 357.
Coomans, A. (1964). *Nematologica* **10**, 601.
Crofton, H. D. (1966). "Nematodes," 160 pp. Hutchinson, London.
Dalmasso, A., and Younes, T. (1970). *Nematologica* **16**, 51.
de Coninck, L. (1965). *In* "Traité de Zoologie" (P. P. Grassé, ed.), Vol. IV, pp. 1–217. Masson, Paris.
Dougherty, E. C., Hansen, E. L., Nicholas, W. L., Mollett, J. A., and Yarwood, E. A. (1959). *Ann. N. Y. Acad. Sci.* **77**, 176.
Favard, P. (1961). *Ann. Sci. Natur., Zool. Ser.* **3**, 53.
Flegg, J. J. M. (1966). *Nematologica* **12**, 174.
Foor, W. E. (1967). *J. Parasitol.* **53**, 1245.
Foor, W. E. (1968a). *Bull. Tulane Univ. Med. Fac.* **27**, 23.
Foor, W. E. (1968b). *J. Cell Biol.* **39**, 119.
Green C. D. (1966). *Ann. Appl. Biol.* **58**, 327.
Green, C. D. (1967). *Nematologica* **13**, 279.
Greet, D. N. (1964). *Nature (London)* **204**, 96.
Greet, D. N., Green, C. D., and Poulton, M. E. (1968). *Ann. Appl. Biol.* **61**, 511.
Hamada, G. S. (1970). *J. Parasitol.* **56**, 523.
Hechler, H. C. (1968). *Proc. Helminthol. Soc. Wash.* **35**, 24.
Hirschmann, H. (1962). *Proc. Helminthol. Soc. Wash.* **29**, 30.
Hirschmann, H., and Sasser, J. N. (1955). *Proc. Helminthol. Soc. Wash.* **22**, 115.
Hirschmann, H., and Triantaphyllou, A. C. (1967). *Nematologica* **13**, 558.

Honda, H. (1925). *J. Morphol. Physiol.* **40**, 191.
Jamuar, M. P. (1966). *J. Cell. Biol.* **31**, 381.
Jones, T. P. (1966). *Nematologica* **12**, 518.
Kaulenas, M. S., and Fairbairn, D. (1968). *Exp. Cell. Res.* **52**, 233.
Kelly, G. W., and Smith, L. J. (1956). *J. Parasitol.* **42**, 587.
Kuhtz, H. (1913). *Arch. Mikrosk. Anat.* **83**, 191.
Lee, D. L. (1962). *Parasitology* **52**, 241.
Lee, D. L. (1969). *Parasitology* **59**, 877.
Lee, D. L., and Anya, A. O. (1967). *J. Cell Sci.* **2**, 537.
Leuckart, R. (1876). "Die Menschlichen Parasiten und die von ihnen Herrührenden Kraukheiten," 410 pp. Winter'sche, Leipzig & Heidelberg.
Looss, A. (1905). *Rec. Egypt. Sch. Med.* **3**, 1.
Luc, M. (1958). *Nematologica* **3**, 57.
Maggenti, A. R. (1970). *J. Nematol.* **2**, 7.
Marchant, H. J. (1970). *J. Parasitol.* **56**, 201.
Maupas, E. (1900). *Arch. Zool. Expt.* **8**, 463.
Mulvey, R. H. (1955). *Can. J. Zool.* **33**, 295.
Mulvey, R. H. (1958). *Can. J. Zool.* **36**, 91.
Nath, V., Gupta, B. L., and Kochhar, D. M. (1961). *Quart. J. Microsc. Sci.* **102**, 39.
Nelson, H. (1852). *Phil Trans. Roy. Soc. London, Ser.* B **142**, 563.
Nigon, V. (1949). *Ann. Sci. Natur., Zool.* **11**, 1.
Nigon, V. (1965). *In* "Traité de Zoologie" (P. P. Grassé, ed.), Vol. IV, pp 218–386. Masson, Paris.
Potts, F. A. (1910). *Quart. J. Microscop. Sci.* **55**, 433.
Roman, J., and Triantaphyllou, A. C. (1969). *J. Nematol.* **1**, 357.
Romeis, B. (1912). *Arch. Mikrosk. Anat.* **80**, 129.
Romieu, M. (1911). *Arch. Zellforsch.* **6**, 254.
Rudall, K. M. (1955). *Symp. Soc. Exp. Biol.* **9**, 49.
Seurat, L. G. (1920). "Histoire naturelle des nematodes de la Barbérie," 221 pp. Algiers.
Sommerville, R. I., and Weinstein, P. P. (1964). *J. Parasitol.* **50**, 401.
Sturdivant, H. P. (1934). *J. Morphol.* **55**, 435.
Terry, A., Terry, R. J., and Worms, M. J. (1961). *J. Parasitol.* **47**, 703.
Triantaphyllou, A. C. (1960). *Ann. Inst. Phytopathol. Benaki* **3**, 12.
Triantaphyllou, A. C. (1962). *Nematologica* **7**, 105.
Triantaphyllou, A. C. (1963). *J. Morphol.* **113**, 489.
Triantaphyllou, A. C. (1966). *J. Morphol.* **118**, 403.
Triantaphyllou, A. C. (1969). *J. Nematol.* **1**, 62.
Triantaphyllou, A. C. (1970). *J. Nematol.* **2**, 26.
Triantaphyllou, A. C. (1971). *In* "Plant Parasitic Nematodes" (B. M. Zuckerman, W. F. Mai, and R. A. Rohde, eds.), pp. 1–34. Academic Press, New York.
Triantaphyllou, A. C., and Hirschmann, H. (1962). *Nematologica* **7**, 235.
Triantaphyllou, A. C., and Hirschmann, H. (1964). *Annu. Rev. Phytopathol.* **2**, 57.
Triantaphyllou, A. C., and Hirschmann, H. (1966). *Nematologica* **12**, 437.
Triantaphyllou, A. C., and Hirschmann, H. (1967). *Nematologica* **13**, 575.
Tyler, J. (1933). *Hilgardia* **7**, 373.
van Beneden, E. (1883a). *Arch. Biol.* **4**, 95.
van Beneden, E. (1883b). *Arch. Biol.* **4**, 265.
van Beneden, E., and Julin, C. (1884). *Bull. Acad. Roy. Sci. Belg.* **7**, 312.
Van Gundy, S. D. (1958). *Nematologica* **3**, 283.
Van Gundy, S. D. (1959). *Proc. Helminthol. Soc. Wash.* **26**, 67.

Van Weerdt, L. G. (1960). *Nematologica* **5**, 43.
von Kemnitz, G. (1912). *Arch. Zellforsch.* **7**, 463.
Walton, A. C. (1959). *J. Parasitol.* **45**, 1.
Wisse, E., and Daems, W. T. (1968). *J. Ultrastruct. Res.* **24**, 210.
Yuen, P. H. (1964). *Nematologica* **10**, 570.
Yuksel, H. S. (1960). *Nematologica* **5**, 289.

12
THE EGG

I. Introduction

The nematode egg has always aroused the curiosity of scientists for a variety of reasons. Its embryology is of interest to zoologists because early studies on development in nematode eggs, with their characteristic orderly cleavage pattern, have profoundly influenced modern thinking in embryology and have also demonstrated certain unique characteristics peculiar to nematodes. The nematode egg also interests those associated with the more specific study of nematodes themselves for a variety of reasons. Thus, to the clinical diagnostician it is often a means of identifying the parasite; to the ecologist it is a stage in the life cycle most likely to resist environmental fluctuations. For similar reasons, it interests pathologists and those working on control measures, as the egg is the stage most resistant to anthelmintics and nematocides and the process of hatching has attracted much attention from physiologists.

Apart from acting as a stage in growth that has to resist environmental hazards more than any other stage (in some parasitic forms it is the only stage outside the host), the egg is both structurally and chemically unique within the Nematoda in that it is the only part of a nematode ever to contain chitin.

279

Various aspects of early research that has been done on the nematode egg have been reviewed and may be considered under the following headings: comparative morphology (Christenson, 1950), chemical composition and physiology (Fairbairn, 1957; Rogers, 1962; Rogers and Sommerville, 1969), and embryology (Hyman, 1951; Nigon, 1965; Crofton, 1966). Studies on the ultrastructure of the egg and its membranes have only been done, so far, on a few species, probably for technical reasons, since these structures are particularly difficult to embed and section properly.

In this chapter I shall consider first of all the general morphology of the nematode egg, second its structure and chemical composition, third the development of the embryo within the egg, and finally the hatching process.

II. Morphology

In free-living and plant parasitic forms, the nematode egg is morphologically similar in most instances. Thus, (Fig. 74A,C, and D) the eggs of *Acrobeloides beutchlii*, *Meloidogyne javanica*, and *Aphelenchus avenae* are examples of this morphological similarity. Some nematodes, usually those parasitic in animals, have a characteristically shaped egg which is a most useful aid to their identification. Drawings of these eggs appear commonly in veterinary and zoological texts and Christenson (1950) provides scale drawings of a number of these. Examples of some of the most characteristically shaped eggs are those of *Trichinella*, *Oxyuris*, *Mermis*, and *Ascaris* (Fig. 74B).

Not only are the majority of nematode eggs morphologically similar but they are also of similar size (Table XII), irrespective of the size of the adult worm. It can be seen in the photographs of eggs (Fig. 74), which are all on the same scale, and from Table XII, that there is more cytoplasm in the egg of *Meloidogyne javanica* than there is in *Ascaris lumbricoides*, despite the enormous disparity in size between the adults of these two nematodes.

In Table XII I show the average measurements of eggs from ten different and unrelated genera of nematodes selected at random from some recent papers. It can be seen that these eggs range from an average of 50–90 μ in length and from an average of 21–47 μ in width. These figures probably represent the average size range into which the majority of nematode eggs will fit.

It is worth noting that, although there appears to be a high degree of uniformity in the average egg size of nematodes, there is often considerable variation within a single species and this may be almost as great as the range given above for the majority of nematodes. Thus, in *Ascaris lumbricoides*, the

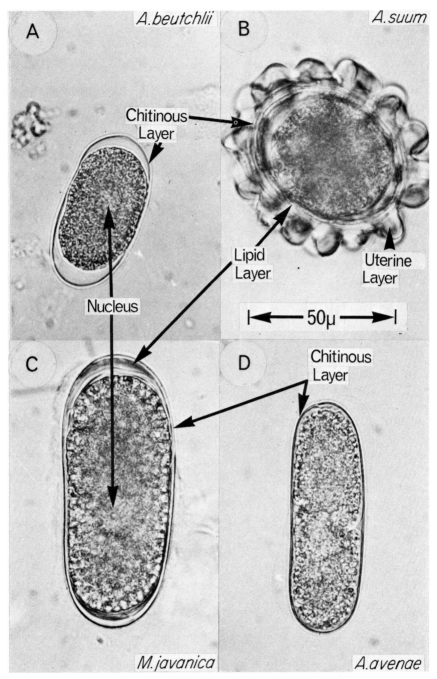

FIG. 74. Photomicrographs of nematode eggs representing both free-living and plant and animal parasitic forms. All at the same magnification. × 800. (A) *Acrobeloides beutchlii*; (B) *Ascaris suum*; (C) *Meloidogyne javanica*; (D) *Aphelenchus avenae*.

TABLE XII
Size of Some Nematode Eggs

Species	Average dimensions (μ)		Reference
	Length	Width	
Asacaris suum (not including uterine layer)	56	47	Fairbairn (1957)
Radopholus similis	64	25	Van Weerdt (1960)
Plectus parietinus	60	40	Maggenti (1961)
Hemicriconemoides chitwoodi	67	21	Fassuliotis (1962)
Meloidogyne javanica	90	42	Bird (1968)
Trichodorus christiei	65	40	G. W. Bird *et al.* (1968)
Diploscapter coronata	50	22	Hechler (1968)
Microtetrameres centuri	51	35	Ellis (1969)
Pratylenchus penetrans	60	24	Hung and Jenkins (1969)
Nematospiroides dubius	78	47	Weinstein *et al.* (1969)

range has been observed (Lýsek, 1967) to vary from 52 to 84 μ for the length of the egg and from 45 to 67 μ for its width. These measurements include the outermost uterine layer (Fig. 74B) which was not included in the measurements for this nematode shown in Table XII, as this layer is not present in the majority of nematodes. In addition to considerable differences in size within species, there may also be differences in shape (Lýsek, 1967). Crofton and Whitlock (1965) have not only observed differences in size of eggs of *Haemonchus contortus* but have also shown "that the volume of an egg determines the length of time required for development to the hatching stage." Thus, the larger eggs took longer to hatch than the smaller ones in *Haemonchus contortus*.

Giant eggs which were thought to be polyploid have been described in *Heterodera trifolii* by Mulvey (1959). These eggs averaged 178 μ long by 45 μ wide. They clearly do not have much survival value, as eggs such as these, which may be twice the length of normal eggs, are very rarely observed. In fact, Johnson and Viglierchio (1970), investigating egg and larval aberrancy in *Heterodera schachtii*, point out that eggs of this size were never observed to develop beyond the four-celled stage.

III. Structure and Chemical Composition

The structure and composition of the eggs of nematodes, and of their shells in particular, have been examined extensively and much of this work has been reviewed by Christenson (1950), Fairbairn (1957), and Rogers (1962). Rogers (1962) pointed out that the results of this research were confusing because of the difficulty in identifying the origin of different layers and because of the paucity of work on the synthesis of various shell components.

Recently a number of papers have been published which describe the ultrastructure of the nematode egg and changes in structure associated either with fertilization and development or hatching (Foor, 1967; Kaulenas and Fairbairn, 1968; Bird, 1968).

Studies on the structure and composition of the egg shell of nematodes are of prime interest and importance to many research workers who may either be interested in controlling various parasitic forms or in the fundamental mechanisms associated with egg shell formation and breakdown. The egg shell consists of three basic layers that are secreted by the egg itself, namely, an inner lipid layer, a middle chitinous layer, and an outer vitelline layer (Fig. 74 and 75). In some forms there is also a fourth outermost layer which is secreted by the uterus and is appropriately known as the uterine layer (Fig. 74B).

There has been some disagreement on the actual number of layers in the egg shell of nematodes and, in the genus *Ascaris*, for instance, various authors have reported from three to five layers (Rogers, 1956). As well as some disagreement on the number of layers, the nomenclature of these layers has varied in a confusing manner. For instance, the innermost lipid layer has been referred to as a vitelline membrane by various workers. However, Foor (1967), in his recent work in which shell formation was examined with the aid of the electron microscope, states that the vitelline layer, which is the first layer formed, lies on the outer surface of the chitinous layer and is thus the outermost of the true egg shell layers (Fig. 75). Foor refers to the innermost layer as the ascaroside layer and states that it "has hitherto been known, improperly, as the vitelline membrane." I shall refer to it as the lipid layer, which is thus synonymous with the vitelline membrane in the older literature. The term vitelline layer now refers to the outermost part of the egg shell and not to the innermost.

The first examination of a nematode egg shell under the electron microscope (Morita, 1953) did not yield very much information, as sectioning techniques had not developed beyond the use of paraffin sections which were too thick to take advantage of the increased resolving power. Thinner sections were ultimately obtained with the use of methacrylate as an embedding medium. R. A. Rogers (1956), working on *Ascaris lumbricoides*, obtained electron micrographs of the chitinous layer, which he considered to be made up of branched microfibers 75–400 Å in diameter, and the uterine layer, which consisted of dense, reticulated material with fibrils about 150 Å in diameter. In this research, the material was either fixed for 2 hours

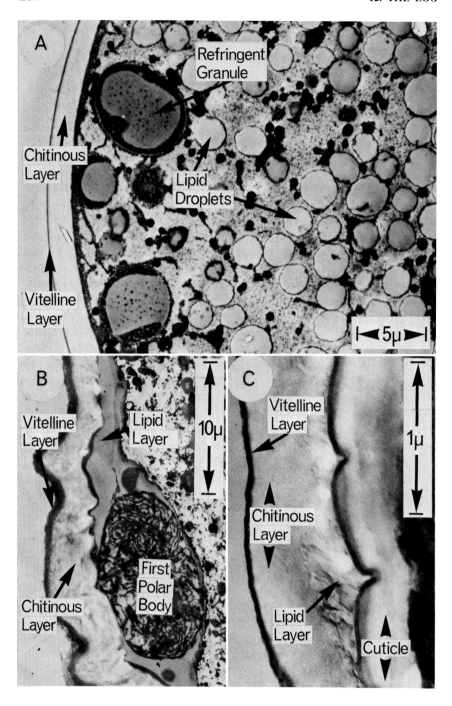

in 1% osmium tetroxide or in Carnoy's fixative for 18–24 hours prior to dehydration. Neither of these two methods appeared to be suitable for fixing the lipid layer, which apparently dissolved in the fat solvents used for dehydrating the material prior to embedding, so that the areas in which it occurs appeared as empty spaces in the electron micrographs. R. A. Rogers (1956) concluded: "The ultrastructure of this region will be of interest when fixation techniques for the study of this material are devised."

This technical problem has now been overcome and the lipid layer can be fixed and rendered relatively insoluble in the dehydrating agents by an initial fixation in gluteraldehyde or formaldehyde for periods of $1\frac{1}{2}$–24 hours, followed by a second fixation in osmium tetroxide (Foor, 1967; Bird, 1968).

It appears from Foor's (1967) excellent studies on shell formation in developing eggs of *Ascaris*, as seen with the aid of the electron microscope, that, in this nematode, there are no more than three layers, excluding the outermost uterine layer which is absent in the majority of nematodes. I think that, generally speaking, the egg shell of nematodes consists of three basic layers, namely, the lipid layer, the chitinous layer, and the third layer mentioned by Foor (1967), which is known as the vitelline layer (Figs. 75 and 76). This layer, which in the majority of nematodes is beyond the resolution of the light microscope, being about 30 mμ thick in *Meloidogyne javanica*, corresponds in general dimensions to the external cortical layer of the cuticle (Fig. 75C). In forms such as *Ascaris*, this layer comes within the resolution of the light microscope, being about 0.5 μ thick, as does the external cortical layer of the ascarid cuticle which may be 1 μ or more in thickness (see Chapter 3). Despite the fact that it is beyond the resolution of the light microscope in the majority of nematodes, I have included the vitelline layer as a distinct layer of the egg shell because Foor has clearly shown that it is a discrete layer formed prior to the other two layers.

It seems possible that the vitelline layer of the egg and the external cortical layer of the cuticle may have much in common. Both represent, in most cases, an outermost layer and, as has been mentioned, have similar dimensions. Both respond to "electron stains" in the same manner and appear to

---

FIG. 75. Electron micrographs of sections cut through the shells of nematode eggs. (A) Low-power view of part of a newly fertilized egg of *Ascaris lumbricoides* showing the incipient chitinous layer and the absence of a definite lipid layer which has yet to be formed, × 3800. (Courtesy of Dr. W. E. Foor; Foor, 1967.) (B) Low-power view of part of an egg of *Ascaris lumbricoides* at a later stage of development showing well-developed chitinous and lipid layers. Note the position of the first polar body in the lipid layer, × 3500. (Courtesy of Dr. W. E. Foor; Foor, 1967.) (C) Part of a fully developed egg of *Meloidogyne javanica* containing a 2nd-stage larva, and showing the larval cuticle adjacent to the lipid layer. × 40,000 (Bird, 1968.)

286   12. THE EGG

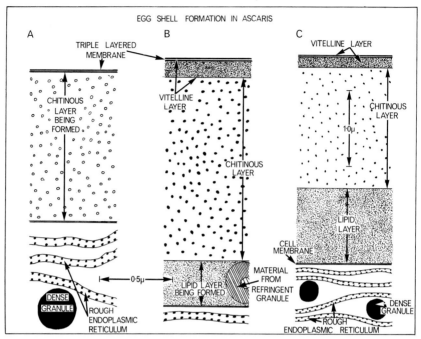

FIG. 76.   Diagrams of egg shell formation in *Ascaris lumbricoides*. (A) Start of shell formation showing the triple-layered outermost part of the vitelline membrane which has separated
from the egg cytoplasm, leaving a relatively clear area which eventually forms the chitinous
layer. (B) Well-developed vitelline and chitinous layers and a lipid layer in the process of
formation. (C) This diagram, which shows all three layers well-developed, has been drawn
at half the magnification of A and B in order to fit in the thickened egg shell.

contain quinone-tanned protein (Monné and Hönig, 1954; Monné, 1963).
Furthermore, a close examination of some of Foor's (1967) electron
micrographs shows that the vitelline layer is bounded by a triple-layered,
plasma membranelike structure which corresponds to a similar structure
on the surface of the external cortical layer of the cuticle (Chapter 3). It
seems quite possible that this structure was the oolemma or unit membrane
which surrounded the oocyte.

Electron micrographs of sections cut through the eggs of *Haemonchus
contortus* and *Trichostrongylus colubriformis* also show a basic three-
layered structure (Donald and Waller, personal communication).

Shell formation in *Ascaris* is an immediate result of fertilization and
incorporates about 39% of the total solids of the egg (Foor, 1967; Kaulenas
and Fairbairn, 1968). It takes place as follows. First of all a dense vitelline
layer separates from the egg cytoplasm (Fig. 76A) leaving a structureless

zone which will eventually contain the chitinous layer. The cortical cyto-plasm of the egg becomes dense with rough endoplasmic reticulum and refringent granules (Figs. 75A and 76A) which, before fertilization, had been randomly distributed throughout the oocyte. Next (Fig. 76B) the structureless zone thickens to about 3 μ and becomes transformed into the chitinous layer. At the same time, an inner lipid layer is formed from the extrusion and fusion of the refringent granules (Fig. 76B and C) and some-times the extruded first polar body (Fig. 75B) is trapped in this lipid layer.

At about this time, the external uterine layer is thought to be formed from uterine cells whose cytoplasm contains an abundance of rough endoplasmic reticulum, glycogen, Golgi bodies, and mitochondria, because the density of material discharged from these cells is similar to that of the external uterine layer.

The lipid layer in *Ascaris* eggs is referred to as the ascaroside layer by Foor (1967) as it appears to consist largely of ascaroside esters. It is a proteolipid in *Ascaris* containing about 25% protein but the entire layer is soluble in lipid solvents. The composition of this layer appears to differ in different nema-todes. Observations made with the aid of the electron microscope on these layers in *Haemonchus contortus* and *Trichostrongylus colubriformis* show that they differ both in their solubility and response to electron stains. It is thought that these differences in the lipid layer may account for differences in the abilities of these two species of nematodes to withstand desiccation within the egg (Donald and Waller, personal communication). In *Ascaris* this layer contains only traces of sterols and, as has been mentioned, is made up of 25% proteins and 75% ascaroside (Fairbairn and Passey, 1955; Fairbairn, 1957). It has been reported that it has a melting point of 73°C in *Ascaris* (Fauré-Fremiet, 1913b) and of 70.2°C in *Meloidogyne* (Chitwood and Chitwood, 1950), but more recent experiments (Bird, unpublished) indicate that there is some variability in the temperatures at which the lipid layers of these two species of nematodes melt.

Flury (1912) and Fauré-Fremiet (1913a) first drew attention to this lipid and its abundance in fertilized eggs. Flury (1912) named it ascaryl alcohol and this was subsequently changed to ascaroside by Fouquey and his co-workers (1957) when they established that it consisted of a mixture of closely related glycosides.

The ascaroside esters in *Ascaris lumbricoides* are found in the neutral lipid fraction and they can be separated from other neutral lipids by means of thin-layer chromatography (Fairbairn, 1969). These lipids are thought (Fairbairn, 1957) to be primarily responsible for the extreme resistance of *Ascaris* eggs to adverse environmental influences. Whether or not ascarosides occur in the lipid layer of the eggs of other nematodes remains to be seen. For the time being, the term lipid layer is a more appropriate general term than ascaroside layer for this innermost layer in the eggs of nematodes.

Chitwood and Graham (1940) have reported that the presence of the lipid layer (which they called the vitelline membrane) is dependent on fertilization in *Strongyloides ratti* and is absent in parthenogenetic forms of this nematode. It is also absent in the parthenogenetic nematode, *Rhabditis filiformis*. However, electron microscope studies have revealed that a lipid layer is present in the egg of the parthenogenetic nematode, *Meloidogyne javanica* (Bird, 1968). This anomaly could, perhaps, be resolved by electron microscope studies of the parthenogenetic eggs of *Strongyloides ratti* and *Rhabditis filiformis*.

The most obvious component of the chitinous layer, or the shell proper, as it is sometimes called, is, of course, chitin. This substance has not been found in oocytes or unfertilized eggs or in any other part of the nematode; it is synthesized in response to the stimulus of fertilization, as described above. The presence of chitin in this layer of the eggs of various nematodes has been demonstrated chemically by color tests, by its solubility in various solutions, and by identifying glucosamine or n-acetylglucosamine in chromatograms of egg hydrolyzates (Chitwood and Chitwood, 1950; Kreuzer, 1953; Rogers, 1962; Anya, 1964). It has been demonstrated physically by X-ray diffraction studies on egg shell material (Rudall, 1955).

The amount of chitin in the chitinous layer appears to vary greatly in different nematodes (Monné and Hönig, 1954). Thus, in the Ascaroidea and Oxyuroidea this layer is largely composed of chitin with a little protein. In other forms, such as the genera *Trichuris* and *Capillaria*, there is only a small amount of chitin and most of the layer consists of protein. Monné and Hönig (1954) came to the conclusion, as a result of solubility tests, that there was little, if any, chitin in this layer of the egg shells of members of the Strongyloidea. However, they pointed out that the egg shells belonging to nematodes of this group "may contain a very small amount of chitin which is not able to influence their solubility properties." In the egg shells of *Heterodera rostochiensis* there is about 9% chitin compared with 59% protein (Clarke *et al.*, 1967). Recent studies on the ultrastructure of the egg shells of two members of the Strongyloidea (Donald and Waller, personal communication) show that morphologically the chitinous layer resembles that of other nematodes in which chitin can be detected chemically.

Monné (1955, 1959, 1962) has studied the chemical composition of the egg shells of many different species of nematodes and provides evidence which suggests that quinone tanning may occur in various layers including the chitinous layer. Anya (1964) has investigated the possible existence of a quinone-tanning mechanism in *Aspiculuris tetraptera* and was unable to detect either polyphenol oxidase or a high concentration of phenolic substances, apart from protein tyrosine, in the egg shell of this nematode. He points out that ammoniacal silver nitrate can be reduced by various reducing substances other than phenols and that it is likely that this response in the egg shells of nematodes is due to the presence of tyrosine in these structures rather than polyphenols.

The chemical composition of the uterine layer of the egg shell (Fig. 74B), found only in some nematodes such as *Ascaris* and *Thelastoma* and produced from the walls of the uterus, resembles the gelatinous matrix found covering the eggs in forms such as *Meloidogyne* in that it consists of an acid mucopolysaccharide-tanned protein complex (Monné and Hönig, 1954; Bird, 1958; Lee, 1961; Monné, 1962, 1963; Bird and Rogers, 1965).

An analysis of the chemical composition of the egg shell of *Heterodera rostochiensis* (Clarke *et al.*, 1967) has revealed that it consists of 59% protein, 9% chitin, 7% carbohydrate, 7% lipid, 3% polyphenols, and 3% ash, the rest being made up of nonhydrolyzed material.

IV. Embryology

The embryology of various different species of nematodes has been investigated by a number of zoologists and nematologists. The most detailed work undoubtedly was done with the eggs of the large ascarids at the turn of the century, notably by Zur Strassen (1896), Boveri (1899), Muller (1903), and, more recently, by Pasteels (1951). All this work has been reviewed and discussed in some detail by Nigon (1965). Other nematodes whose embryology was studied in the earlier days of this research include the genera *Rhabdias* (Neuhaus, 1903), *Camallanus* (Martini, 1903), and *Turbatrix* (Pai, 1928).

More recently, the embryology of a number of free-living and plant parasitic genera has been described; these include *Radopholus* (Van Weerdt, 1960), *Ditylenchus* (Yuksel, 1960; Anderson and Darling, 1964), *Plectus* (Maggenti, 1961), *Nacobbus* (Clark, 1967), *Xiphinema* and *Longidorus* (Flegg, 1968), *Rotylenchulus* (Dasgupta and Raski, 1968), and *Pratylenchus* (Hung and Jenkins, 1969).

The embryology of a nematode is best followed with the aid of a diagram. Most of the diagrams published in textbooks are based on the classic work of Boveri (1899) on the embryology of *Parascaris equorum*. It appears that the embryology of all nematodes is basically similar, although few of the more recent studies approach those of Boveri in detail.

In general, the first cleavage of the egg (Fig. 77B) gives rise to two equal cells or blastomeres which are the first somatic cell (S_1) and the parental

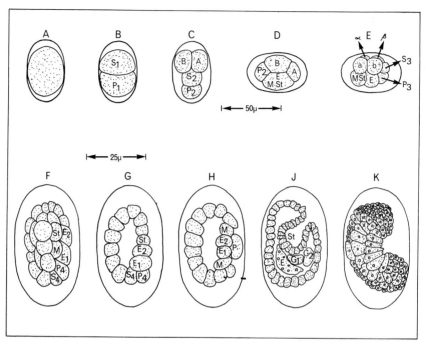

FIG. 77.   Diagrams illustrating nematode embryogenesis.

germinal cell (P_1) from which the gonads of the adult can be traced. This, as Crofton (1966) points out, "is the clearest and best documented example of germinal lineage in the animal kingdom." In some cases, this first cleavage may give rise to blastomeres which are unequal, as has been reported by Yuksel (1960) in *Ditylenchus dipsaci* and Van Weerdt (1960) in *Radopholus similis*. In other instances, this first cleavage and even the second and third cleavages may be equal, as in *Rotylenchulus parvus* (Dasgupta and Raski, 1968), *Plectus parietinus* (Maggenti, 1961), and *Xiphinema diversicaudatum* (Flegg, 1968).

The second cleavage in *Parascaris equorum* gives rise, at first, to four cells arranged in a T-shape (Fig. 77C). This is achieved by the blastomere S_1 dividing longitudinally to form A and B and the blastomere P_1 dividing transversely to form P_2 and S_2. These blastomeres become rearranged to form a rhomboid (Fig. 77D) which is the characteristic shape of the typical nematode four-celled stage. There are, of course, exceptions to this pattern of development, as in *Ditylenchus destructor* (Anderson and Darling, 1964) where mitosis is delayed in one of the blastomeres after the first cleavage until the other blastomere has divided twice, to give a five-cell stage.

Similarly, in *Meloidogyne naasi* (Siddiqui and Taylor, 1970), mitosis in one blastomere precedes that in the other to give rise to a three-celled stage. However, generally, the pattern described above appears to be fairly typical. The S_1 blastomere is the primary somatic cell and its descendants A and B give rise to most of the nematode's ectodermal cells. The blastomere S_2 also only gives rise to somatic tissue and will give rise to endoderm, mesoderm, and stomodeum (EMSt) tissues (Fig. 77D). The nematode's gonads, will, of course, be derived from P_1.

It is interesting to note that not only are the two primary blastomeres going to give rise to predictable and different tissues but each has its own cleavage rhythm. In addition, nematodes are unusual in that for a period of time the descendants of the somatic cells A and B undergo what is known as chromatin diminution, in which the end portions of the chromosomes are extruded into the cytoplasm where they appear to degenerate. Thus, only the germ-line chromosomes can be seen to be of normal size at each mitosis.

The cells A and B divide to give a, b, α, and β, and P_2 divides to give P_3 and S_3 (Fig. 77E). The S_2 cell or EMSt divides into E and MSt. The dorsal cells derived from A and B continue to divide and eventually give rise to most of the hypodermis, the nervous system, and the excretory cells. The cell P_3 divides to give P_4 and S_4 (Fig. 77E). Both S_3 and S_4 are ectodermal and give rise to the hypodermis in the posterior region of the nematode's body.

The endodermal tissue is derived from the descendants of cell E_1 (Fig. 77G) and P_4 divides into P_5 and S_5. The descendants of cell S_5 produce the epithelium which covers the gonads and their ducts and the descendants of P_5, G_1, and G_2, and their descendants proliferate germ cells only (Fig. 77H and J).

The nematode's body-wall musculature and its pseudocoelomic cells are derived from the primary mesodermal cell M (Fig. 77F and H) and its pharynx from the descendants of the cell St. In the early embryonic stages, these primary cells St, M, and E lie on the ventral surface of the embryo and are taken within the embryo by a process of gastrulation (Fig. 77H and J). This is achieved usually, either by a type of cell overgrowth known as epiboly, or, more commonly, by a type of invagination (Fig. 77H and J) in which cell E proliferates a chain of cells that will eventually become the midgut, the descendants of cell M form on either side of these cells, and St proliferates a mass of cells which become invaginated into the interior.

Development involving the formation of a coeloblastula followed by gastrulation involving invagination of the endoderm and the stomodeum, as described above, appears to be typical for many different species of nematodes studied. The gastrula stage superficially resembles the single cell stage and may be distinguished from it by the manner in which the cytoplasm entirely fills the egg membranes in the single cell stage and, of course, by the latter's single nucleus when this is visible.

By the process of gastrulation, the flattened embryo becomes cylindrical and the embryo starts to become worm-shaped. It continues to grow and elongate and eventually develops into a larva. This process of development has been well illustrated recently in a series of cinephotomicrographs of the embryology of the plant parasitic nematodes *Nacobbus serendipiticus* (Clark, 1967) and *Meloidogyne naasi* (Siddiqui and Taylor, 1970). Details of gastrulation in these nematodes were difficult to follow but cell differentiation was clear and the outermost smaller and lighter-colored ectodermal cells were easily distinguished from the internal larger and darker endodermal cells. The ectodermal cells divide actively at the anterior end to form a hyaline region which eventually gives rise to the head and esophageal regions.

Coordinated movements of the embryo were first observed when it had developed to the elongated form of the future larva (Clark, 1967; Siddiqui and Taylor, 1970). This started in the posterior region as sudden twitches and this ability to move spread over the whole embryo over a period of between 2 and 3 hr until the entire embryo could rotate on its axis. This movement was accompanied by narrowing and rapid lengthening, the tail became pointed, the head broadly triangular, and the stomodeum developed as a small depression in its center. In both *Nacobbus serendipiticus* and *Meloidogyne naasi*, the 1st-stage larva is formed about a week after the first cell division.

Once the nematode embryo has completed its development, there is no further cell division except in the genital and intestinal cells. Thus, further growth is due to an increase in size of the cells rather than to an increase in cell numbers. This has led to the production of some very large cells in nematodes, particularly in the large parasitic forms.

The time taken for complete embryological development within the egg, that is, from the first cell division to hatching of the larva from the egg, varies considerably in different species of nematodes. It is generally more rapid in the free-living forms. In *Rhabditis teres* (Chuang, 1962) at 18°C, the larvae hatch 20 hr after fertilization. However, another rhabditid, *Acrobeles complexus* (Thomas, 1965), has a much slower development and takes 4 to 5 days. This rapid rate of reproduction of free-living nematodes such as the rhabditids makes them suitable experimental animals. Thus, *Caenorhadbitis briggsae*, which can pass through one complete generation, under optimal conditions, in $3\frac{1}{2}$ days (Nicholas *et al.*, 1959), has been used extensively in axenic culture work.

The period of time taken to hatch in plant parasitic nematodes is often considerably greater than in the free-living forms. Thus, in *Pratylenchus penetrans* it is about 10 days at 23°C (Hung and Jenkins, 1969), it takes from 15 to 19 days in *Hemicriconemoides chitwoodi* (Fassuliotis, 1962), from 19 to 24 days in three species of *Xiphinema*, 25 to 30 days in two species of *Longidorus* (Flegg, 1968), and 15 to 17 days at 22°–26°C in *Meloidogyne naasi* (Siddiqui and Taylor, 1970).

The time of development to the hatching stage in many forms parasitic in animals varies considerably. In many of these forms hatching will only take place when the embryonated egg is ingested by the host. It takes up to 20 days for these eggs to become infective for *Ascaris* and 10 days for *Parascaris* (Fairbairn, 1957). These types of eggs appear to develop more slowly than those which hatch outside the host to give a free-living larva. Thus, the eggs of *Trichuris trichiura* take 21 days at 30°C to develop to the embryonated stage whereas those of *Ancylostoma caninum* only take a day for the corresponding period of development (Rogers, 1962); Crofton (1965) has shown that the eggs of various trichostrongyle species, dissected from the uterus of each worm, all hatched, under optimal conditions, within 24 hours to give the free-living larval stage. The nematode *Neoaplectana glaseri*, which parasitizes the larvae and adults of various beetles, takes about a week to complete a generation and has been grown axenically over many generations (Stoll, 1959).

I have selected these examples at random to illustrate the variability in rate of embryological development that occurs in nematodes. This rate of development does not appear to be influenced by the number of molts that occur in the egg, as some forms which only molt once in the egg develop much more slowly than others which molt twice. The rate at which embryological development takes place in a particular nematode appears to be an intrinsic property of that nematode. There may be a greater variation in embryological developmental times between closely related genera such as *Ascaris* (20 days) and *Parascaris* (10 days) than between nematodes such as *Ditylenchus distructor*, a member of the superfamily Tylenchoidea (Anderson and Darling, 1964) and *Seinura celeris*, a member of the superfamily Aphelenchoidea (Hechler and Taylor, 1966) both of which have a developmental period of 2 to 3 days.

The nature of the forces responsible for determining the fate of the various blastomeres of the nematode egg, from the first cleavage onward, has aroused much curiosity, and Nigon (1965) has reviewed and discussed some of the hypotheses that have been formulated on this topic.

This question of cellular differentiation concerns all living organisms; it is complex, fundamental, and, perhaps, beyond the scope of this book. However, I feel that it is worth pointing out that, because of their unique, predetermined, and orderly early cleavages, nematode eggs must provide those workers interested in the ultrastructure of early embryonic differentiation with very suitable material for their studies. So far as I know, the dividing nematode egg has not been examined at high resolution with the aid of the electron microscope in an attempt to find out if structural changes occur which can be related to the process of differentiation. The results of research with other animals in this field have been reviewed by Sherbet and Lakshmi (1967), who describe some of the structural changes which take place in the cells of various embryos during differentiation.

Studies on cell division during early cleavage stages in the eggs of various animals have been reviewed by Fautrez-Firlefyn and Fautrez (1967). These workers state: "The mitotic cycles of cleaving eggs are characterized by the fact that no growth periods separate them." They also point out that many important questions remain unanswered. We do not know, for instance, precisely what factors initiate the start of cleavage or what determines the cleavage pattern or the orientation of the successive planes of cleavage. It is possible that when synthesis of an essential constituent, such as the protein of the achromatic apparatus, reaches a given level, the processes of cell division are triggered off simultaneously. At the moment, however, no particular substance has been found which is capable of inducing the onset of cell division.

V. Hatching

In this section I propose to restrict myself largely to a discussion of the structural changes that take place in a nematode egg during the process of hatching. I shall only briefly mention what I consider to be some important aspects of the physiology and biochemistry of egg hatching in nematodes, as I feel that any ramifications of these topics, however interesting, lie beyond the scope of this book.

Hatching occurs either in response to a stimulus or stimuli from the host, as in some parasitic forms, or it takes place under normal environmental conditions in response to stimuli which are part of this normal environment. In this latter case, hatching may be inhibited by a change in some component of the environment, such as temperature or moisture content.

In the former case, a great deal of research has been done on the nature of the stimulus, which may be quite specific. A classic example of this is, of course, the plant parasitic nematode, *Heterodera rostochiensis*, which has been studied in some detail because of its economic importance. The eggs of this nematode, which normally hatch in response to stimuli provided by the exudations from roots of its solanaceous plant hosts, will only hatch *in vitro* in the presence of a hatching factor isolated from these roots or in

3mM aqueous solutions of several compounds, notably anhydrotetronic acid, picrolonic acid, and vanadates, out of the many hundreds tested (Clarke and Widdowson, 1966; Clarke and Shepherd, 1966, 1968). By contrast, eggs of the closely related plant parasitic nematode, *Heterodera schachtii*, will hatch in response to the stimuli of over fifty synthetic hatching agents.

The actual process of hatching in eggs of *Heterodera rostochiensis*, stimulated in either potato root exudate or in 3 mM aqueous sodium metavanadate, has been recorded using time lapse cinephotomicrography (Doncaster and Shepherd, 1967). This nematode cuts a slit in the shell by using the tip of its stylet to make a line of close perforations through the shell, which merge to make the slit. This process is remarkably precise and is a good example of the high degree of nervous coordination that can be achieved in nematodes.

Doncaster and Shepherd consider that the process of hatching in this nematode is largely mechanical and that pharyngeal gland secretions are unimportant in this process, as they were unable to detect them. However, they did notice that, in larvae stimulated by potato root exudate, "the three pharyngeal glands were active before locomotion was detected and the distensible distal ends of the gland ducts were swollen with globular secretions by the time the larvae emerged." These changes were not so pronounced in larvae stimulated by sodium metavanadate. Larval movement in stimulated eggs did not start for at least a day and stylet movement was not observed for at least another day.

It seems to me that it is possible that larval movement prior to hatching may occur in association with an enzymatic breakdown of the lipid layer which would permit the larva to have much more freedom of movement within the egg. Examination of the ultrastructure of the egg shell before and during hatching would determine whether or not this assumption is correct, or, in other words, whether hatching in *Heterodera rostochiensis* is entirely mechanical, or partly mechanical and partly chemical. Certainly there are many recorded instances of mechanical force being used by the hatching larvae just prior to emergence from the egg. These include widely separated genera such as *Pratylenchus* (Di Edwardo, 1960), *Paratylenchus* (Rhoades and Linford, 1961), *Haemonchus* (Silverman and Campbell, 1959), *Trichostrongylus* (Wilson, 1958), *Aphelenchus avenae* (Taylor, 1962), *Nacobbus* (Clark, 1967), and *Meloidogyne* Dropkin *et al.*, 1958; Bird, 1968; Wallace, 1968b).

Active movement of a nematode within the egg shell provides some form of mechanical force and it is possible that prehatch movement of this sort is necessary in nematodes that hatch into an environment outside the host in order to bring their muscles to a high level of efficiency (Wallace, 1968b).

The work of Rogers (1958, 1960) and Fairbairn (1961) on the hatching of eggs of *Ascaris lumbricoides* has clearly demonstrated the important role that enzymes play in the hatching of this species. They have provided evidence which indicates that an esterase, a chitinase, and possible a proteinase are secreted by the larva in the egg in response to stimuli from the host. There is some evidence (Justus and Ivey, 1969) that this larva can secrete chitinase without being induced by host stimuli. It seems that the lipid layer acts as a barrier between the chitinase and its substrate in the egg shell. It appears (Rogers, 1958) that the enzymes produced by the larvae in response to host stimuli alter the permeability of the lipid layer and allow the chitinase to come in contact with the chitinous layer.

A pattern of events similar to this may occur in the hatching processes of many nematodes; Wallace (1966a, 1968a, b) has suggested that in *Meloidogyne javanica*, at about the time of the first larval molt in the egg, either an enzyme is secreted which dissolves the lipid layer or, alternatively, this layer is emulsified by the active movement of the larva within the egg, in a manner similar to that reported for *Trichostrongylus retortaeformis* (Wilson, 1958). As a result of studies on the ultrastructure of the egg of *Meloidogyne javanica* during hatching (Bird, 1968), it appears that enzymes associated with the hydrolysis of lipids do play an important part in the hatching process of this nematode (Fig. 78). It appears that the lipid layer is not hydrolyzed at about the time of the first larval molt but later when hatching commences (Fig. 78C and D), as this layer appears quite intact in eggs containing 2nd-stage larvae (Fig. 78B). Furthermore, the lipid-hydrolyzing enzymes appear to be synthesized in the subventral esophageal glands of the larva and these structures only appear to become active just before hatching.

It seems to me that the basic mechanism of hatching is similar throughout the Nematoda. Generally, it seems to take place as follows: "The stimulus elicits a behavioral response in the larva which brings about increased larval activity, breakdown of the lipid layer, and an increase in plasticity of the egg shell leading to its distortion" (Bird, 1968). As mentioned above, responses similar to these have been observed in a number of different genera.

There are also other examples such as in *Xiphinema* (Flegg, 1968) where an exudation from the mouth of the nematode appears to bring about changes in the structure of the egg which lead to its rupture.

The stimulus which initiates the hatching process in nematodes may either function as a direct stimulus, such as dissolved gaseous carbon dioxide, or a specific substance in a root exudate, in the case of some nematodes parasitic in animals or plants, or indirectly through the removal of an inhibitor, which may have been acting as a brake on an internal biological clock mechanism, as is probably the case in the majority of nematodes. Inhibition may be caused by a deficiency of a component of the nematode's

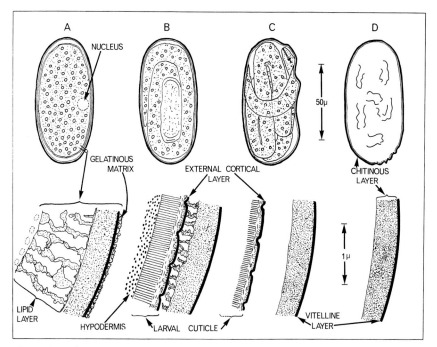

FIG. 78.   Diagrams illustrating the structure of the egg shell during development and hatching in *Meloidogyne javanica*. (After Bird, 1968.)

normal environment, such as water or oxygen. For instance, in the case of *Meloidogyne*, water loss leads to a shrinkage of the gelatinous matrix surrounding the eggs (Wallace, 1968a). This process results in a mechanical pressure being placed on the egg shell which prevents swelling and distortion of the egg taking place and so inhibits hatching. Inhibition of hatching may also be due to factors which act directly as inhibitors. For instance, microorganisms are known to be able to influence development and hatching of various species of nematodes (Johnston, 1957; Lýsek, 1966; Wallace, 1966b).

It is difficult, at times, to draw a clear distinction between the application of a stimulus and the removal of an inhibitor but it seems that the basic mechanism of hatching itself may be similar throughout the Nematoda.

VI. Summary

The majority of nematode eggs are similar in shape and size irrespective of the size of the adult nematode.

There are three layers in a typical nematode egg shell, namely, an inner lipid layer, a middle chitinous layer, and an outer vitelline layer which normally lies beyond the resolution of the light microscope and is about 30 mμ thick in *Meloidogyne javanica*. In some eggs, for example, *Ascaris*, there is a layer outside the vitelline layer which is secreted by the uterus and is called the uterine layer.

The lipid layer is soluble in various dehydrating agents unless fixed for long periods of time. It is made up of 25% protein and 75% lipid in *Ascaris*, has a melting point of about 72°C in some nematodes, and is soluble in fat solvents. This layer is thought to be responsible for the extreme resistance of eggs such as those of *Ascaris* to adverse environmental conditions.

The amount of chitin in the chitinous layer varies in different nematodes. It is synthesized in response to the stimulus of fertilization and has been detected in this layer by a variety of techniques.

The vitelline layer of the egg shell resembles the external cortical layer of the larval cuticle in many respects and appears to be bounded in much the same manner by a triple-layered plasma membrane which may be derived from the unit membrane surrounding the oocyte.

The egg shell, which incorporates about 39% of the total solids of the egg, is formed when the vitelline layer comes away from the egg cytoplasm, leaving a structureless zone which eventually develops into the chitinous layer. At the same time, the lipid layer is formed beneath this from fusion of the refringent granules.

The embryogenesis of a typical nematode is described. This sequence of events appears to be basically similar throughout the group. The embryology of nematodes is unique in that the fate of some of the blastomeres is determined from the first cleavage onward, so that embryonic differentiation takes place right from the beginning of embryogenesis in these animals. The embryo develops within the egg into a larva which molts once and sometimes twice before hatching. The larva hatches in response to stimuli which can be remarkably specific in some forms and very general in others.

Studies on the physiology and ultrastructure of eggs during the process of hatching support the contention that this process takes place by mechanical movement of the larva after the lipid layer has been hydrolyzed by enzymes synthesized and exuded by the larva.

REFERENCES

Anderson, R. V., and Darling, H. M. (1964). *Proc. Helminthol. Soc. Wash.* **31**, 240.
Anya, A. O. (1964). *Parasitology* **54**, 699.
Bird, A. F. (1958). *Nematologica* **3**, 205.
Bird, A. F. (1968). *J. Parasitol.* **54**, 475.

Bird, A. F., and Rogers, G. E. (1965). *Nematologica* **11**, 231.
Bird, G. W., Goodman, R. M., and Mai, W. F. (1968). *Can. J. Zool.* **46**, 292.
Boveri, T. (1899). Die Entwicklung von *Ascaris megalocephala* mit besonderer Rücksicht au die Kernverhältnisse. *Festschr. Kupfer* pp. 383–430.
Chitwood, B. G., and Chitwood, M. B. eds. (1950). "An Introduction to Nematology," 213 pp. Monumental Printing Co., Baltimore, Maryland.
Chitwood, B. G., and Graham, G. L. (1940). *J. Parasitol.* **26**, 183.
Christenson, R. O. (1950). *In* "An Introduction to Nematology" (B. G. Chitwood and M. B. Chitwood, eds.), pp. 175–190. Monumental Printing Co., Baltimore, Maryland.
Chuang, S. H. (1962). *Nematologica* **7**, 317.
Clark, S. A. (1967). *Nematologica* **13**, 91.
Clarke, A. J., and Shepherd, A. M. (1966). *Nature (London)* **211**, 546.
Clarke, A. J., and Shepherd, A. M. (1968). *Ann. Appl. Biol.* **61**, 139.
Clarke, A. J., and Widdowson, E. (1966). *Biochem. J.* **98**, 862.
Clarke, A. J., Cox, P. M., and Shepherd, A. M. (1967). *Biochem. J.* **104**, 1056.
Crofton, H. D. (1965). *Cornell Vet.* **55**, 242.
Crofton, H. D. (1966). "Nematodes," 160 pp. Hutchinson, London.
Crofton, H. D., and Whitlock, J. H. (1965). *Cornell Vet.* **55**, 274.
Dasgupta, D. R., and Raski, D. J. (1968). *Nematologica* **14**, 429.
Di Edwardo, A. A. (1960). *Phytopathology* **50**, 570.
Doncaster, C. C., and Shepherd, A. M. (1967). *Nematologica* **13**, 476.
Dropkin, V. H., Martin, G. C., and Johnson, R. W. (1958). *Nematologica* **3**, 115.
Ellis, C. J. (1969). *J. Nematol.* **1**, 84.
Fairbairn, D. (1957). *Exp. Parasitol.* **6**, 491.
Fairbairn, D. (1961). *Can. J. Zool.* **39**, 153.
Fairbairn, D. (1969). *In* "Chemical Zoology" (M. Florkin and B. T. Scheer, eds.), Vol. III, pp. 361–378. Academic Press, New York.
Fairbairn, D., and Passey, B. I. (1955). *Can. J. Biochem. Physiol.* **33**, 130.
Fassuliotis, G. (1962). *Nematologica* **8**, 110.
Fauré-Fremiet, E. (1913a). *Arch. Anat. Microsc. Morphol. Exp.* **15**, 435.
Fauré-Fremiet, E. (1913b). *C. R. Soc. Biol.* **74**, 1183.
Fautrez-Firlefyn, N., and Fautrez, J. (1967). *Int. Rev. Cytol.* **22**, 171–204.
Flegg, J. J. M. (1968). *Nematologica* **14**, 137.
Flury, F. (1912). *Arch. Exp. Pathol. Pharmakol.* **67**, 275.
Foor, W. E. (1967). *J. Parasitol.* **53**, 1245.
Fouquey, C., Polonsky, J., and Lederer, E. (1957). *Bull. Soc. Chim. Biol.* **39**, 101.
Hechler, H. C. (1968). *Proc. Helminthol. Soc. Wash.* **35**, 24.
Hechler, H. C., and Taylor, D. P. (1966). *Proc. Helminthol. Soc. Wash.* **33**, 71.
Hung, C. L., and Jenkins, W. R. (1969). *J. Nematol.* **1**, 352.
Hyman, L. H. (1951). "The Invertebrates," 572 pp. McGraw-Hill, New York.
Johnson, R. N., and Viglierchio, D. R. (1970). *Nematologica* **16**, 33.
Johnston, T. (1957). *Phytopathology* **47**, 525.
Justus, D. E., and Ivey, M. H. (1969). *J. Parasitol.* **55**, 472.
Kaulenas, M. S., and Fairbairn, D. (1968). *Exp. Cell Res.* **52**, 233.
Kreuzer, L. (1953). *Z. Vergl. Physiol.* **35**, 13.
Lee, D. L. (1961). *Parasitology* **51**, 379.
Lýsek, H. (1966). *Acta Univ. Palacki Olomuc. Fac. Med.* **40**, 83.
Lýsek, H. (1967). *Folio Parasitol. (Prague)* **14**, 381.
Maggenti, A. R. (1961). *Proc. Helminthol. Soc. Wash.* **28**, 118.
Martini, E. (1903). *Z. Wiss. Zool.* **84**, 501.

Monné, L. (1955). *Ark. Zool.* **7**, 559.
Monné, L. (1959). *Ark. Zool.* **12**, 99.
Monné, L. (1962). *Ark. Zool.* **15**, 277.
Monné L. (1963). *Z. Parasitenk.* **22**, 475.
Monné, L., and Hönig, G. (1954). *Ark. Zool.* **7**, 261.
Morita, S. (1953). *Med. J. Osaka Univ.* **3**, 669.
Muller, H. (1903). *Zoologica (New York)* **17**, 1.
Mulvey, R. H. (1959). *Nature (London)* **184**, 1662.
Neuhaus, C. (1903). *Jena. Z. Naturwiss.* **37**, 653.
Nicholas, W. L., Dougherty, E. C., and Hansen, L. H. (1959). *Ann. N.Y. Acad. Sci.* **77**, 218.
Nigon, V. (1965). *In* "Traité de Zoologie" (P. P. Grassé, ed.), Vol. IV, pp. 218–386. Masson, Paris.
Pai, S. (1928). *Z. Wiss. Zool.* **131**, 293.
Pasteels, J. (1951). *Arch. Biol.* **59**, 405.
Rhoades, H. L., and Linford, M. B. (1961). *Proc. Helminthol. Soc. Wash.* **28**, 51.
Rogers. R. A. (1956), *J. Parasitol.* **42**, 97.
Rogers, W. P. (1958). *Nature (London)* **181**, 1410.
Rogers, W. P. (1960). *Proc. Roy. Soc., Ser. B* **152**, 367.
Rogers, W. P. (1962). "The Nature of Parasitism," 287 pp. Academic Press, New York.
Rogers, W. P., and Sommerville, R. I. (1969). *In* "Chemical Zoology" (M. Florkin and B. T. Scheer, eds.), Vol. III, pp. 465–499. Academic Press, New York.
Rudall, K. M. (1955). *Symp. Soc. Exp. Biol.* **9**, 49.
Sherbet, G. V., and Lakshmi, M. S. (1967). *Int. Rev. Cytol.* **22**, 147–170.
Siddiqui, I. A., and Taylor, D. P. (1970). *Nematologica* **16**, 133.
Silverman, P. H., and Campbell, J. A. (1959). *Parasitology* **49**, 23.
Stoll, N. R., (1959). *Ann. N.Y. Acad. Sci.* **77**, 126.
Taylor, D. P. (1962). *Proc. Helminthol. Soc. Wash.* **29**, 52.
Thomas, P. R. (1965). *Nematologica* **11**, 395.
Van Weerdt, L. G. (1960). *Nematologica* **5**, 43
Wallace, H. R. (1966a). *Nematologica* **12**, 57.
Wallace, H. R. (1966b). *Proc. Roy. Soc., Ser. B* **164**, 592.
Wallace, H. R. (1968a). *Nematologica* **14**, 231.
Wallace, H. R. (1968b). *Parasitology* **58**, 377.
Weinstein, P. P., Newton, W. L., Sawyer, T. K., and Sommerville, R. I. (1969). *Trans. Amer. Microsc. Soc.* **88**, 95.
Wilson, P. A. G. (1958). *J. Exp. Biol.* **35**, 584.
Yuksel, H. S. (1960). *Nematologica* **5**, 289.
Zur Strassen, O. (1896). *Arch. Entwicklungsmech Organismen* **3**, 27.

AUTHOR INDEX

Numbers in *italics* refer to the pages on which the complete references are listed.

301

SUBJECT INDEX

A

Acanthocephala, 58
Acanthonchus duplicatus, 46, 51, 54, 55, 61, 63, 64, 97
Acanthonchus rostratus, 146
Acetic-orcein, 22
Acetylcholine, 123, 124, 125
Acid mucopolysaccaride, 64
Acid phosphatase, 26, 99
Acrobeles complexus, 292
Acrobeloides beutchli, 280
Acrosome, 256
Actin, 123, 127
Agamermis, 222, 223
Alae, 48, 49, 92
Aldehyde-fuchsin, 25
Alimentary tract, 112
Amblystoma mexicanum, 230
Amphidelphic, 262
Amphids, 45, 83, 131, 132, 133, 135, 137, 140, 147, 148, 203
Amphimixis, 273
Amplicaecum, 107, 212, 213
Ampulla, 179, 188, 192, 195
Ancylostoma, 112, 155, 158, 201, 209, 211, 212, 229, 238

Ancylostoma caninum, 49, 51, 64, 80, 131, 177, 192, 193, 213–216, 234, 252, 266, 293
Ancylostoma duodenale, 49, 51, 55, 64, 96, 107, 109, 112, 114, 131, 144, 160, 208, 260, 268, 269
Anesthetics, 7
Angiostrongylus cantonensis, 80
Anguilla, 160
Anguina, 266
Anguina calamagrostis, 215
Anguina tritici, 73, 254, 255, 264
Angusticaecum, 163
Anisakis, 182
Annulations, 47, 48, 74, 83
Anus, 112, 113, 198, 221
Aphelenchus avenae, 58, 66, 73, 80, 84, 86, 280, 295
Aplectana, 212, 234
Apochromatic objectives, 33
Arcade, 96
Arginine, 59
Ascaridae, 47, 49
Ascaridia, 160
Ascaridia lineata, 80
Ascaris, 107, 112, 115, 120–125, 131–133, 137, 152, 155–157, 160–163,

310